2001 Distinguished Instructor Short Course
Distinguished Instructor Series, No. 4

sponsored by the

Society of Exploration Geophysicists

European Association of Geoscientists & Engineers

Seismic Amplitude Interpretation

presented by

Fred J. Hilterman

EAGE

EUROPEAN
ASSOCIATION OF
GEOSCIENTISTS &
ENGINEERS

ISBN 1-56080-086-0 (Series)
ISBN 1-56080-109-3 (Volume)

Copyright © 2001 Fred Hilterman
Geophysical Development Corporation
8401 Westheimer, Suite 150
Houston, TX 77063-2799 U.S.A.

web site: www.geodev.com
e-mail: fred@geodev.com
phone: 713-782-1234

Printed in U.S.A.
Second printing 2006

Table of Contents

About the author

Fred J. Hilterman received a geophysical engineering degree and PhD in geophysics from the Colorado School of Mines. During his tenure with Mobil (1963-1973), his assignments ranged from field work and prospect evaluation to Activity Leader at the Field Research Laboratory. In 1973, he joined the University of Houston (UH) as a Professor of Geophysics. While at UH, Fred co-founded the Seismic Acoustics Laboratory (SAL) and he was Principal Investigator there until 1981. At that time he co-founded Geophysical Development Corporation, where he is currently Vice-President of Development. Fred also lectures at UH as a Distinguished Research Professor.

Fred's early research and publications were in the field of theoretical and physical 3-D modeling. Since 1984, his interests and papers have dealt with the calibration and integration of rock properties to seismic, mainly through AVO techniques. In addition, Fred continues an active interest in all aspects of seismic techniques.

Fred is a long-standing member of SEG, EAGE, AGU, GSH, and AAPG, with honorary memberships in SEG and GSH. His services to the societies include Associate Editor of GEOPHYSICS, Chairman of THE LEADING EDGE Editorial Board, SEG and AAPG Distinguished Lecturer, and both Technical and General Chairman of SEG Annual Meetings. Fred received the SEG Best Paper Award, Best Presentation Award, and Virgil Kauffman Gold Medal. He also received the Colorado School of Mines VanDiest Gold Medal and Distinguished Alumni Medal. He has been an instructor for SEG and AAPG Continuing Education courses since the 1970s. Fred was 1996–1997 SEG President.

Fred has two children and six grandchildren and enjoys time spent with his wife, Kathi, at their cattle ranch (Belly Acres Ranch) near Houston.

**EUROPEAN
ASSOCIATION OF
GEOSCIENTISTS &
ENGINEERS**

Dear DISC Participant:

It is a great pleasure to welcome you to the fourth annual SEG/EAGE Distinguished Instructor Short Course (DISC), "Seismic Amplitude Interpretation," by Dr. Fred J. Hilterman. The SEG, EAGE, and your local society are proud to provide this premier course in geophysics education.

With rapidly changing technologies, geoscientists around the world have an increasing need to acquire expert geophysical knowledge. SEG's Distinguished Programs, which include the joint SEG/EAGE Distinguished Instructor Short Course, the Distinguished Lecture, and the joint SEG/AAPG Distinguished Lecture, aid in the promotion of technologies that will have a significant impact on geophysics and geology.

Previous DISC programs included: "Time-Lapse Seismic in Reservoir Management," by Mr. Ian Jack of BP Amoco in 1998; "The Seismic Velocity Model as an Interpretation Asset," by Dr. Phil Schultz of Spirit Energy, a division of Unocal Corporation, in 1999; and "Shear Waves from Acquisition to Interpretation," by Mr. Robert Garotta in 2000.

Geophysics education is one of SEG/EAGE's top priorities. Because the DISC is an annually renewed program, your participation is key to its success. The Distinguished Programs and DISC have become highly sought opportunities for financial sponsorship and endowment by companies and organizations. In partnership and collaboration with the EAGE, the DISC is sponsored and coordinated throughout Europe by EAGE. The DISC program affords important opportunities for local organizations to provide first-rate geophysical education opportunities at modest cost. The DISC is truly a cooperative effort of many people dedicated to the promotion and advancement of geophysics.

Fred Hilterman has prepared an extremely comprehensive examination of seismic amplitude attributes and their applications. We encourage you to take full advantage of this opportunity to broaden your perspectives through participation in the 2001 DISC.

Sincerely,

Sally G. Zinke
SEG President

Etienne Robein
EAGE President

Section 1. Course Introduction

Objective:

1. **Present philosophy of amplitude interpretation**
2. **Track our history in amplitude interpretation**
3. **Outline course direction**

1A. Seismic Interpretation Philosophy

What are the objectives of a seismic interpretation? Are the objectives the same today as they were 40 years ago? Certainly today's 3-D seismic data and computer workstations have added tremendous interpretative abilities that weren't present 40 years ago—or even dreamed of! However, these are only tools for accomplishing the objectives. Unlike the frequency content of seismic data, the objectives of a seismic interpretation aren't time varying.

The objectives listed in Fig. 1.A.1 are paraphrased from Jakosky's book published in 1960. The first objective, "Recognizing a hydrocarbon anomaly," is still paramount in *predominant* today's seismic interpretation. However, our recognition criteria have been greatly enhanced with modern *true* amplitude acquisition and processing. Seismic amplitude is now one of the major criteria for recognizing potential hydrocarbon reserves.

The second objective, "Validating an anomaly," might be expanded to include stratigraphic framework through the interpretation of the seismic waveform patterns. However, let's incorporate stratigraphic validation in the structural interpretation of the geologic framework. In short, find an anomaly, map the structure, and make sure the seismic reflection amplitude is consistent with the structural interpretation.

While the recognition and validation of a potential seismic anomaly might be the interpreter's objectives, management also has its own. Besides the upside economic value of the prospect, some aspect of risk must be assigned to the prospect, if for no other reason than for trying to decide which prospect to drill first. The management requirement can be stated several ways. One is: "Identify where art dominates and science deviates in the structural and amplitude interpretations." This philosophy is paraphrased from a late evening discussion several years ago with a fellow colleague, Jack Caldwell. By stating risk assignment in these terms, the old adage "Seismic interpretation is an art that takes years of experience to acquire" takes on a different meaning. Seismic interpretation is both an art and a science. As Fig. 1.A.2 indicates, the *years of experience* inferred by the old adage is nothing but the development of a systematic set of rules to produce an initial estimate of the anomaly's structure and composition. Without this first estimate of the earth model, it is difficult to scientifically validate the prospect, and thus it is difficult to reduce the ambiguity associated with risk.

Four Steps of Interpretation

This interpretation philosophy was introduced to me in 1961 as I walked into my first lecture on seismic prospecting. In bold letters on the blackboard, Professor Hasbrouck had written *ACCH* (Fig. 1.A.3). This acronym represented the art and science of an interpretation. In *A* (Assume an earth model), the systematic rules one developed from past experience are drawn upon to visualize an earth model. The two *C*'s (Compute and Compare) represent the validation step through science. The final *H* is the pleasure of waiting for the drill bit to reach the anomaly's target depth and Hoping for success. Beneath ACCH, Professor Hasbrouck had also written a corollary on the blackboard: "Geophysical data can't be interpreted without knowing the answer." To the young geophysicists in the class, this was a contradictory statement that definitely needed additional explanation.

The seismic section displayed in Fig. 1.A.4 will help illustrate the *ACCH* method and its corollary. In the figure, there is an obvious time anomaly beneath the question mark. Is this anomaly a time high caused by a lateral velocity variation, or a true anticline that could be a potential hydrocarbon trap? Let's apply ACCH. For the *A* portion, one might *assume* salt sits on a flat horizon (assuming a velocity anomaly). The validation portion, *Compute and Compare*, can be quite simple. The anomaly has a time interval of 1.0 s and the lower horizon has a 0.4 s time high for a total of 1.4 s. If the interval velocity between 1.3 s and 2.7 s off the structure is equal to [salt velocity] × [1.0 s / 1.4 s], then salt on a flat horizon appears to be a good estimate of the earth model. And, the potential hydrocarbon trap disappears. However, in order to execute the ACCH method, several items had to be known: the shape of salt structures, the petrophysical properties of salt and the surrounding sediments, and so forth.

In short, the validation of the structural interpretation employed a set of rules that included petrophysical relationships. If this structural interpretation were complemented with a modern interpretation workstation, the validation process would approach a science as stated in Fig. 1.A.5. When an interpretation reaches the science stage, quality-control (QC) standards can be developed and easily verified by others. In fact, there are several companies today that have developed these QC standards, thus freeing geoscientists from the initial structural mapping.

However, is the current status of amplitude validation approaching a science? If not, where is Art dominating the amplitude interpretation, and what is necessary to raise amplitude interpretation to a Science? What is obviously missing is a modern set of rules that are based on past experience (the corollary). This is the course objective: to review the current rules for recognizing and validating an amplitude interpretation, with particular emphasis on the seismic amplitude relationship to petrophysics.

Expansion of Interpretation Objectives

As presented so far, the validation of a seismic anomaly is quite restrictive. Normally, most oil companies validate all components of the hydrocarbon system rather than just the reservoir composition and structure. Gordon Greve, in his 1996 SEG presidential talk, briefly described the importance of the team effort to answer questions about the seven elements of the hydrocarbon system (Fig. 1.A.6). All elements must be in place for hydrocarbons to exist. Can an amplitude interpretation assist in this analysis?

With respect to the source rock, does it have unique rock properties that will allow amplitude to define the richness and presence of kerogen? While seismic velocity has been related to effective pressure measurements, will there be significant amplitude variations that can be related to pressure regimes? If fault planes are possible fluid-flow paths for hydrocarbon migration, will active faults display more amplitude or less than inactive faults do? Will this recognition of fault activity relate to the timing of trap generation? If the petrophysical properties of a seal are related to its pressure capacity, will seismic amplitude be able to quantify shale rock properties? As before, all these questions place a particular emphasis on the seismic amplitude relationship to petrophysics.

1B. Historical Overview

If a comprehensive documentation of amplitude interpretation of seismic data were attempted, reports from the archives of the oil companies would be necessary. Unfortunately, any amplitude interpretation technique found in these archives that offered to be a Direct Detection Indicator (DDI) or Hydrocarbon Indicator (HCI) would have *confidential* stamped on the cover. Thus, these rules for amplitude interpretation are lost.

However, Mike Forrest recently discussed Shell's entry into bright spot or DDI efforts in the late 1960s (Forrest, 2000). From the article, it was obvious that this new technique was Shell's confidential leading edge in lease sales. Widespread application of the bright-spot technology in the oil industry occurred around 1972. Thus, early publications that documented the use of seismic amplitude to predict lithology or pore-fluid content are scarce.

The Russian literature, however, documented amplitude interpretation techniques to find hydrocarbons well before the Western world did. Sengbush noted that the Russians were using amplitude in 1952-1953 on structures to locate water-oil and gas-liquid contacts. In 1963, Churlin and Sergeyev reported on four significant DDI's that they were applying to seismic data: bright-spot measurements, reservoir-edge interference patterns, flat spots, and absorption.

For the Western world, Savit (1960) presented two case histories on amplitude interpretations from the Summarizer, which was invented by Merlini of AGIP. Basically, the Summarizer integrated the seismic trace and produced a trace that resembled an acoustic impedance log. Figure 1.B.1 contains an example from Western Canada. The figure indicates that there are two producing wells and a dry hole for petrophysical calibration. On the Summarizer section, the increase in amplitude associated with the horizon labeled C defines the limits of the stratigraphic oil field. Savit noted, and I am sure you will also, that it is difficult to find this same amplitude relationship on the seismic section.

In 1970, Pan and de Bremaecker published results from Pan's 1969 PhD dissertation on direct location of hydrocarbons using seismic amplitude. Figure 1.B.2 is a colored version of a figure taken from their article. The figure contains a structural map overlain with a colored amplitude map. The seismic amplitudes (A) on the hydrocarbon portion of the structure were normalized by an amplitude (*B*) from an off-structure water-saturated reflection. There is a strong correlation between the structure map and normalized reflection amplitude (*A/B*, or anomaly/background). Typical seismic data that were used in this analysis are shown in Fig. 1.B.3. Yes ... 8-trace, split-continuous analog data with AGC were interpreted! It is obvious that the authors developed an interpretation philosophy before they examined the seismic data. As depicted in Fig. 1.B.4, the philosophy included techniques that are part of today's amplitude interpretation: petrophysical calibration, inversion to acoustic impedance, and relative-amplitude calibration. The goal was to determine porosity, pore-fluid saturant, and field limits. What is surprising is that the oil field is not a bright-spot anomaly, it is a dim out; the seismic amplitude map in Fig. 1.B.2 decays over the hydrocarbon zones.

In 1973, the Geophysical Society of Houston organized a symposium on direct detection indicators. Numerous field examples and theoretical models for tying seismic to rock physics were presented. In addition, the number of direct detection indicators was vastly expanded to include such features as flat spots, velocity pushdowns, frequency attenuation, etc. It was obvious from this symposium that the recognition and validation of seismic amplitude anomalies from stack sections was a procedure accepted by the oil industry. The bright-spot technology of the 1970s established the first era of seismic amplitude interpretation. An abbreviated timeline for the amplitude interpretation eras is suggested in Fig. 1.B.5.

The second era of amplitude interpretation, the analysis of Amplitude Variation with respect to source-receiver Offset (AVO), was actually happening simultaneously. AVO is also referred to as AVA for Amplitude Variation with incident Angle. Before the second era is discussed, an important contribution to both the bright-spot era and the current era of AVO that is often overlooked is Gassmann's contribution. His work was essential for calibrating the petrophysical properties to the seismic velocities, especially for pore-fluid predictions.

Around 1900, Knott and Zoeppritz developed the theoretical work necessary for AVO theory (Knott, 1899; Zoeppritz, 1919). Given the *P*-wave and *S*-wave velocities along with the densities of the two bounding media, they developed equations for plane-wave reflection amplitudes as a function of incident angle. However, the exact mathematical expression of the reflection coefficient is exceptionally long, thus making it difficult to perceive how reflection amplitude varies if a rock property is changed slightly. Therefore, when it comes to visualizing the interplay of rock properties and reflection amplitudes, the work of Bortfeld in 1961 is called upon. Bortfeld's work simplified Zoeppritz's equation, and surprisingly it came six years after Koefoed (1955) described the relationship of AVO to changes in Poisson's ratio across a boundary. Koefoed's results were based on the exact Zoeppritz's equation. The conclusions drawn by Koefoed are the basis of today's AVO interpretation.

Recognizing the significance of Koefoed's work for predicting lithology, Rosa in 1976 investigated the elastic properties that could be extracted robustly from AVO inversion. His work tied very closely to the linear-approximation equation developed by Shuey (1985). Interestingly, Shuey also was inspired to examine AVO after learning of Koefoed's article.

However, it was 27 years after Koefoed's work that the relationship between AVO and lithology was dramatically brought into the limelight by Ostrander (1982). Ostrander's work was the verification that the industry needed in order to react. Once Ostrander illustrated the interpretation benefits of AVO with field data, the second era of amplitude interpretation accelerated. Interest in (A) petrophysics, (B) forward and inverse modeling, and (C) preservation, imaging, and inversion of seismic amplitudes received new attention.

The dissemination of integrated AVO case histories still remained a problem for the geophysical industry. In the early 1990s, through the auspices of the Gas Research Institute (GRI) and SEG, Allen and Peddy collected seismic data, well information, and interpretations from several exploration companies working the Gulf Coast of Texas. They published (Allen and Peddy, 1993) a practical look at AVO that was documented not only with successes but also the interpretational lessons learned from dry holes. The majority of the case histories centered on the Eocene Yegua Formation. In fact, Yegua plays were so successfully detected with AVO, that locals claimed that *Yegua* was the American Indian pronunciation of *AVO*.

With the advent of AVO, the amplitude interpretation principles developed during the bright-spot era have become a subset of AVO.

1C. Basic Principles

The article by Pan and de Bremaecker (1970) provided an excellent philosophy for an amplitude interpretation based on the bright-spot technique: amplitude analysis of normal-incident reflections. This needs to be expanded for AVO. What additional information resides in an AVO interpretation?

A stack section and three common depth point (CDP) gathers are illustrated in Fig. 1.C.1. On the stack section, the amplitude associated with the upper horizon is bright (large amplitude values) around CDP 110. Is this amplitude variation caused by a change in rock type, porosity, pore-fluid content, or thickness? The CDP gather at location 20, off the anomaly, is examined. Within CDP gather 20, the amplitude variation for the upper horizon is constant with offset. How does this amplitude variation with offset compare with a CDP gather located on the prospect? The figure depicts two possible CDP gathers that might be found at location 110 on the amplitude anomaly. If the CDP traces for Case 1 or Case 2 were stacked, the results would be identical. Thus, by examining the stack amplitude alone, the fact is lost that the amplitude decreases with offset in Case 1 but increases with offset in Case 2. Yet as Koefoed stated in 1955, this difference in amplitude variation provides insight to the lithology. What media properties would cause the two different AVOs? How is lithology correlated to petrophysics?

Following the suggestion of Koefoed, a Poisson's ratio curve derived from a shear-dipole log is displayed with its respective gamma log in Fig. 1.C.2. The well is located in a Tertiary basin composed of sand-shale sequences. Thus, the gamma log provides an indication of sand percentage or shale volume. There is a strong correlation between Poisson's ratio and the inferred sand percentage for this logged interval. Does this always occur? Are all the sands wet? How much does the Poisson's ratio value change if the pore-fluid is substituted with hydrocarbons? What other petrophysical possibilities should be considered as this AVO anomaly is validated?

Once the possible petrophysical changes have been cataloged, their seismic effect must be compared with the field data. The equation in Fig. 1.C.3 relates the reflection coefficient (RC) to changes in the petrophysical properties; that is, changes in acoustic impedance ($\rho\alpha$) and Poisson's ratio (σ). This is a simplified version of Shuey's equation (which will be discussed later), but it provides a qualitative tie of the petrophysics to the AVO. The equation also quantifies Koefoed's observations.

The individual contributions to $RC(\theta)$ from $\rho\alpha$ and σ variations are graphed in the lower right of the figure. *PR* (σ variation) has no influence on normal-incident reflections ($\theta = 0°$). However, if σ is related to lithology as suggested by Fig. 1.C.2, then large-angle reflections are desired so that $RC(\theta)$ has lithologic information.

Three basic principles are outlined in this first section. They are: first, recognize an amplitude anomaly on the stack or CDP gathers; second, establish the possible variations in the rock properties that could relate to the amplitude anomaly; and third, validate the rock-property predictions with the seismic field data. Simple!

1D. Course Objective

A cut-and-dry version of the course objective is: Using seismic amplitudes, develop a systematic method for calibrating the earth's rock properties to seismic in an effort to validate the economic potential of a hydrocarbon play. But this doesn't really relate to the three basic principles outlined. So, let's expand on these principles as suggested in Fig. 1.D.1.

The first two topics, petrophysical transforms and reflection-coefficient equations, provide rules-of-thumb for predicting the change in magnitude and shape of the AVO curve from rock-property variations. For instance, how do pore-fluid variations translate to changes in AVO shape? Once these are understood, then rules-of-thumb for recognizing hydrocarbon signatures can be developed.

In the previous interpretation of the time anomaly beneath the salt structure, a "quick-look" solution was employed without the use of a computer. Methods similar to this will be examined for amplitude interpretation of AVO signatures.

Just as Shuey advocated a particular mathematical expression relating rock properties to reflection amplitude, numerous other authors have proposed different expressions. These various expressions lead to numerous AVO attributes that are available for amplitude interpretation. Examples of the AVO attributes found in the literature and that will be discussed in detail in Section 6 are (A, B), (NI_P, NI_S), (NI_P, PR), $(\rho\lambda, \rho\mu)$, and (AI, EI). What are the advantages of one set of AVO attributes over another?

Finally, case histories will illustrate the selection of one set of amplitude attributes over another, based on the geologic environment.

To many readers, an obvious omission might be noticed in Figure 1.D.1 and the Table of Contents. There is no mention of seismic data processing or acquisition. Comments will be made throughout the course on these subjects, but each subject deserves a course by itself, to do it justice.

Figures

Figure 1.A.1

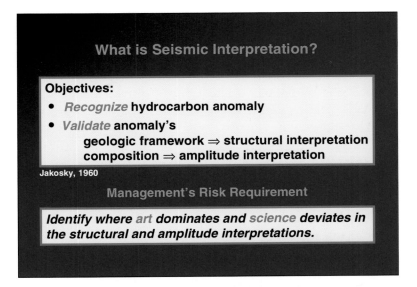

Figure 1.A.2

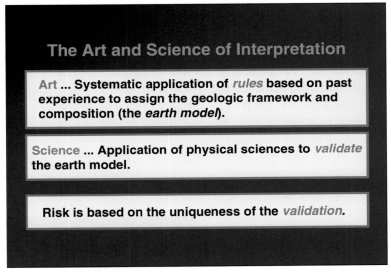

Figure 1.A.3

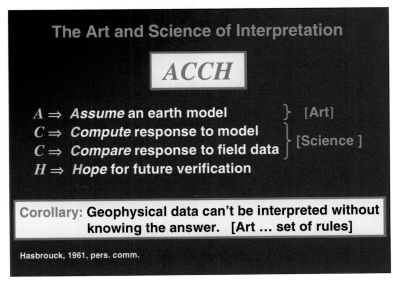

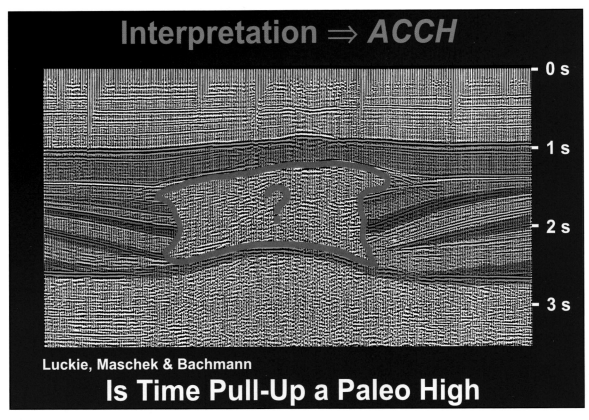

Figure 1.A.4

Figure 1.A.5

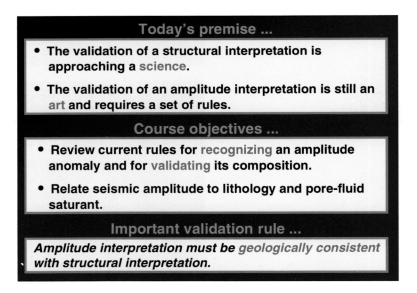

Figure 1.A.6

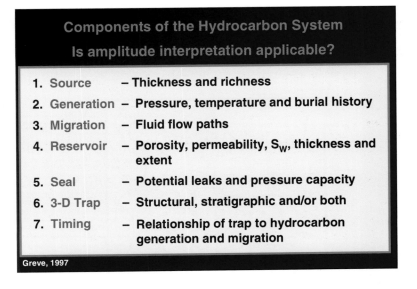

Figure 1.B.1

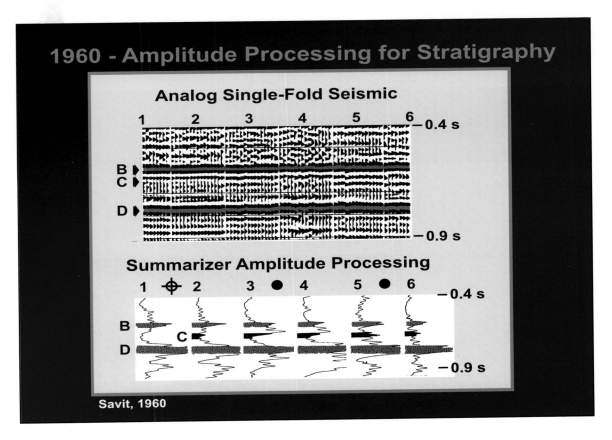

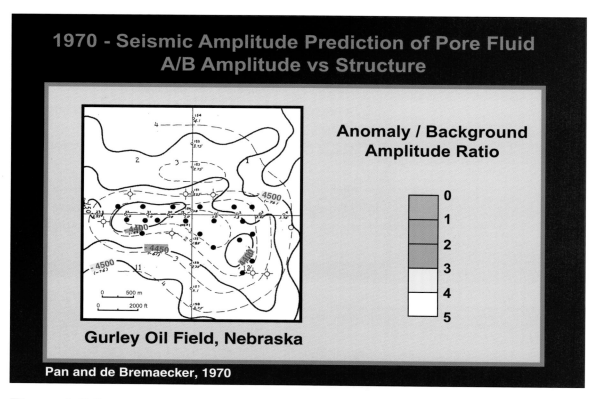

Figure 1.B.2

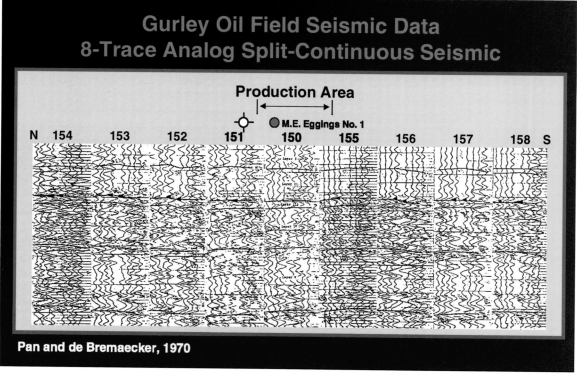

Figure 1.B.3

Figure 1.B.4

Pan and de Bremaecker's 1970 Interpretation

- **Petrophysics** - **Applied rock-property transforms**
  - **- Included pore-fluid substitution**
  - **- Calibrated borehole to seismic**
- **Inversion** **- Estimated acoustic impedance**
- **A/B** **- [Anomaly/Background] amplitude maps**

Predictions from amplitude

- **Pore-fluid saturant**
- **Porosity**
- **Structural limits of pore-fluid contact**

Oil reservoir was Dim Out, not Bright Spot

Figure 1.B.5

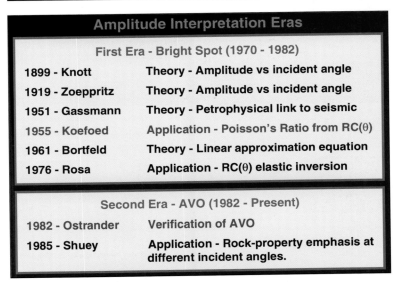

Amplitude Interpretation Eras

First Era - Bright Spot (1970 - 1982)

1899 - Knott	**Theory - Amplitude vs incident angle**
1919 - Zoeppritz	**Theory - Amplitude vs incident angle**
1951 - Gassmann	**Theory - Petrophysical link to seismic**
1955 - Koefoed	**Application - Poisson's Ratio from RC(θ)**
1961 - Bortfeld	**Theory - Linear approximation equation**
1976 - Rosa	**Application - RC(θ) elastic inversion**

Second Era - AVO (1982 - Present)

1982 - Ostrander	**Verification of AVO**
1985 - Shuey	**Application - Rock-property emphasis at different incident angles.**

Figure 1.C.1

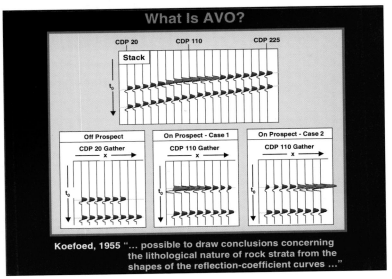

Koefoed, 1955 "... possible to draw conclusions concerning the lithological nature of rock strata from the shapes of the reflection-coefficient curves ..."

Figure 1.C.2

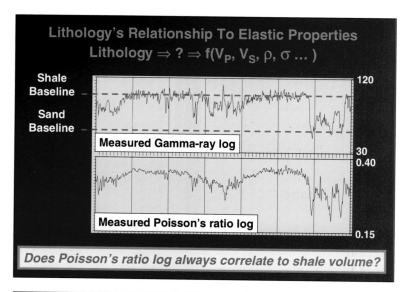

Figure 1.C.3

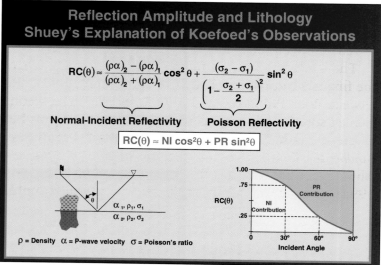

Figure 1.D.1

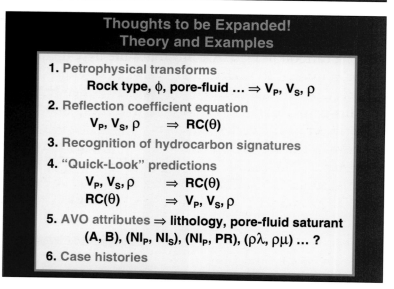

Section 2. Rock Physics

Objective:

1. Illustrate velocity dependence and sensitivity to elastic constants and environmental factors

2. Examine rock-property transforms

3. Estimate *P*-wave and *S*-wave velocities when pore-fluid and/or porosity changes

One of the primary goals of amplitude interpretation is to determine whether a water-saturated rock or a hydrocarbon-saturated rock generated the reflection of interest. In order to accomplish this task, an estimate of the difference in rock properties between the water-saturated and hydrocarbon-saturated states is required. Thus, a few basic relationships of rock physics are necessary. There are both empirical and theoretical relationships between seismic rock properties and elastic constants that will be called upon, as well as wave-propagation models.

The work presented in these notes has drawn heavily from two excellent references. The first is a tutorial article by Castagna et al. (1993): "Rock Physics—The Link Between Rock Properties and AVO Response." The second is a book for those who want detailed solutions to various rock-property transforms but don't want to wade through the messy math. The book is written by Mavko et al. (1998): *The Rock Physics Handbook—Tools for Seismic Analysis in Porous Media*. In addition, the two SEG reprint volumes, *Seismic Acoustic Velocities in Reservoir Rocks*, compiled by Wang and Nur (1992), provide easy access to classic articles on petrophysics.

2A. *P*-waves, *S*-waves, Density, and Poisson's Ratio

Before a theory can be formulated for wave motion in a medium, a relationship between stress and strain is needed. For waves of infinitesimal amplitude, Hooke's empirical law supplies this relationship. The three most commonly used elastic constants to quantitatively describe the strength of a body are the shear (μ), bulk (K), and Young's (E) moduli. The cartoon in Fig.2.A.1 illustrates the hypothetical experiments that measure these elastic constants. In reality, it is difficult to measure the shear modulus (rigidity) as described in the figure and obtain useable results. However, the other two moduli measurements are conducive to lab measurements. As an example, if the bulk modulus of a solid rubber ball were desired, a simple experiment could be conducted. Measure the diameter of the ball and then dive into a deep lake and measure the ball's diameter at the depth of 500 ft (150 m). At 500 ft, the stress (or hydrostatic pressure) is approximately 230 psi (1590 kPa). Knowing the change in stress and the change in volume, the bulk modulus can be computed. Young's modulus is normally measured on thin rodlike specimens.

The experiments described in Fig. 2.A.1 would yield the necessary elastic constants for developing a wave theory if the material were nonporous. For porous material, the bulk modulus needs to be separated into its components (Fig. 2.A.2). The bulk-modulus components selected in the figure are pertinent to Gassmann's wave propagation theory, which will be introduced later. The three components are the pore-fluid (K_f), matrix-material (K_{ma}), and dry-rock (K_{dry}) bulk moduli. If the pore fluid and matrix material (grains) are known from well-log measurements, their associated bulk moduli can be estimated fairly easily. The dry-rock bulk modulus is a bit more difficult to come by and other relationships will be developed to assist in estimating it.

In Fig. 2.A.3, two of the rock moduli are related to the *P*-wave and *S*-wave velocities. Throughout these notes, the Greek letters α and β will be used interchangeably with V_P and V_S to refer to the *P*-wave (primary or compressional) and *S*-wave (shear) velocities, respectively. While current convention requires that the metric system be employed in geophysical literature, many of the graphs and figures shown in these notes are reproduced from literature and are annotated in the English system. If the bulk moduli of the rock are expressed in gigapascals (GPa) and the density in gm/cc (gm/cm^3), then the resulting velocity is expressed in km/s. The bottom of the figure contains an example with appropriate units for nonporous sandstone.

In order to solve for velocities in the equations of Fig. 2.A.3, the density, ρ, is required. Density is expressed as a function of porosity, ϕ, as shown in Fig. 2.A.4. The bulk density of the rock, ρ, is related to the matrix (grains) and pore-fluid densities. As the bulk density depends on porosity, the fluid density depends on the water saturation, S_W, which is the percentage of the pore space filled with water (brine). What is not indicated is that most rocks are composed of more than one mineral. Thus, the matrix density, ρ_{ma}, needs to be expressed as a volumetric average of the individual mineral densities.

During rock-squeezing experiments in the lab, Poisson's ratio, σ, can also be measured as shown in Fig. 2.A.5 (static measurement). Poisson's ratio, which is Koefoed's lithologic identifier, is simply the negative ratio of the transverse strain to the longitudinal strain. Normally, however, geophysicists express Poisson's ratio as a function of the *P*-wave and *S*-wave velocities (dynamic measurement).

For isotropic media, the value of Poisson's ratio falls between 0.0 and 0.5. The two extremes are useful to examine. When the strained volume is equal to the initial volume, Poisson's ratio is 0.5. This is the case for fluids, which include water, air, and oil. In addition, for the first hundred feet beneath the ocean bottom, Poisson's ratio approaches 0.5 for recent sediments. For those involved in physical modeling experiments, rubber has a Poisson's ratio very close to 0.5. The other extreme occurs when the strained volume has no transverse strain, or as Mike Graul has quoted, "It has zero *fatticity;* it doesn't get fat as you squeeze it vertically." What doesn't get fatter when you squeeze it? A sponge! In exploration geophysics, this occurs in some sense when water is replaced with gas in the pores. Poisson's ratio of the rock always decreases when gas is substituted for water in the pore space.

Substantial differences between the static and dynamic measurements of Poisson's ratio for the same rock are reported in literature. The dynamic Poisson's ratio is normally higher. Wang offered an explanation for these discrepancies. In the dynamic measurements, the propagating waves have strain amplitudes smaller than 10^{-6}, while the static measurements (squeezing in a vise) have strain amplitudes greater than 10^{-3}. That is, static measurements squeeze the rock more than dynamic methods. Most sedimentary rocks have pores or cracks that are elongated (not spherical) and the propagating waves in the dynamic method do not squeeze these cracks closed. Thus, the rock appears to be stronger (less compressible) than in the situation where the cracks close. In the static method, the cracks close and the rock will appear to have a lower strength. If the experiments are conducted at higher confining pressures so that the cracks are closed at the beginning of the experiment, then static and dynamic measurements of Poisson's ratio approach one another.

A brief preview of the significance of V_P/V_S or Poisson's ratio for discriminating different lithologies is shown in Fig. 2.A.6. This is an idealized plot. At a particular depth, shales tend to have a Poisson's ratio that is larger than that for sands, especially gas-saturated sands. As the depth of investigation becomes shallower, sand and shale Poisson's ratio values move toward 0.5. Also, the sand and shale trends tend to overlap more. Conversely, as the depth of investigation increases, the sand and shale trends tend to separate and have lower Poisson's ratio values—with sand still having a Poisson's ratio lower than shale does. However, with changes of depth, Poisson's ratio for limestone and dolomite does not vary as much as it does for sandstone and shale.

2B. Establishing Regional and Local Rock-Property Trends

Whenever an amplitude anomaly is recognized on a seismic section, the trick is to distinguish what rock-property variation caused the amplitude change. In order to assist in this decision, rules-of-thumb are desired on how velocity is affected by changes in (a) elastic moduli, (b) densities, and (c) various environmental conditions (Fig. 2.B.1). A few of the primary factors affecting velocity are as follows.

Fluid Density—For unconsolidated clastics, pore-fluid variations can significantly change the velocity of the rock. As the pore-fluid density increases, the rock's velocity increases. However, for well-consolidated rocks, porosity variations become more significant than pore-fluid variations for changing the rock's velocity.

Matrix Density—Denser rocks normally have a higher velocity than lighter rocks. Density variations are often the primary component of the reflection coefficient for shallow wet unconsolidated rocks.

Age/Depth—Age, by itself, does not affect the rock's velocity. It is all the other factors that occur over time, such as increased cementation, loss of porosity, compaction, and diagenetic changes. High-velocity rocks tend to have a rapid increase in velocity with depth for the first 3000 ft (900 m) as the micro-cracks close. Then, the velocity increases slowly with depth until the velocity approaches the terminal zero-porosity end member. For unconsolidated rocks, velocity tends to increase linearly with depth, or, more exactly, with increases in effective pressure, which is discussed later.

Water Saturation—As mentioned, if the pore-fluid density increases, the *P*-wave velocity increases. However, this increase in velocity is not necessarily linear with the increase of pore-fluid density. For shallow unconsolidated sediments, a small percentage of gas in the pores significantly decreases the velocity of the rock compared with the water-saturated state. However, once the rock is saturated with 5–10% gas, further gas saturation has little effect on the rock's velocity. Unfortunately, this means that economic gas reservoirs have almost the same *P*-wave seismic amplitude as a depleted reservoir.

Porosity—There are numerous empirical formulas that log analysts have derived over the years to evaluate a reservoir's porosity in terms of sonic-log traveltime (inverse of velocity). Porosity alters both the density of a rock and its elastic moduli, such that porosity increases yield velocity decreases.

Cementation—Cementation of the grains, which normally increases with age, reduces the porosity and increases the elastic moduli of the rock. Thus cementation increases the velocity of the rock.

Pore Pressure and Overburden Pressure—It is necessary to consider overburden pressure and pore pressure together when analyzing velocity. The overburden pressure on a formation results from the total weight of the rock above it, including the fluid in the rock. If the rock has hydrostatic communication with the surface, then the pore pressure in the rock is equal to the pressure at the base of a column of brine that has a height equal to the formation's depth (hydrostatic pressure). If the overburden pressure is increased while holding the pore pressure constant, the solid matrix will be squeezed closer together and the rock's elastic moduli increase while the density changes little. Similarly, if the pore pressure increases while the overburden pressure remains the same, the pore fluid tends to support more of the overburden and the rock appears weaker and the formation has a lower velocity. This last scenario is an abnormally pressured formation. For our purposes, the overburden pressure minus the pore pressure is called the effective pressure. If the effective pressure is held constant, then no apparent change in velocity is recognized. With an overburden pressure gradient of 1 psi/ft and a pore pressure gradient of 0.47 psi/ft, the effective pressure on the rock increases at 0.53 psi/ft. Thus velocity generally increases with depth.

Shale Content—Normally, the *P*-wave velocity decreases as the shale content is increased. However, this is not always the case. The direction of the velocity change depends on how shale enters the rock: fills the pores, breaches the grain contacts, or replaces part of the skeleton.

From the factors listed above, which one influences velocity the most? Generally, the dominant factors that influence velocity must be determined for an individual area. The different factors are introduced as either filters or variables in trend analyses for regional and local amplitude interpretations. A trend example from the Gulf of Mexico (GOM), which contains essentially unconsolidated clastic sediments, illustrates the concept by filtering the samples based on lithology and the presence of abnormal pressure. Effective pressure is a variable approximated by depth. Velocity and density trends for both sand and shale are desired for quantifying future amplitude interpretations.

Sea-Level Versus Ocean-Bottom Datum

The six well locations illustrated in Fig. 2.B.2 have water depths ranging from 1000 to 7000 ft (300 to 2000 m). Velocity and density histogram trends were developed from these six wells and they are illustrated in Fig. 2.B.3. A histogram trend contains statistical analyses at 500-ft (150-m) depth intervals from a specified datum to approximately 18,000 ft (6000 m) beneath the datum. Velocity and density samples from well-log curves were taken at 1-ft intervals. All lithologies were included and the datum was set at sea level. The vertical line near the maximum-frequency point for each 500-ft histogram represents the average value. The small red dot represents a recomputed average after samples more than one standard deviation from the original average were omitted. It is difficult to predict a reliable trend for either velocity or density from the plots in Fig. 2.B.3. The histograms are too disjointed from one depth to the next to be considered reliable. The first impulse is to rerun the data and produce separate histogram trends for sand and shale. However, this is not the primary factor to consider for developing reliable trend curves in this area.

The same six well-log curves were reexamined, but with the depth datum set at ocean bottom (Fig 2.B.4). More continuous and thus reliable trends are produced. Obviously, velocity and density trend curves to be used in amplitude interpretation should be referenced from the ocean bottom. Why?

Effective Pressure

As mentioned earlier, the effective pressure can be a primary factor controlling velocity. The effective pressure is zero in the water column and does not change until sediments are reached. The empirical relationship of effective pressure to in-situ velocity is cartooned in Fig. 2.B.5. The effective pressure, which is approximately the overburden pressure minus the pore pressure, increases linearly until the onset of abnormal pore pressure is reached (at 7500 ft [2300 m] in the figure). The velocity profile also increases linearly to the onset of abnormal pressure. Below the onset of abnormal pore pressure, the fluid in the pores begins to support the overburden rock, and the effective pressure decreases. The two points labeled as V_A on the velocity profile have the same effective pressure and thus have approximately the same in-situ velocity. As a side note, it was this empirical velocity-to-effective-pressure relationship, which can be determined from seismic interval-velocity analyses, that formed the basis of predicting mud-weight programs for drilling engineers (Hottman and Johnson, 1965; Pennebaker, 1968; Dutta and Levin, 1987). This is a very simplistic relationship of interval velocity to effective pressure that needs to be adjusted slightly for actual field conditions.

The expected rock properties beneath the onset of abnormal geopressure depend not only on the effective pressure but also on the environmental reasons for the abnormal pressure. Often, the environmental reasons can be inferred by the change in the shape of the effective pressure curve. In drilling terminology, these changes in effective-pressure curves are called *soft* and *hard* onsets of abnormal geopressure.

A soft onset is illustrated with shale histogram trends from a single well in the southern portion of offshore Louisiana, Vermilion Block 395 (Fig. 2.B.6). At the 6500-ft (2000-m) depth, the onset of abnormal pressure occurred and the mud weight at this depth was gradually increased from 10.3 lbs/gal to 12.4 lbs/gal at the bottom of the hole. The velocity and density values beneath 6500-ft depth are essentially the same as the values at 6500 ft. This indicates that the effective pressure is constant over the depth interval beneath the onset of abnormal pressure. This type of overpressure commonly occurs when the pore fluid trapped by low-permeability shale is squeezed by the weight of newly deposited sediments. This abnormal pressure is referred to as undercompaction or compaction disequilibrium (Bowers, 1995).

A hard onset of abnormal pressure is depicted by the shale histogram trend curves in Fig. 2.B.7. Above the onset of abnormal pressure, the shale rock-property trends are essentially the same as the soft-onset trend curves, but they differ dramatically below. In the soft onset, the density values beneath the onset have a somewhat predictable trend, but in the hard onset, density values may increase, decrease, or remain constant. Also, the velocity drops significantly when abnormal pressure is reached in the hard-onset case. Bower emphasized the importance of distinguishing this mechanism of overpressure from undercompaction. This overpressure can be generated by fluid expansion such as heating, hydrocarbon maturation, and expulsion/expansion of intergranular water during clay diagenesis. This is an unloading mechanism, and normally the effective pressure decreases more than is predicted from interval velocity. The rock undergoes a plastic and not an elastic rebound.

These significant changes in the velocity and density trends suggest that a horizon map indicating the depth to the onset of abnormal pressure should be incorporated into all amplitude interpretations.

The different mechanisms for generating abnormal geopressure were also correlated to stratigraphy by Verm et al. (1998). The study used over 2700 wells and included GOM regional trend analyses. The maps in Fig. 2.B.8 indicate a strong correlation between the depth to abnormal-pressure onset and the major sand deposits. In the northern portion of the upper map, the onset of abnormal geopressure isn't reached until 14,000 ft (4000 m) in some places, while in the southern portion, the onset occurs as shallow as 2000 ft (600 m). In the upper map, there is a sharp break in the north-south gradient at the 8000-ft (2400-m) contour (red color). This is not surprising because large sand deposits in the northern part of the Gulf provide the pore-fluid conduit for communication to the surface. This is evident in the sand percentage map in the lower portion of the figure that also has the 8000-ft contour overlain. North of the 8000-ft contour line, the expected onset of geopressure is hard and diagenetic changes are responsible for abnormal pressure; while south of the 8000-ft contour, it is mainly soft and caused by undercompaction.

Up to this point, the significance of knowing the effective pressure has been emphasized for unconsolidated sediments. How does lithology affect the velocity and density trend curves?

Velocity and Density Trend Curves for Sand and Shale

In Fig. 2.B.9, sand velocity and density histograms were generated from a 2500-mi^2 (6400-km^2) area in the northern portion of the map shown in Fig. 2.B.8. In this area, the depth to the onset of geopressure was picked for 220 exploration wells. Only data above the onset of geopressure were included in the statistical analyses. There is a surprisingly linear depth trend for both sand velocity and density.

Similar trends for shale were obtained, and the average trend values for the sand and shale properties were fitted with linear equations as shown in Fig. 2.B.10. The best-fit linear trends to the average rock-property values are

$$V_{SAND} \text{ (ft/s)} = 5530 + .464 \, z \text{ (ft)}$$
$$V_{SHALE} \text{ (ft/s)} = 5820 + .417 \, z \text{ (ft)}$$
$$\rho_{SAND} \text{ (gm/cm}^3) = 2.02 + .0000226 \, z \text{ (ft)}$$
$$\rho_{SHALE} \text{ (gm/cm}^3) = 2.06 + .0000291 \, z \text{ (ft)}$$

where z is depth, in feet.

The sand velocity is less than the shale velocity down to approximately 6000-ft (2000-m) depth and then the sand velocity becomes faster than shale velocity. The density contrast between sand and shale increases with depth, with sand being less dense than shale. However, the more important aspect with respect to amplitude interpretation is the reflection coefficient trend as displayed in Fig. 2.B.11. This is based on shale over water-saturated sands. The figure indicates that the acoustic impedance ($\rho\alpha$) of sand is less than shale from the surface to 13,000 ft (4000 m). Even though the velocity of shale is less than sand in the deeper zones, the smaller density values of sand dominate the contrast of the acoustic impedances at depth. The next logical step would be to investigate these relationships below the onset of abnormal geopressure. However, this is a more difficult problem.

In Fig. 2.B.12, a shale-velocity histogram trend for a single well that encounters abnormal pressure is illustrated. This well is from the deep-water area of GOM. There are several interesting points. First, end-member lithologies were analyzed in order to establish upper and lower bounds for the shale properties. The velocity trends for two end-member shale lithologies are shown. The lower-velocity bound is the clay-rich shale trend in abnormal pressure. This is essentially the minimum shale velocity in abnormal pressure. The other end-member is the shale normal-compaction curve for samples above the onset of geopressure. Above the onset of abnormal pressure in the figure, the trend from the single-well histogram is near the normal-compaction trend curve. In abnormal pressure, the shale velocity from the single well falls between the two end-member curves.

Another point is that shale-over-shale reflection amplitudes can be larger than shale-over-sand amplitudes in some areas. This is indicated on the histogram in Fig. 2.B.12 by the large velocity spread within a single 500-ft (150-m) depth interval. The figure indicates that the reflection amplitude from the velocity contrast between the shales within one 500-ft interval could be as large as 0.086. This number is several times larger than the shale-over-sand reflection amplitudes shown in Fig. 2.B.11. In the GOM, areas that are near the 8000-ft (2400-m) contour of abnormal geopressure (Fig. 2.B.8, by Verm et al.) exhibit large shale-over-shale reflections.

For unconsolidated rocks, velocity values are strongly correlated to effective pressure. The effective pressure is related to depth until the onset of abnormal pressure is reached. Beneath the onset of abnormal pressure, the effective pressure can be strongly correlated to the effective pressure just above the onset depth. This suggests that only local trend curves in abnormal pressure should be applied in amplitude interpretation, not regional ones where the onset of abnormal pressure varies significantly with depth.

In summary, in order to determine the significance of amplitude anomalies, local calibrations of rules-of-thumb are needed. These include quantitative rock-property measurements as a function of the anticipated lithologies and environmental conditions. Not only are average trends required, but we also need variations of the rock properties within short depth intervals. As illustrated above, linear-with-depth trends appear to fit unconsolidated rocks in the GOM. However, this is an isolated example and the trend values are applicable in this one area. Petrophysicists have reported numerous other empirical relationships, and these will now be examined.

2C. Empirical Relationships between Velocity and Density

Fig. 2.C.1 suggests several reasons for wanting empirical velocity-density relationships. The applications range from generating missing well-log curves and quality-controlling logs in questionable zones, to explaining anomalous seismic amplitudes. With the advent of AVO, new empirical transforms have been advocated for predicting S-wave velocity from other logs and also for predicting velocity changes when the pore-fluid is varied. However, as a warning beforehand, many of the transforms to be discussed are not only highly dependent on lithology, but are also very dependent on local conditions and shouldn't be extrapolated to other areas without recalibration.

Gardner's Velocity-Density Transform

At the 38th Annual International SEG Meeting in Denver (1968), Gardner et al. presented petrophysical principles for distinguishing gas-saturated sands from water-saturated sands using the seismic method. Gardner et al.'s published results (1974) were similar to Domenico's (1974). These authors had an impact on how pore-fluid content is analyzed from seismic data.

Gardner et al.'s velocity-density crossplots (1974) for various lithologies along with the average transform of $\rho = .23V^{.25}$ (gm/cm^3 and ft/s) are shown in Fig. 2.C.2. This average transform is a best-fit curve for all lithologies and was not intended for application to individual lithologies. Overall, however, the average transform fits the velocity-density pairs with only a couple of outliers. Salt is too light for its velocity, and anhydrite is too heavy. Gardner et al.'s average transform falls between the sand and shale trend lines.

Castagna (1993) extended Gardner's work by developing velocity-density transforms for lithologies plotted in Fig. 2.C.2. The revised transforms in gm/cm^3 and ft/s are

Sand:	$\rho = .200 \; V_P^{.261}$
Shale:	$\rho = .204 \; V_P^{.265}$
Limestone:	$\rho = .243 \; V_P^{.225}$
Dolomite:	$\rho = .226 \; V_P^{.243}$
Anhydrite:	$\rho = .600 \; V_P^{.160}$

In order to emphasize the importance of developing individual lithologic transforms, Castagna overplotted his best-fit sand and shale transforms on a set of well-log and laboratory measurements of velocity-density pairs (Fig. 2.C.3). As has been observed by many geophysicists, the average transform, $\rho = .23V^{.25}$, overestimates the density of sand and underestimates the density of shale. With the revised transforms, there is a better correlation to the raw data.

However, when Castagna's transforms for sand and shale are applied to the data sets previously displayed in Fig. 2.B.10, the correlation is not satisfactory (Fig. 2.C.4). Using the data themselves, the log-log best fits are shown in Fig. 2.C.4. Castagna's shale transform and the transform derived from the data themselves yield approximately the same results. However, the significant differences between the two sand transforms highlights a statement that Mavko et al. (1998) frequently note in their book: "These relations are empirical and thus strictly speaking they apply only to the set of rocks studied."

Wyllie's Velocity-Porosity Transform

In 1956 and in subsequent publications (1958 and 1963), Wyllie et al. proposed the empirical relationship between velocity and porosity for brine-filled porous media of

$$1/V = (1-\phi)/V_{ma} + \phi/V_{fl} \tag{1}$$

where V = velocity of total rock, V_{ma} = velocity of the matrix material, V_{fl} = velocity of pore fluid and ϕ = porosity. This is often expressed in terms of interval traveltime (μs/ft) as

$$\Delta t = (1-\phi)\,\Delta t_{ma} + \phi\,\Delta t_{fl} \tag{2}$$

where the Δt's represent the respective traveltimes (Fig. 2.C.5). When expressed in interval traveltimes, Wyllie's equation represents the total time it takes to pass through the porous material and matrix material individually. This heuristic interpretation is illustrated in the figure.

Obviously, the variable Δt_{ma} is dependent on lithology. Commonly used values for Δt_{ma} (μs/ft) as reported by Schlumberger are

Sandstone	55.5 or 51.0
Limestone	47.5
Dolomite	43.5
Anhydrite	50.0
Salt	67.0
Brine	189.0 (Δt_{fl})

When applying Wyllie's transform, there are numerous assumptions and conditions that should be considered. Notwithstanding this, Wyllie's transform is still very popular. In order to apply Wyllie's transform when an assumption has been violated, numerous authors have suggested empirical corrections for shaliness, mixed lithologies, hydrocarbon saturation, etc. A couple of examples will demonstrate these limitations and corrections.

In Fig.2.C.6, velocity-density pairs from porous limestone reefs were crossplotted and three empirical transforms were overplotted. The limestone is considered to be consolidated material. Two expressions are similar to Wyllie's suggested transform. The transform with a Δt_{ma} of 47.5 is the commonly used equation for limestone and the one with 46.6 is an "eyeball" adjustment to better fit the data. The third equation is a linear-fit of velocity to porosity. The porosity values ranged from 0% to 44%. All three expressions provide adequate transformations between velocity and density.

However, a satisfactory correlation does not exist for lower-velocity unconsolidated rocks. Using the measured velocity-density pairs from Fig. 2.B.10 again, the time-average curve for sandstone is overplotted in Fig. 2.C.7. The red curve represents the time-average equation with commonly used values of 55 and 189 μs/ft for the matrix and fluid traveltimes, respectively. The results are poor. A least-squares fit from the actual data set yields matrix and pore-fluid traveltimes of −22.3 and 467, respectively. This is plotted as the blue curve. The blue curve provides an adequate fit for densities below 2.25 gm/cm^3 but then the fit begins to diverge quickly for larger density values. Obviously, with a negative traveltime of −22.3 μs/ft for the matrix material, no physical meaning can be associated with the best-fit traveltimes. Matrix materials don't have negative velocities.

As mentioned, there are several assumptions and limitations that are inherent in the application of Wyllie's time-average equation (Mavko et al., 1998). A few are:

• Use for brine pore fluid,
• Use for rocks beneath 8700-ft (2700-m) depth (equivalent to 30 MPa if an effective pressure gradient of 0.5 psi/ft is assumed),
• Use for consolidated cemented rocks, and
• Use for intermediate porosity.

In shallow uncompacted sands, an adjustment to the porosity term in Wyllie's time-average equation has been suggested to make the transform more accurate. The original porosity term, ϕ, is replaced with $[t_{SH}/100]\phi$. When estimating the porosity of sand, any time the neighboring shale sonic traveltime is over 100, apply the adjustment with t_{SH} representing the shale traveltime. This adjustment lowers the value of the estimated porosity.

Raymer-Hunt-Gardner's (R-H-G) Velocity-Porosity Transform

In an effort to improve upon Wyllie's empirical time-average equation, Raymer et al. (1980) proposed the following velocity-porosity relationships (from Mavko et al., 1998):

$$V = (1- \phi)^2 V_{ma} + \phi \, V_{fl} \qquad\qquad \phi < 37\% \qquad\qquad [3]$$
$$1/V = (0.47 - \phi)/(.1 \, V_{37}) + (\phi - .37)/(.1 \, V_{47}) \qquad 37 < \phi < 47\% \qquad [4]$$
$$1/\rho V^2 = (1- \phi)/(\rho_{ma}V_{ma}^2) + \phi/(\rho_{fl}V_{fl}^2) \qquad\qquad \phi > 47\% \qquad\qquad [5]$$

where V_{37} is calculated from the low-porosity equation at $\phi = .37$ and V_{47} is calculated from the high-porosity equation at $\phi = .47$.

Once again, the data set in Fig. 2.B.10 was used to analyze the R-H-G equation. The results are shown in Fig. 2.C. 8. With the suggested values of 18,182 ft (5546 m)/s and 5291 ft (1614 m)/s for V_{ma} and V_{fl} respectively, the R-H-G match to the measured velocity-density pairs is unacceptable. Thus, even though the R-H-G transform was developed to better estimate lower-porosity values from sonic readings, it is still not adequate for all areas.

A least-squares fit from the data themselves for V_{ma} and V_{fl} yields acceptable correlation between velocity and density. However, once again, no physical meaning should be attached to the two variables. In fact from the data themselves, the influence of the pore-fluid was in the negative direction with $V_{fl} = −5000$ ft (1525 m)/s.

In summary, log analysts have provided the industry with numerous velocity-density (velocity-porosity) transforms that have inherent limitations and assumptions. In the above, three different mathematical expressions were examined. Often, constants for the matrix and pore-fluid properties are selected to ensure that the transform equations are realistic at the end-member porosity values of 0% and 100%. Additional mathematical forms with higher-order porosity terms are often entertained. However, for seismic modeling, it appears that mathematical predictions based on fitting regional and local trend analyses would be more robust. To apply any of the transforms blindly is dangerous. For instance, if a density curve has to be estimated for forward modeling, the 1-D synthetic might match quite adequately with the estimated density curve because of the overriding influence of in-situ velocity. However, the velocity estimate obtained during a pore-fluid substitution is sensitive to the original porosity value. Errors made in estimating the in-situ density curve will then visibly affect pore-fluid substitution AVO modeling.

Han's Velocity-Porosity-Clay Volume Transform

Empirical transforms are often valuable not only for the direct estimates of a rock-property value, but for the functional relationship they provide between the variables. For instance, they may provide insight into the relative changes in *P*-wave and *S*-wave velocities as the porosity content and clay content are varied.

Han (1986) and Han et al. (1986) developed empirical relationships among velocity, porosity, and clay content, C, using ultrasonic measurements on 75 well-consolidated sandstones. Measurements were conducted with variations of effective pressure and water saturation. A few results from the minimum and maximum effective-pressure measurements will be examined. Han's transforms are

Clean sandstones:
40MPa $V_P = 6.08 - 8.06\phi$ $V_S = 4.06 - 6.28\phi$ [6]

Shaly Sandstones:
40MPa $V_P = 5.59 - 6.93\phi - 2.18C$ $V_S = 3.52 - 4.91\phi - 1.89C$ [7]
5MPa $V_P = 5.26 - 7.08\phi - 2.02C$ $V_S = 3.16 - 4.77\phi - 1.64C$ [8]

With the conversion of 1MPa = 145 psi and an effective pressure gradient ≈ 0.5 psi/ft, the measurements at 40 MPa and 5 MPa correspond to approximate depths of 12000 ft and 1500 ft, respectively.

The relationships of porosity and clay content to velocity and Poisson's ratio are shown in the graphs of Fig. 2.C.9. In the crossplots in the left of Fig. 2.C.9, the porosity was set to 15% as the clay volume, C, varied. In the crossplots in the right of Fig. 2.C.9, the clay volume was set to 20% as the porosity varied. For these well-consolidated sandstones, a few observations can be drawn.

- Velocity variations as a function of depth are smaller for well-consolidated sandstones than for unconsolidated sands (as shown in Fig. 2.B.10).

- As the percentage of porosity or clay volume increases, the velocity decreases about 2.5 times more for porosity than for clay volume.
- As the percentage of porosity or clay volume increases, Poisson's ratio increases.
- Poisson's ratio decreases with depth.

Han noted an interesting petrophysical property for clean sandstones. This resulted by subdividing the data set. The clean-sandstone equations were derived using a subset of samples, with only 10 clean-sandstone samples. However, all samples were used, including the clean sandstones, when the shaly-sandstone equations were derived. The clean-sandstone equations listed above have no clay component. However, clean-sandstone velocities can also be estimated with the shaly-sandstone equation by setting C=0. The results of computing clean-sandstone velocities from the two equations at an effective pressure of 40 MPa are depicted in Fig. 2.C.10.

There are significant differences in the estimated Poisson's ratio values depending on which equation was used. Han et al. noted the petrophysical significance of this by stating "... a very small amount of clay (1% or a few percent of volume fraction) significantly reduces the elastic moduli of sandstones." The reduction is more for the shear modulus than for the bulk modulus.

In a typical clastic basin, most sands contain a small amount of clay. Thus, when a clean sand is encountered, there is a significant reduction in its Poisson's ratio when compared with surrounding shaly sands. This Poisson's ratio reduction can make clean, water-saturated sand appear as if it is hydrocarbon-saturated during an AVO interpretation.

Castagna's V_P-to-V_S Transforms

Pickett (1963) introduced the concept that V_P/V_S ratios could be used for identifying lithology. This concept didn't receive much attention until Ostrander (1982) verified that V_P/V_S ratios could be inferred from seismic data. In 1985, Castagna et al. published additional laboratory and in-situ measurements of V_P/V_S ratios. An interesting result that came from this article was the robustness of the V_P/V_S ratio for clastic silicate rocks composed primarily of clay- or silt-sized particles. Castagna et al. called this relationship the mudrock line and expressed the velocity relationship as

$$V_P = 1.16V_S + 1.36 \qquad [9]$$

where the velocities are expressed in km/s.

Greenberg and Castagna (1992) published additional V_P-to-V_S transforms in their work on pore-fluid substitution techniques, based on the Gassmann equation. They assumed that a conventional suite of well-log curves would normally be available for modeling. As they noted, however, when no in-situ V_S information is available, additional empirical information is needed to solve Gassmann's equation for the fluid-substitution problem. Greenberg and Castagna provided this needed information in the form of V_P-to-V_S transforms for various water-saturated lithologies. Their transforms, in km/s, are:

Sandstone:	$V_S = -0.856 + 0.804\ V_P$	[10]
Limestone:	$V_S = -1.030 + 1.017\ V_P - 0.055\ V_P^2$	[11]
Dolomite:	$V_S = -0.078 + 0.583\ V_P$	[12]
Shale:	$V_S = -0.867 + 0.770\ V_P$	[13]

To convert the above equations to ft/s, multiply the V_P^2 term by (1/3280), the V_P term by 1, and the constant by 3280. These transforms are graphed in Fig. 2.C.11. In addition, Gassmann's estimate of Poisson's ratio for a gas-saturated sandstone is plotted. Note, however, that the velocity of the gas-saturated sand *cannot* be obtained from this plot. The x-axis is based on the water-saturated sand velocity. An example will demonstrate the proper reading of this graph. A water-saturated sand that has a velocity of 12,000 ft/s has a Poisson's ratio of approximately 0.275 and when this sand is fluid substituted with gas, its Poisson's ratio lowers to 0.200, the value vertically beneath the water-saturated Poisson's ratio.

The reason for plotting Poisson's ratio against V_P rather than V_S can be found in Fig. 1.C.3. The AVO equation in this figure is

$$RC(\theta) \approx \frac{(\rho\alpha)_2 - (\rho\alpha)_1}{(\rho\alpha)_2 + (\rho\alpha)_1}\ \cos^2(\theta) + \frac{\sigma_2 - \sigma_1}{(1-\sigma_{avg})^2}\ \sin^2(\theta). \qquad [14]$$

This equation indicates that the amplitude at non-zero incident angles will be a function of the lower medium's Poisson's ratio minus the upper's. Thus, Poisson's ratio appears to be a rock property that links directly to AVO.

There are other interesting observations that are depicted in Fig. 2.C.11.

- The difference between Poisson's ratio for water-saturated sand and for shale increases as velocity increases.
- Poisson's ratios for water-saturated sand and for shale approach each other for low-velocity unconsolidated sediments.
- The difference between Poisson's ratio for gas-saturated and for water-saturated sands decreases as velocity increases.
- Above 11000 ft/s, Poisson's ratio for limestone is essentially constant.
- Poisson's ratio for dolomite is essentially constant.

As a warning, the gas-saturated Poisson's ratio curve in Fig. 2.C.11 was based on a density function derived from the expression, $\rho = .200\ V_P^{.261}$. The gas-saturated velocity that is estimated for a specific in-situ wet sand is sensitive to porosity. In short, density-velocity relationships or trends should be derived locally for the creation of the gas-saturated Poisson's ratio curve. The V_P-to-V_S transforms are more robust than velocity-density transforms (Castagna, 2000, personal communication).

2D. Relationships for Bulk Moduli

Just outside Golden, Colorado, the highway department has built a series of walking paths alongside a large road cut that traverses numerous outcropping formations. An observer will notice that within a particular formation, the rock properties vary significantly with respect to porosity, grain size, fracture patterns, rock types, etc. Any geophysicist who has taken the time to view these outcrops has to marvel at the simplistic averaging that is employed in the seismic method. Do we really assign just one velocity and one density to represent a formation's properties? In essence, yes. Effective-medium theory is applied.

An effective medium is assumed to be macroscopically homogeneous and isotropic, so that only two elastic constants are necessary to define the entire medium or formation. The key is to define an adequate mixing model of the composite material. Wang and Nur (1992) provide an excellent tutorial on the various petrophysical models and theories that are commonly applied by geophysicists. In a sense, the Wyllie and R-H-G transforms are effective-medium theories that incorporate a mixing model in the choice of V_{ma} and V_{fl}.

But why are we examining effective-medium theories? One of the primary reasons is to estimate the changes in V_P and V_S for different pore-fluid saturants (Fig. 2. D.1). This process is often called fluid-replacement or fluid-substitution modeling. Most rocks are composed of at least two different materials: the matrix or grain material and the pore-fluid material. The example in the figure has two mineral components, quartz sand and shale. In addition, the pore fluid will have two components for the hydrocarbon state.

It was noted earlier that the velocities of the rock depend upon the bulk and shear moduli of the total rock, along with the density. When the pore-fluid is changed in a rock, the dry-rock bulk modulus (K_{dry}) and mineral bulk modulus (K_{ma}) normally remain the same. Only the fluid properties change. How does the total or effective moduli (K) of the rock change when only one component (pore-fluid) is changed? In order to answer this question, methods to estimate K_{ma}, K_{dry} and K_{fl} are needed.

In this section, I discuss several effective-medium theories that average the elastic constants rather than the composite velocities of the medium. In addition, empirical relationships between the individual bulk moduli (K_{ma}, K_{dry} and K_{fl}) will be examined.

Voigt, Reuss, and Hill's (V-R-H) Moduli Models—K_{ma} Estimate

In Fig. 2.D.2, V_P and V_S are expressed as a function of two effective moduli, K_{eff} and μ_{eff}. These moduli represent the macroscopic scale of the material. In the late 1920s, Voigt (1928) and Reuss (1929) proposed two different mixing laws to compute these effective moduli from the individual moduli of the composite material. Reuss's method provided the lower limit for the effective moduli, while Voigt's provided the upper limit. However, Hill (1952) suggested that an average taken from the Voigt and Reuss models would yield a better estimate.

Wang and Nur (1992) tested the V-R-H model with laboratory data, and their results are shown in Fig. 2.D.3. As noted, the Voigt and Reuss models place upper and lower bounds on the effective moduli of the composite material. The Hill model comes close to matching the best-fit curve for the bulk modulus, but the Hill model should not be used to estimate the shear moduli. They also note that the V-R-H model should not be used for gas-saturated rocks. These last two constraints limit the direct application of the V-R-H model for predicting V_P and V_S from a volumetric analysis of a rock. In short, the V-R-H model is used to estimate the effective bulk modulus of the mineral (grain) components, K_{ma}, not the total bulk modulus.

In order to estimate the effective bulk modulus of the various minerals with the V-R-H model, the volumetric percentage of each mineral and the porosity must be known. In addition, the bulk moduli of the minerals and pore fluid are required. Mineral bulk moduli and density values (at porosity = 0%) from a list compiled by Mavko et al. (1998) and other authors are expressed in GPa and gm/cm^3 as:

Mineral	Bulk Modulus	Density
Clay	25	2.55
Coal	5	1.40
Quartz	40	2.65
Halite salt	25	2.16
Calcite	71	2.71
Anhydrite	54	2.98
Dolomite	80	2.87
Plagioclase feldspar	76	2.63

Wood's Pore-Fluid Modulus Model—K_{fl} Estimate

There are two scenarios where Wood's model (1955) is of use to the geoscientist: for estimating the effective bulk modulus of pore-fluid K_{fl} and for estimating the effective bulk modulus of shallow-marine sediments that are essentially in suspension. Wood's velocity equation (Fig. 2.D.4) employs the Reuss model to compute the effective bulk modulus and assigns a value of zero to the shear modulus.

Three suspension models are given at the bottom of the figure. The first model has both the porosity and water saturation equal to one. This is the trivial case for an all-water model where $K_R = K_{WATER}$. The second model has porosity = 1 and the water saturation is a variable. This is designed for determining the pore-fluid bulk modulus, K_{fl}, for a mixture of hydrocarbons and water. The last model determines the bulk modulus for ocean-bottom sediments. That is, $K_R = K$, the total bulk modulus.

Fig. 2.D.5 illustrates two applications of Wood's equation. The left graph represents an ocean-bottom sediment model. The composite material has quartz grains and water with $S_W = 1$. The densities and bulk moduli are listed under the graph. At $\phi = 0.0$, the composite material is all quartz. For porosity values between 50% and 100%, the model represents ocean-bottom sediments. The velocity associated with this porosity range is essentially that of water. On the right graph, a pore-fluid mixture of gas and water is modeled as a function of water saturation (S_W). The most obvious feature on this plot is that a little bit of gas ($S_W = 95\%$) immediately drops both the velocity and effective bulk modulus of the pore fluid. Once 5% gas has been introduced into the pore volume, there is little change in the pore-fluid bulk modulus or pore-fluid velocity. Obviously, this pore-fluid effect relates to the elastic properties of sands that have partial gas saturation.

One difficulty with Wood's model is that the shear modulus and thus V_S are assumed to be zero. While the V_P predicted from Wood's model for shallow ocean-bottom sediments is fairly accurate when compared with actual field experiments, measured V_S is not zero. If V_S were zero for suspended loads, then ocean-bottom horizontal phones would have difficulty recording converted *PS* waves. Hamilton (1979) published measured V_S values for ocean-bottom (OB) sediments and his results indicate a change in the V_S gradient at approximately 60 m beneath the ocean bottom. Marfurt (2000, personal communication) emphasized the importance of this V_S gradient in separating *PP* from *PS* wavefields in OB multicomponent data.

The effective pressure for shallow OB sediments is also akin to highly overpressured sediments. Here, pore pressure approaches the overburden pressure (small effective pressure) and the P-wave velocity decreases but the S-wave velocity decreases more dramatically: same as with shallow OB sediments. This rapid decrease in V_S was emphasized to the author while examining an unpublished walkaway *VSP*. The *PP* waves from the *VSP* were very poor for detailing structure beneath the onset of abnormal pressure. However, the converted *PS* waves clearly imaged the reservoir and fault planes.

Batzle and Wang's Estimation of Pore-Fluid Properties

In order to apply Wood's equation for estimating the bulk modulus of the pore fluid, the bulk moduli of water and hydrocarbons are required. The values listed at the bottom of Fig. 2.D.5 were taken from Domenico's (1974) graphs shown in Fig. 2.D.6 for a depth of 5000 ft (1500 m). While the density and bulk-moduli curves for oil and brine appear to be near one another in Figure 2.D.6, an increase in the gas-oil ratio will move the oil curves quickly toward methane values.

A more detailed and recommended approach for determining the pore-fluid bulk moduli and density has been given by Batzle and Wang (1992). Current pore-fluid modeling programs implement some version of their algorithms. In their procedure, the bulk moduli and density of a pore-fluid component are expressed in terms of pore temperature, pressure, salinity, GOR, API number, and specific gas gravity. After the bulk moduli of the pore-fluid components are determined, the effective bulk modulus of the total fluid is determined using Wood's equation.

Biot's Coefficient

In Fig. 2.A.2, the bulk modulus of the total rock K (effective rock bulk modulus) was shown to be dependent on three bulk moduli: the pore-fluid bulk modulus, K_{fl}; the matrix bulk modulus, K_{ma}; and, the dry-rock bulk modulus, K_{dry}. As has been discussed, two of these bulk moduli, K_{fl} and K_{ma}, can be estimated if the volumetric mineral and pore-fluid components of the rock are known. The third, K_{dry}, is elusive and yet, is a very important component for validating amplitude interpretations and providing sensitivity analyses (the what-ifs). Thus, numerous petrophysicists have developed empirical approximations to estimate this property based on other known properties of the rock. Many of the techniques are related to Biot's coefficient as expressed in Fig. 2.D.7.

Biot's coefficient, B, is a function of K_{ma}, which can be estimated, and K_{dry}, the desired dry-rock bulk modulus. B values range from 0 (well-consolidated sediments) to 1 (unconsolidated sediments and suspended loads). One of the most popular experimental approaches has been to approximate B as a function of porosity. The following have been suggested.

1. Geertsma (1961) $B = 1 - [1 + 50\phi]^{-1}$ [15]
2. Krief et al. (1990) $B = 1 - [1 - \phi]^{[3/(1-\phi)]}$ [16]
3. Nur et al. (1991) $B = \phi/\phi_{crit}$ $\phi < \phi_{crit}$ [17]
   $B = 1$ $\phi \geq \phi_{crit}$ [18]

where (Mavko et al., 1998):

Material	*Critical porosity* (ϕ_{crit})
Sandstone	40%
Limestone	60%
Dolomite	40%
Pumice	80%
Chalk	65%

4. Polynomial expansion of $K_{dry}/K_{ma} = a_0 + a_1 (\phi/\phi_{crit}) + a_2 (\phi/\phi_{crit})^2$ [19]
   leads to $B = 2(\phi/\phi_{crit}) - (\phi/\phi_{crit})^2$ [20]
   from the initial conditions of:

$K_{dry}/K_{ma} = 1$ at $(\phi/\phi_{crit}) = 0$

$K_{dry}/K_{ma} = 0$ at $(\phi/\phi_{crit}) = 1$

$d(K_{dry}/K_{ma})/d(\phi/\phi_{crit}) = 0$ at $(\phi/\phi_{crit}) = 1$

The Krief model incorporates the H-R-G relationship. The Nur model is based on empirical observations from laboratory measurements and the introduction of the critical porosity term.

With $\phi_{crit} = 50\%$ for the polynomial equation and $\phi_{crit} = 40\%$ for Nur's, the above four expressions for Biot's coefficient are graphed in Fig. 2.D.8 as a function of porosity. As depicted in the figure, the Krief, Nur, and polynomial equations yield similar results.

With methods to estimate K_{ma} and K_{fl} developed, pore-fluid substitution techniques and predictions of V_S are possible. The significance of the Biot coefficient will also become evident in later discussions.

2E. Wave Propagation Theories

Of the many wave-propagation theories in the geophysical literature, Gassmann's (1951) has been the most widely applied by geophysicists (Fig 2.E.1). Gassmann's equation is popular because of the ease in providing values for the parameters in his equation. Basically, Gassmann derived an equation that relates the effective bulk-modulus of a fluid-saturated rock to that of the bulk moduli of the matrix material (K_{ma}), the frame (K_{dry}), pore fluid (K_{fl}) and porosity (ϕ). Methods to estimate K_{ma} and K_{fl} were discussed in the previous section.

Biot's (1956a) theory is an extension of Gassmann's (1951) theory. Biot included fluid viscosity and the fact that the pore fluid could move relative to the frame. With viscosity, Biot's model exhibited attenuation and the possibility of having two *P*-waves propagating at different velocities through the medium. However, values for the parameters required in Biot's equation are more difficult to derive, and quite frankly more difficult to understand intuitively.

The Kuster-Toksöz (1974) theory is a low-porosity model that provides options to change the size, shape and distribution of cracks in the rock. Xu and White (1995) provided a technique to model mixtures of clay and sand that incorporates Gassmann, Wyllie, and Kuster-Toksöz theories.

If only the conventional well-log suite of gamma, SP, resistivity, neutron, density, and *P*-wave sonic curves are available, none of the theoretical models mentioned above have enough information to estimate V_S. Thus, geophysicists need additional empirical models. The fact that Gassmann's equation only requires one additional piece of information and correlates fairly accurately to field measurements makes it an obvious choice. In addition, the empirical models selected to provide the additional information needed to solve Gassmann's equation can be adjusted regionally.

Gassmann's Equation

Gassmann's equation can be separated into two components: the dry rock and fluid (Fig. 2.E.2). The dry-rock bulk moduli are a function of the frame and are independent of the pore-fluid properties. Thus, K_{dry} and μ_{dry} remain the same for computing V_P when the pore space has hydrocarbons or is totally water saturated. The dry-rock moduli are not independent of porosity, so if porosity is changed, then new K_{dry} and μ_{dry} are required. There are two equations and nine variables listed in the figure.

Let's start with a typical scenario of having a suite of conventional well-log curves. Now, an estimate of V_P and V_S is desired when the pore-fluid is changed from the in-situ condition. All that is necessary is to plug in values for the variables listed in Gassmann's equation. But as Fig. 2.E.3 questions: "What's known and what's unknown?" Starting with the in-situ well-log curves, the *P*-wave velocity and density can be measured. Likewise, an estimate of the porosity can be made. The bulk modulus of the matrix material, K_{ma}, can be computed from numerous mixing laws such as the V-R-H. However, a volumetric analysis and the mineral bulk-moduli values are required. An additional component of the volumetric analysis is the in-situ description of the pore-fluid components. From this, the pore-fluid bulk moduli, K_{fl}, can be estimated using the Batzle-Wang algorithms or taken from graphs such as Domenico's. In short, this leaves three unknown parameters, K_{dry}, μ_{dry}, and the desired V_S, but only two equations. This is why empirical models, such as the ones previously discussed, are called upon. Fig. 2.E.4 summarizes a few choices. Additional empirical relationships besides those listed in Fig. 2.E.4 are suggested by Mavko et al. (1998).

A popular choice is to estimate V_S using the known volumetric analyses and V_P. Once this is done, then K_{dry} and μ_{dry} can be determined. Although these V_P-to-V_S transforms are based on water-saturated rocks, Greenberg and Castagna (1992), provide an iterative solution when the in-situ pore space contains hydrocarbons.

Greenberg and Castagna also emphasized the importance of recalibrating the V_P-to-V_S coefficients for the local area when a measured V_S is available.

Once the variables in Gassmann's equation are solved for the in-situ case, the fluid substitution case is straightforward. With a description of the pore fluid to be substituted, a new density and bulk modulus, K_{fl}, are computed. Then estimates of V_P and V_S with the new pore fluid are made.

The same procedure is followed if another choice besides the Greenberg and Castagna equation from Fig. 2.E.4 is selected. For consolidated rocks, empirical relationships based on Biot's coefficient are often chosen. These relationships should also be calibrated to local areas when possible. The previous section describes four different relationships of the Biot coefficient versus porosity.

Gregory (1977) suggested using a value of 0.10 for the dry-rock Poisson's ratio as the additional seed for inverting Gassmann's equation for unconsolidated sands. He noted that σ_{dry} is independent of pressure, and the calculated V_P was not very sensitive to this estimate. In an effort to extend Gregory's relationship to shale and limestone, Hilterman (1990) suggested a relationship of dry-rock Poisson's ratio to clay content. This was based on amplitude correlations of AVO models to seismic field CDP gathers.

Frequently, authors indicate that their empirical relationship is applicable to unconsolidated but not consolidated rocks, or the other way around. The significance of these statements can be understood by examining the limits of Gassmann's equation in Fig. 2.E.5.

Consolidated and unconsolidated rock examples are given in this figure. The analysis centers on the fact that Gassmann's equation can be separated into a dry-rock contribution and a pore-fluid contribution. Using the velocity and density values listed in the figure and Greenberg and Castagna's V_P-to-V_S relationship, Gassmann's equation was solved for the dry-rock and pore-fluid contributions. Two pore-fluid contributions are given: one for water saturation, the other for gas saturation. For the unconsolidated case, Gassmann's equation essentially tends toward the suspended-load model as suggested by Wood. The dry-rock contribution (1.63 GPa) is only 30% that of the contribution from the fluid (5.51 GPa). The choice of pore-fluid saturant dominates the value obtained for V_P. As Gregory noted, the choice of the dry-rock properties is not the most significant factor for unconsolidated rocks. However, the opposite is true for consolidated rocks. The pore-fluid contribution, be it water or gas, contributes little to the rock's total moduli. Accurate estimates of lithology and porosity are important when dealing with consolidated rocks.

These last two observations are reinforced by the graphs displayed in Figs 2.E.6 and 2.E.7. The change in V_P, V_S, and Poisson's ratio due to variations in porosity and water-saturation are shown for unconsolidated rocks and consolidated rocks. In Fig. 2.E.6, the left graph indicates a rapid and large decrease in V_P as the water saturation varies from 100% to 95%. This rapid decline was also previously depicted for the pore-fluid bulk modulus, K_{fl}, as a function of water saturation. This emphasizes the close correlation of V_P to pore-fluid properties for unconsolidated rocks. Since V_S is not that sensitive to pore-fluid content, Poisson's ratio correlates strongly to V_P.

Estimates of V_P and V_S for fluid substitution are fairly reliable if conventional well-log curves are provided. However, when porosity substitutions for the initial rock are requested, then the results are not as reliable. Basically, if the porosity is changed, then the dry-rock moduli also have the opportunity to change in Gassmann's equation. As noted in the section on empirical relationships for velocity and density, there is a wide variance for unconsolidated and well-consolidated rocks.

For consolidated rocks (Fig. 2.E.7), the introduction of gas into the pores has little effect on V_P or Poisson's ratio. The change of porosity (or increase in fracture density) is more significant. This was noted in the bottom of Fig. 2.E.5 also.

In Figs. 2.E.6 and 2.E.7, it was assumed that the different fluids in the pore spaces were mixed at very fine scales. If the fluids are not well mixed with respect to the propagating wavelength, a patchy model is more appropriate for modeling the bulk modulus of the pore fluid rather than Wood's equation. The patchy model predicts a more linear drop in the fluid bulk modulus and thus in the P-wave velocity as the water saturation is varied. There are no abrupt changes in the P-wave velocity when 5% gas is introduced into a totally water-saturated rock. The current thought is that a patchy model is more appropriate for the sonic log response in hydrocarbon-charged formations, while Wood's model is more appropriate for the surface seismic. In short, sonic logs in gas zones can yield higher velocities than should be used in AVO modeling. Mavko et al. (1998) describe several patchy models for correcting sonic traveltimes for AVO modeling.

Fluid-Substitution Verification

Greenberg and Castagna (1992) verified their V_S estimation technique with measured laboratory data and well-log curves. The well-log verification is shown in Fig. 2.E.8. The correlation is excellent. In fact, it is difficult to see any separation between the dotted-curve (measured V_S) and the continuous curve (predicted V_S). However, the authors warned that the initial V_S estimate was not acceptable. A revised estimate of the lithology had to be conducted using sonic, neutron, and density curves to get the excellent match. The V_P values in the figure range from 10,000 to 16,000 ft (3000 to 5000 m)/s. These are consolidated rocks, and as noted, Gassmann's equation then requires an accurate lithologic estimate.

When a V_S curve is not available in a well, verification of the fluid-substitution technique can be preformed if two different pore fluids are present in the same formation. The well-log curves in Fig. 2.E.9 depict a thick sand zone that has three different pore-fluid states: gas, fizz, and water. The in-situ curves for the sonic, density, Poisson's ratio, and ln(acoustic impedance) are plotted in blue. The gas zone (8597-8630 ft) has low velocity, high resistivity, and neutron-density crossover. The fizz zone (8630-8670 ft) has a low velocity and a resistivity value slightly elevated over the water zone value (8670-8717 ft). The gas and fizz zones were replaced with water and the new rock properties are displayed by the red curves in the gas and fizz zones. Assuming that the only difference in the sand zone was the pore-fluid state, then the rock properties after fluid substitution to water should match the in-situ water-saturated rock properties. There is a good correlation.

Often a measured V_S log is "noisy" and questions are raised regarding whether it should be used for modeling. Fig. 2.E.10 shows measured and estimated curves for V_S and Poisson's ratio for a GOM deep-water well. The measured V_S curve (blue color) has high-frequency variations that are not present on the other logs. The extreme values for these V_S fluctuations do not appear to be real. In situations such as this, the "good" zones of the measured V_S curve can be used to develop new regression coefficients for V_P-to-V_S transforms and then the estimated V_S is used for AVO modeling (Chesser, 1997).

Summary—Example of Fluid-Substitution Modeling

Numerous empirical and theoretical models have been described up to this point and the average reader should be swamped with thoughts such as "When to apply what." An example of a typical fluid substitution for AVO modeling should answer some of these questions.

Let's assume that a prospect has been defined near a well that has conventional well-log curves. Migrated CDP gathers have been obtained near the well and an AVO synthetic is desired to compare to the gathers. The well doesn't have hydrocarbons and an AVO synthetic is also desired to determine the seismic signature when various pore fluids are substituted for the in-situ brine. The petrophysical problem is to determine V_S for the in-situ AVO modeling and V_P, V_S, and ρ for the fluid-replacement AVO modeling.

The V_S prediction for the water-saturated in-situ rocks is simple, as illustrated in Fig. 2.E.11. The subscripts [,WET] and [,GAS] on the rock-property variables refer to the water-saturated and hydrocarbon-saturated states, respectively. Using the lithologic curves, the volume of each mineral component is determined at each depth point. The example rock is composed of 85% sand and 15% shale with an in-situ velocity of 11,400 ft (3500 m)/s. The simplest method of predicting V_S is by V_P-to-V_S transforms, such as those published by Greenberg and Castagna (1992). Once V_S is determined for the shale and sand components, the component velocities are averaged using the Voigt-Reuss-Hill effective-medium model. This procedure is repeated for the entire depth of the well. With V_P and density values taken from the in-situ logs and V_S predicted as shown, the in-situ AVO synthetic can now be generated.

The petrophysical work needed for fluid-substitution AVO modeling is covered in the next four figures. As shown in the upper portion of Fig. 2.E.12, porosity and density are additional parameters required for pore-fluid substitution. Of course, the desired S_W and the pore-fluid description (API, GOR, etc.) need to be defined.

The solution is broken into two parts. In the first part, (A), the elastic constants for the water-saturated rock are estimated and then these elastic constants are used in the second part (B) when new pore fluids are introduced. In Fig. 2.E.12, model equations and numeric values for estimating the bulk moduli of the total rock (K_{WET}), pore fluid ($K_{fl,WET}$), and minerals (K_{ma}) are given. For convenience in this example, the density and modulus for the pore fluid were taken from Domenico's table. However, it is recommended that Batzle-Wang's method of estimating the pore-fluid properties be followed. Domenico's values were derived for a specific set of environmental conditions (pressure and temperature gradients, specific gas density, salinity, etc.) and these conditions would normally not match other areas. Mavko et al. (1998) provided step-by-step numeric examples for calculating the pore-fluid properties with the Batzle-Wang equations.

The next step, shown in Fig. 2.E.13, contains the Greenberg-Castagna inversion of Gassmann's equation to find K_{dry}. The X, Y, and b shown in Part A.3 have no physical meaning; they are only intermediate variables to aid in the solution.

This is not the only technique for estimating K_{dry}. In Fig. 2.E.4, two other methods for obtaining K_{dry} were suggested. One is the Biot coefficient technique. If Biot's coefficient is approximated with one of the models described in Fig. 2.D.8, then $K_{dry} = (1-B) K_{ma}$. Remember B is based on the known porosity and K_{ma} has been determined in the previous figure. Now, the only variable that is unknown in Gassmann's equation for V_P is μ_{dry}. Once this is found, the new pore fluids can be introduced (following step A.4 in Fig. 2.E.13).

The other method suggested in Fig. 2.E.4 for estimating K_{dry} is to use the dry-rock Poisson's ratio. If this model is selected for providing additional information to Gassmann's equation, then a solution proposed by Gregory (1977) can be employed. Application of any of these three methods (Greenberg-Castagna, Biot's coefficient, or dry-rock Poisson's ratio) will supply the information listed in Fig. 2.E.13 at the end of Part A.3. The last portion for estimating the properties of the water-saturated rock is given in Part A.4 of Fig. 2.E.13.

The last petrophysical stage for AVO modeling with fluid-substitution properties is rather straightforward. The only additional rock properties needed, beyond what was calculated from the water-saturated case, are the hydrocarbon-charged values for the total rock density and the pore-fluid bulk modulus. Then the rock properties associated with the hydrocarbon-charged state are inserted into Gassmann's equation. These steps are worked out with numeric values in Figs. 2.E.14 and 2.E.15.

2F. Back to Geology through Anstey

With all the theoretical and empirical relationships presented in this section, the author seems to have lost sight of geologic processes. How does one return to the basics? There is no better way than through the geophysicist's own Shakespearean orator, Nigel Anstey. All geophysicists who have made Society presentations and also listened to one of Nigel's inspiring presentations develop a fear for the future. That fear is, "Oh Lord, please never make me follow Nigel in a technical presentation!"

Nigel gave such an illuminating presentation at Cambridge in 1990 that it was reproduced in *First Break*. After a few cartoons on squeezing and distorting the shape of a rock, it became obvious that a grain's shape and the number of contacts it has with other grains were going to be an important factor in predicting the *S*-wave velocity of the rock. Several of his intuitive observations are summarized in Fig. 2.F.1. His conclusions of the factors that control *S*-wave velocity were:

- First and foremost [is], probably, the cementation. Advanced cementation makes all rocks look much the same.
- But if there is no cementation, then [there are] those factors that control the number and angularity of the grain contacts—shape, then sorting, then overburden pressure.

- Now—where's lithology? Well, we will list it; the intrinsic rigidity of the grain material must be there, as must that of the cement. But not very clearly—partly because different lithologies often imply different angularity of the grain contacts, different natural cements, different susceptibility to pressure solution, different susceptibility to fracture, and so on ... [and] partly because the lithology becomes less important at porosities of reservoir quality.
- Then [there is] clay content—ranging from the low side of modest if the clay particles are just passengers in the pores, to the high side of modest if they are actually in the contacts. Then [there is] the saturant (just the minor effect of density), and the grain size (insofar as it controls the closing effect of overburden pressure, and preferential cementation).

Also noted was that porosity, as such, is not a major control on S-wave velocity.

But Nigel also wanted his conclusions to be phrased in terms that geologists know and understand, and this is accomplished as shown in the Fig. 2.F.2. The emphasis is that the number of grain contacts affects the rigidity of the rock. For fine-grained rocks, cement is likely to form preferentially in small pores and thus the rocks will have a higher rigidity than do coarse-grained rocks. Coarse-grained rocks that are well-rounded and well-sorted have fairly good porosity, and have many rigid contacts and thus a high shear-wave velocity for that porosity. This relates to the previous discussion on Han's observation of very-clean sand specimens. For angular-grained rocks, the sorting and packing, which can be related to geologic processes, control the number of contacts and thus the S-wave velocity.

While Anstey wanted to emphasize that examination of thin sections will provide insight into the geologic processes and thus predictions about the S-wave velocity, one has to wonder if these same predictions can be made from an interpretation based on seismic sequence stratigraphy.

Figures

Figure 2.A.1

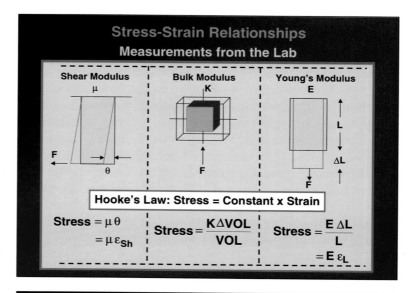

Figure 2.A.2

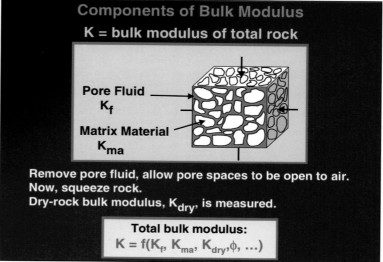

Figure 2.A.3

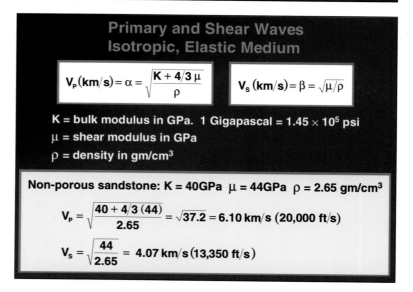

Figure 2.A.4

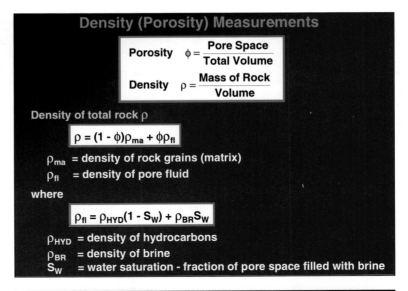

Figure 2.A.5

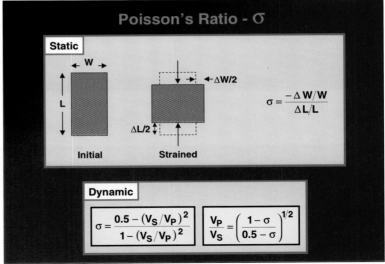

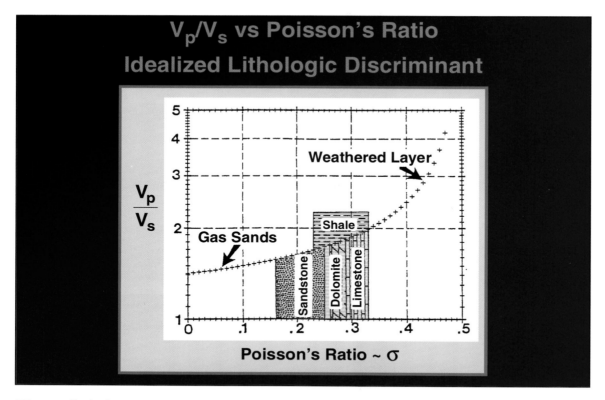

Figure 2.A.6

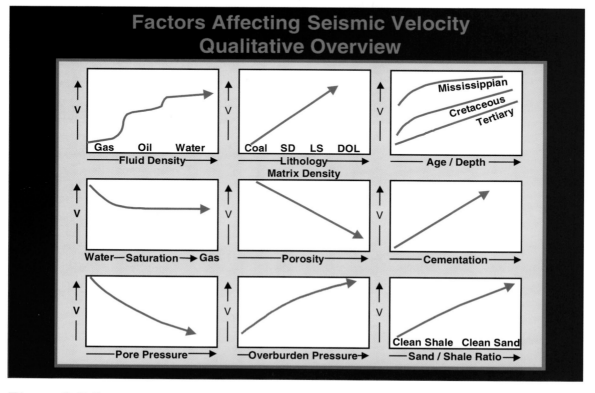

Figure 2.B.1

Figure 2.B.2

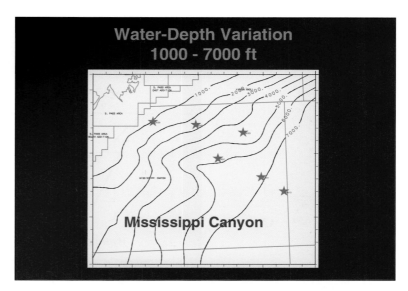

Figure 2.B.3

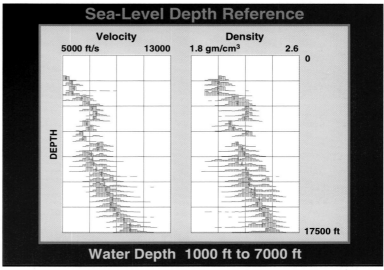

Figure 2.B.4

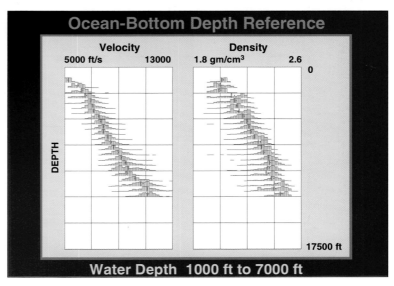

Figure 2.B.5

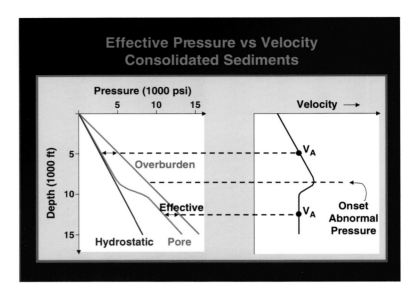

Figure 2.B.6

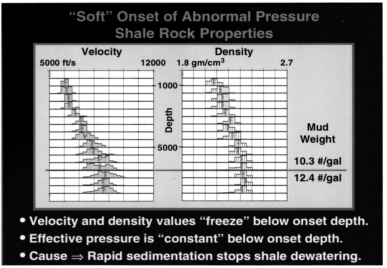

Figure 2.B.7

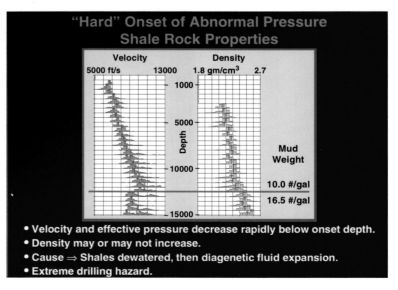

Figure 2.B.8

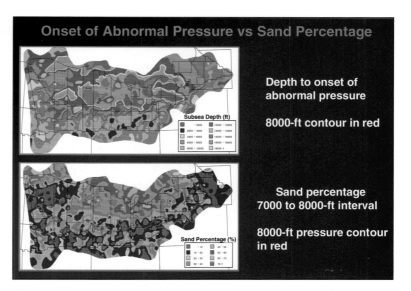

Figure 2.B.9

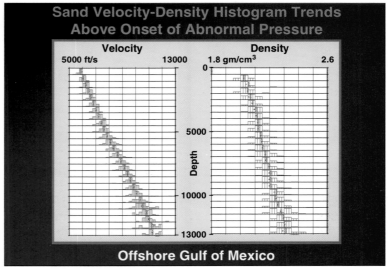

Figure 2.B.10

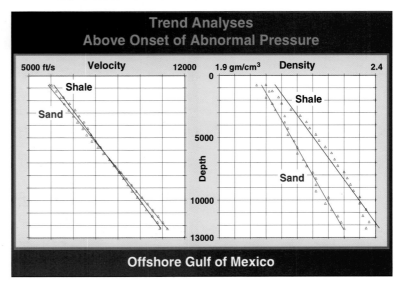

Figure 2.B.11

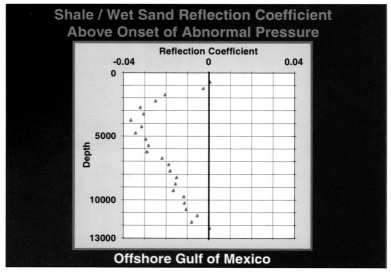

Figure 2.B.12

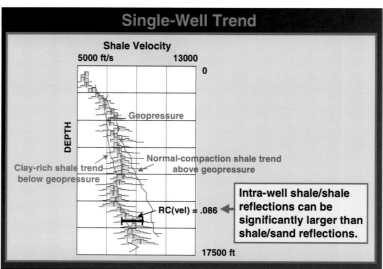

Figure 2.C.1

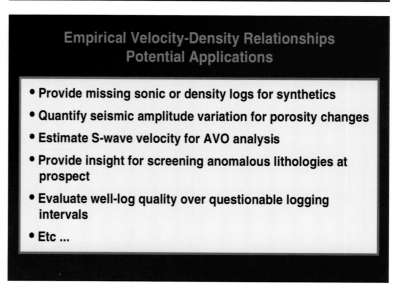

Figure 2.C.2

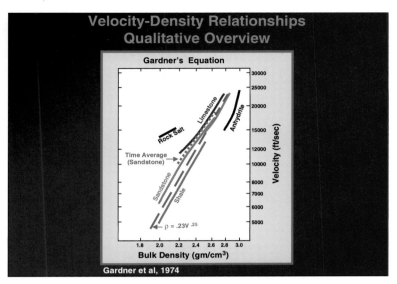

Figure 2.C.3

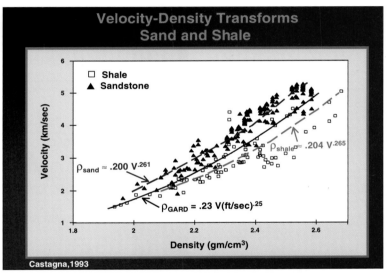

Figure 2.C.4

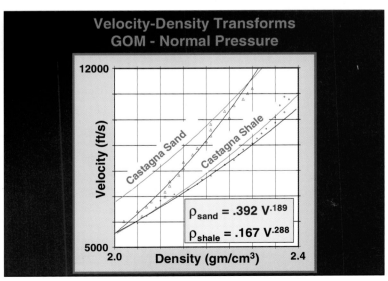

Figure 2.C.5

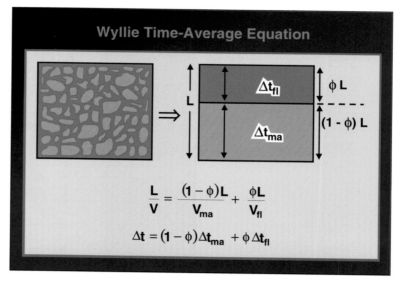

Figure 2.C.6

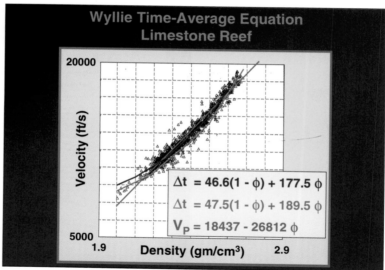

Figure 2.C.7

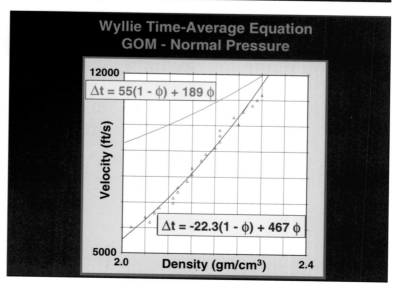

Figure 2.C.8

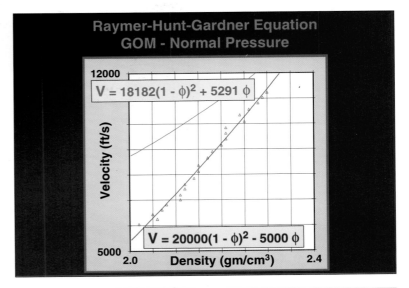

Figure 2.C.9

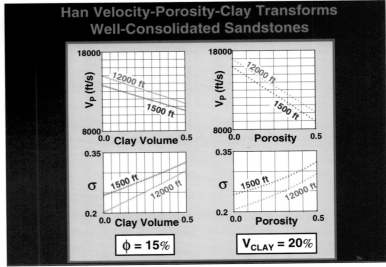

Figure 2.C.10

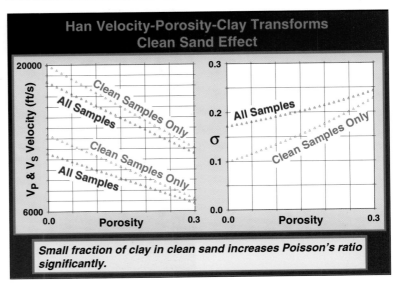

Figure 2.C.11

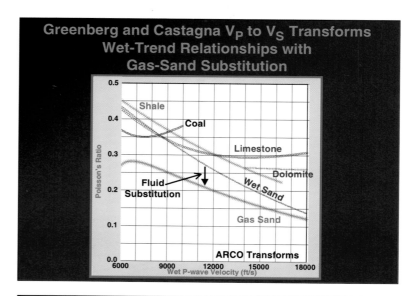

Figure 2.D.1

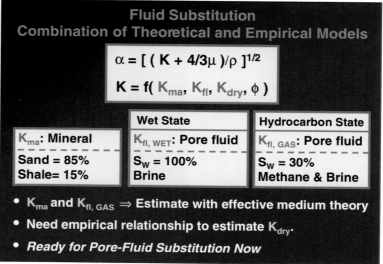

Figure 2.D.2

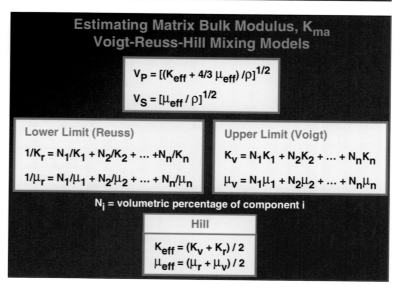

Figure 2.D.3

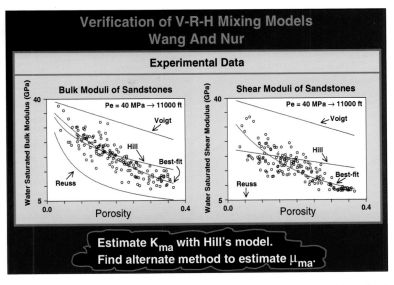

Figure 2.D.4

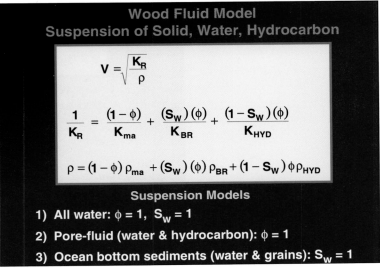

Figure 2.D.5

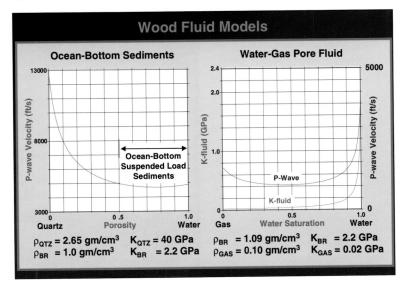

Figure 2.D.6

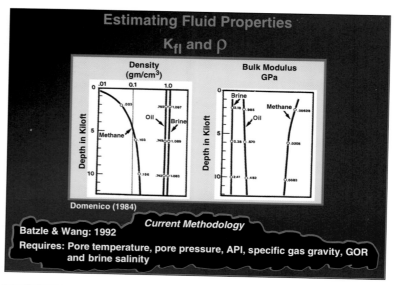

Figure 2.D.7

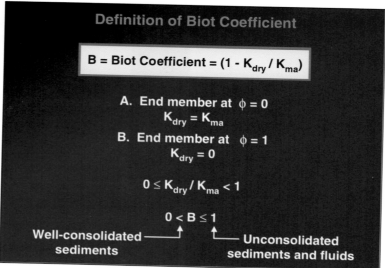

Figure 2.D.8

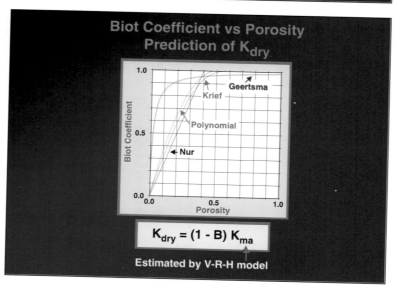

Figure 2.E.1

Wave Propagation and Fluid Substitution Models

- Gassmann (1951) - Related fluid, frame and matrix strengths.

- Biot (1956)   - Extended Gassmann to include viscosity.
                    Applicable for various frequency ranges.

- Kuster &
    Toksöz (1974) - Handled fractures, low porosity.

- Xu & White (1995) - Combined Gassmann & Toksöz for
                      shaly sandstones.

- Etc ...

Figure 2.E.2

Gassmann's Equation - Fluid Substitution Model

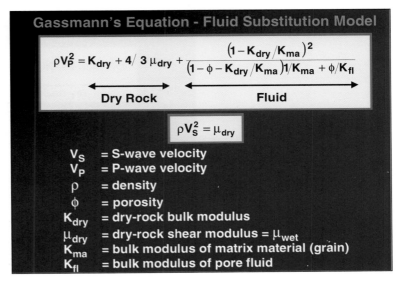

$$\rho V_P^2 = K_{dry} + 4/3\,\mu_{dry} + \frac{\left(1 - K_{dry}/K_{ma}\right)^2}{\left(1 - \phi - K_{dry}/K_{ma}\right)1/K_{ma} + \phi/K_{fl}}$$

$\longleftrightarrow$ Dry Rock $\longleftrightarrow$ $\longleftrightarrow$ Fluid $\longleftrightarrow$

$$\rho V_S^2 = \mu_{dry}$$

V_S = S-wave velocity
V_P = P-wave velocity
ρ = density
ϕ = porosity
K_{dry} = dry-rock bulk modulus
μ_{dry} = dry-rock shear modulus = μ_{wet}
K_{ma} = bulk modulus of matrix material (grain)
K_{fl} = bulk modulus of pore fluid

Figure 2.E.3

What's Known ... What's Unknown?
Gassmann Equation.

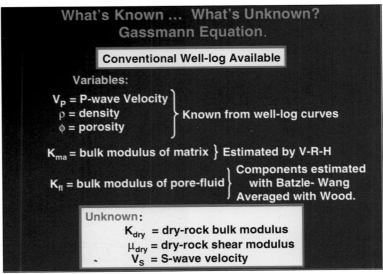

| Conventional Well-log Available |

Variables:

V_P = P-wave Velocity
ρ = density   } Known from well-log curves
ϕ = porosity

K_{ma} = bulk modulus of matrix } Estimated by V-R-H

K_{fl} = bulk modulus of pore-fluid } Components estimated
with Batzle- Wang
Averaged with Wood.

Unknown:
K_{dry} = dry-rock bulk modulus
μ_{dry} = dry-rock shear modulus
V_S = S-wave velocity

Figure 2.E.4

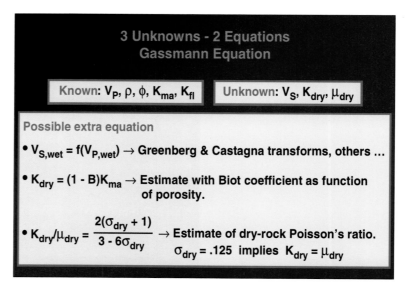

Figure 2.E.5

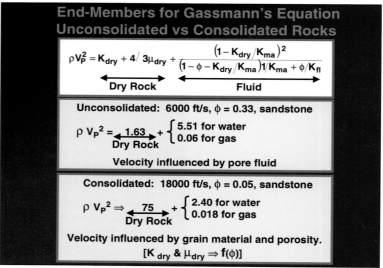

Figure 2.E.6

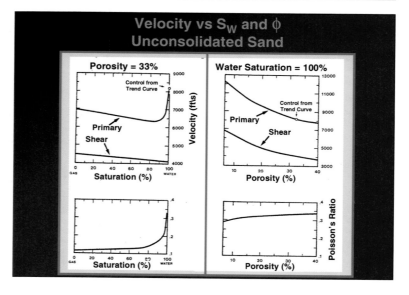

Figure 2.E.7

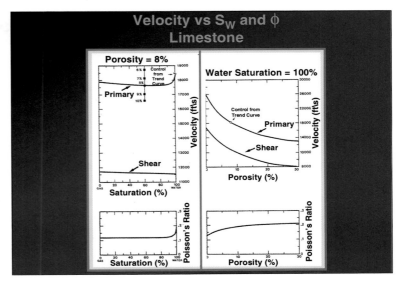

Figure 2.E.8

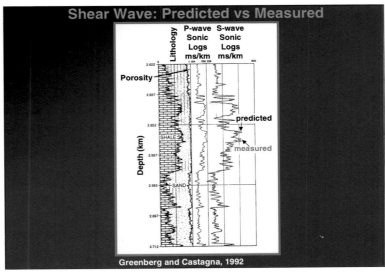

Figure 2.E.9

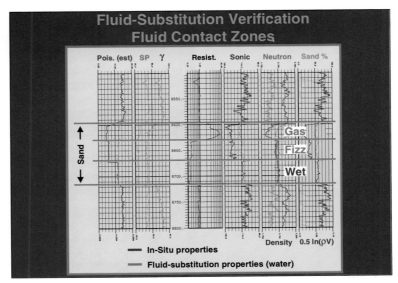

Figure 2.E.10

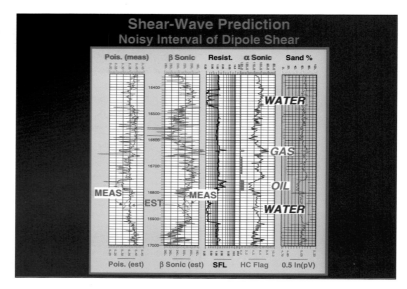

Figure 2.E.11

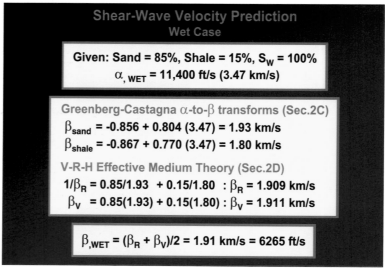

Figure 2.E.12

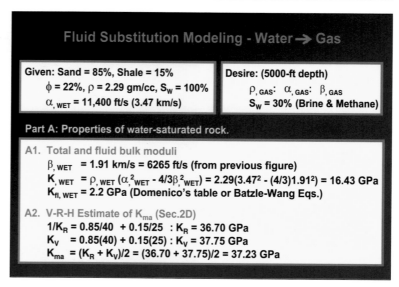

Figure 2.E.13

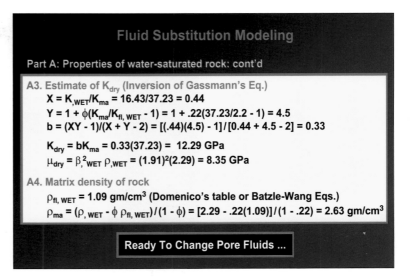

Figure 2.E.14

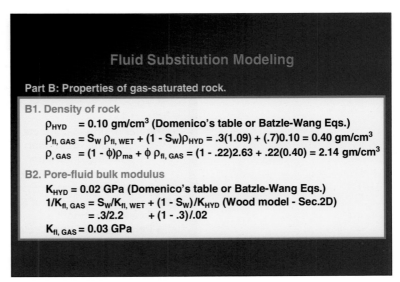

Figure 2.E.15

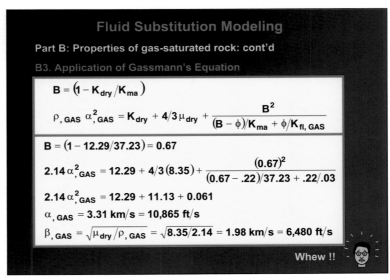

Figure 2.F.1

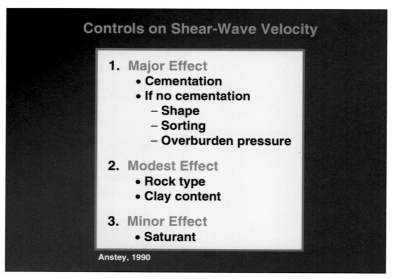

Figure 2.F.2

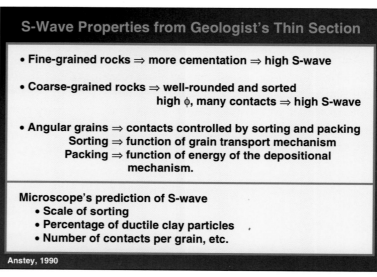

Section 3. Seismic Reflection Amplitude

Objective:

1. Provide rules-of-thumb for reflection amplitude associated with various shapes of geologic boundaries

2. Present reflection-coefficient equations that separate lithologic from pore-fluid contributions to the AVO response

After loading the seismic data on the workstation, one of the first questions an interpreter asks the data processor is: "What's the polarity?" The processor assures the interpreter that the final seismic has true-amplitude processing with a zero-phase wavelet, so that a peak represents a reflection from a high-velocity bed. Knowing the complexities that mother earth can introduce, and having a little bit of processing experience, seasoned interpreters are often heard mumbling quotes such as, "It's your dream, tell it the way you want to."

But even if the processor has produced his dream section, there are amplitude and phase anomalies that are often not associated with rock type or pore-fluid changes. Once these anomalies are reconciled, reflection amplitudes both on the stack and within CDP gathers can be investigated for rock type and pore-fluid predictions. These predictions from the amplitude interpretation are normally conducted using simplified versions of the reflection-amplitude equation. Which equation is employed depends on what the interpreter is trying to emphasize.

3A. Normal-Incident Amplitude

Polarity Issues

A variety of geophysical receivers are used by the oil industry to measure the particle motion of seismic waves. Likewise, these receivers can be planted on land, towed as streamers, deployed in vertical cables, or planted on the ocean bottom. With respect to polarity, two issues arise: type of receiver, and direction of wavefront.

Particle-velocity geophones and pressure-sensitive hydrophones are the two receivers commonly employed in seismic. Starting with a displacement wavelet, the amplitude relationship between a particle-velocity phone and a hydrophone is shown in Fig. 3.A.1. The theory is based on plane-wave propagation, which is a good approximation for the far-field signature. The strain can be found by taking the partial derivative of the displacement wavelet as a function of the spatial coordinate. Likewise the particle-velocity wavelet is found by taking the partial derivative of the displacement wavelet as a function of time. Note that v_x is particle-velocity motion while V refers to propagation velocity; i.e. $V=5000$ ft/s for water.

Next, Hooke's Law is called upon to relate stress to strain through an elastic constant E. The final step in the pressure development requires $V=(E/\rho)^{1/2}$. Finally, the theoretical pressure signature is the negative of particle velocity modified by the acoustic impedance.

As mentioned earlier, the direction of the wavefront needs to be considered when analyzing amplitude. As shown in the bottom of Fig. 3.A.2, the signature that a particle-velocity phone records depends on the direction that the wavefront takes. Pressure phones are insensitive to the wavefront direction. Likewise, the placement of the receiver influences the recorded amplitude. If pressure phones were allowed to float on the water surface, they would record amplitudes very near zero. However, particle-velocity phones located on the earth's surface record twice the amplitude of waves approaching the surface vertically. Because pressure phones must be located beneath sea level, they are normally positioned so that the initial upcoming wave is reinforced with the negative reflection from the wave reflected downward from the air-water interface. This pressure-phone phenomenon is called a ghost. A ghost basically introduces a 90°-phase shift with respect to the upcoming wave. The marine source, which is also beneath the surface, can produce another ghost, so that the total effect is a 180°-phase shift.

To add to the confusion of phase determination, there are two polarity standards in common usage (Fig. 3.A.3). Brown (1999) refers to them as the "American" and "European" polarities. Rather than rely on the notation American or European, most interpreters want statements such as "Positive values on the tape are reflections from a hard boundary." Even with this notation, interpreters still need to confirm the polarity by tying synthetics to the seismic, examining reflections from the ocean bottom, evaluating obvious shallow thin-bed gas zones, etc. More correctly, the statement should be, "Interpreters need to verify the phase of the data." Marine data, especially older vintages, are notoriously 90° (+ or −) out-of-phase from the desired zero-phase wavelet.

Reflection and Transmission Coefficients

By applying the boundary conditions of continuity of vertical displacement and stress, the equations for normal-incident reflection and transmission coefficients as shown in Fig. 3.A.4 can be derived. The reflection coefficient is the difference of acoustic impedances ($\rho\alpha$) over the sum of the acoustic impedances of the two bounding media. The reflection and transmission coefficients are dimensionless because the respective amplitudes have been normalized to the incident-wave amplitude. The reflection coefficient has values between −1.0 and +1.0, but the seismic range is usually between −0.3 and 0.3.

One aspect of the reflection coefficient that hasn't been mentioned is the reference coordinate system. Is the positive z-axis pointing upward or downward? If a fixed-coordinate system is selected, then the normal-incident (NI) equation will only be true for the particle-velocity or pressure—not for both. Also, it becomes more confusing when amplitude for oblique raypaths are considered in a fixed-coordinate system. To avoid this confusion, the coordinate system is assumed to have the positive z-axis pointing in the direction of the ray path being considered. Then a positive amplitude particle-velocity wavelet traveling downward will reflect from a hard boundary and travel upward as a positive-amplitude particle-velocity wavelet. The same is true for a pressure wavelet.

The transmission coefficient can also be written as (1 − reflection coefficient). However, this is only true for particle-velocity phones if the coordinate system is defined as suggested. For pressure phones, the particle-velocity amplitudes need to be modified by the acoustic impedance of the medium in which the wave is traveling. When this is done, the transmission coefficient for pressure phones is expressed as (1 + reflection coefficient).

While the reflection-coefficient expression in Fig. 3.A.4 is the one most often quoted, alternate forms are given in Fig. 3.A.5. The first equation expresses the reflection coefficient as a function of two variables, the velocity and density ratios of the two media. The second equation indicates the amount that the velocity and density contrasts individually contribute to the total reflection. The right side of the second equation indicates that the reflection coefficient can be expressed as a difference (Δ) of the two media properties over the average.

The third expression comes from the approximation, $\Delta[\ln(\rho\alpha)] \approx [\Delta(\rho\alpha) / \rho\alpha]$. If the natural log of an acoustic impedance curve is plotted, then the ratio of one reflection amplitude to another can be found by graphically measuring the excursion at each boundary and taking the ratio. This concept is expanded in the fourth equation to graphically illustrate the contributions of velocity and density to the total reflection coefficient. Fig. 3.A.6 contains an example.

The sand formation, which is in the middle of the well-log plot (Fig. 3.A.6), has a higher velocity but a lower density than the encasing shale. However, the scales for the sonic and density curves are deceiving in that it appears that the velocity increase will be cancelled by the density decrease at the upper boundary of the sand formation. A quick visual evaluation is made from the natural logarithm plot on the right. The length of the line NI_{Vel} in the figure is a graphical representation of the velocity contribution to the normal-incident reflection coefficient. The line's origin is at the center of the upper medium's cluster of shale points and vertically goes to the middle of the sand cluster. NI_{Vel} is positive for this reflection, while NI_{Den} is negative. In this example, the negative contribution of the density, NI_{Den}, is only one-sixth the magnitude of the positive contribution of the velocity, NI_{Vel}.

3B. Geometric Considerations of Amplitude

Wavelets Reflected from Geologic Boundaries

While the processor promised zero-phase seismic data, trying to find this wavelet shape in the seismic data is similar to finding a needle in a haystack. On most seismic sections, flat-lying, thick constant-velocity beds that produce zero-phase reflections are seldom observed. Seismic data consist of a "convoluted" form of various wavelet shapes; some are easy to predict—others not so easy. A few of the predictable wavelet shapes are shown in Fig. 3.B.1. Starting with the basic zero-phase wavelet, the integral, 1st derivative and 2nd derivative, wavelet shapes are cartooned.

The time on the wavelet that is associated with the reflection is indicated by the reference 0 at the bottom of the figure. The integral and 1st derivative shapes have the reflection time at a zero-crossing point. The integral has the lowest apparent frequency content and the frequency content increases steadily from the integral to the 2nd derivative.

If the thick-bed response is the shape of the basic wavelet, then other wavelet shapes will exist for reflections from:

thin bed	1st derivative
refraction	integral
velocity gradient	integral
small area	1st derivative
small volume	2nd derivative
buried-focus syncline	90°-phase change
buried-foci basin	180°-phase change

Of course, each of the above is also associated with an amplitude change.

The variation from the basic wavelet shape results from either a vertical change in the acoustic impedance or a lateral change from a flat boundary. If 3-D seismic is employed, then the phase variation associated with nonflat boundaries will revert to zero-phase after 3-D migration. However, a 2-D line across any of the last four geometric shapes listed can lead to some perplexing wavelet shapes and reflection patterns after migration. This is introduced as a warning when amplitude interpretation is based on an extracted 3-D line that is 2-D processed.

Thin-Bed and Transitional Velocity Responses

Wavelet changes associated with vertical variations in acoustic impedance are illustrated in Fig. 3.B.2. For simplicity, the density curve was held constant in this model. There are three factors to consider for each reflection sequence. They are the reflection event timing, the additional amplitude scalar over the reflection coefficient, and the shape of the wavelet. In the 1-D synthetic, the velocity curve was selected so that the velocity ratio and thus the reflection coefficients are the same for each bed response. The principle being illustrated is, "If a thick bed has a reflection amplitude of one (1), what additional scalar is needed for a thin-bed or transitional velocity change?"

In a classic paper by Widess (1973), the thin-bed response shown in Fig. 3.B.2 was given. Widess was awarded the Virgil Kauffman Gold Medal for the significance that this paper had on stratigraphic interpretation using amplitude. When the thickness of a bed is less than one-eighth of the seismic wavelength (computed with the interval velocity of the thin bed), the composite reflection amplitude is directly proportional to the thickness of the bed. The composite reflection takes the shape of the derivative of the zero-phase wavelet. That assumes zero-phase processing.

When the bed thickness is greater than one-fourth the wavelength, thickness estimates are determined from the time interval measured between the reflections from the top and bottom. Essentially, the reflections are resolvable in time. Time and amplitude analyses of thin beds are often referred to as TAMP. Two TAMP examples are given in Fig. 3.B.3. The wedge model on the left was generated with a zero-phase Ricker wavelet, and the one on the right with a minimum-phase wavelet. The time separation between the upper and lower reflections varies continuously from 45 ms to 1 ms. In both models, the maximum peak-to-trough amplitude occurs at the tuning thickness of $\lambda/4$. For the Ricker model, the time separation between the peak and trough decreases linearly until the tuning thickness is reached, and then the peak-trough time separation remains essentially constant. The time-interval and amplitude plots for the minimum-phase wavelet are not as smooth as the Ricker-wavelet example because of the *ringing* nature of the specified minimum-phase wavelet.

In TAMP analyses, one uses time separation to estimate thick beds and amplitude to estimate thin beds. However, additional information or assumptions are necessary in order to relate amplitude to thickness. For instance, the interval velocity of the thin bed and the reflection coefficients at the top and base of the thin bed are needed for comparison to background reflections. Neidell and Poggiagliolmi (1977) detailed the principles and assumptions of thin-bed analyses with practical examples. Neff's (1992) incremental pay thickness modeling was an extension of thin-bed analysis for 3-D data that led to reservoir pay volume and pay distribution estimates.

Besides TAMP, several authors proposed techniques for estimating thickness in the frequency domain. Fig. 3.B.4 contains amplitude spectra for each trace of the wedge models in Fig. 3.B.3. The thickness of the bed (in two-way traveltime) can be estimated in the frequency domain by noting the periodicity of the notches in the amplitude spectra. In the figure, the spectra associated with 45-ms thickness have notches at approximately 22, 44, and 66 Hz. This corresponds to the time-frequency relationship of 1/45 ms = 22.22 Hz. As the bed thickness decreases, the spectral notches move to higher frequencies. With this notch movement, the amplitude-spectra contour plots in the bottom of the figure illustrate the difficulty of estimating thickness with frequency analyses. The contours are essentially the same for the thickness interval from 0 to $\lambda/4$. Thus differentiating 20-ft (6-m) thick beds from 40-ft (12-m) ones would be questionable using the shape of amplitude spectra.

Because the minimum-phase wavelet was designed with a flat band-pass spectrum, the derivative effect of the thin bed can be observed. In the right plot, the high-frequency content increases as the bed separation approaches zero thickness. The amplitude spectra in Fig. 3.B.4 were normalized to the same maximum value.

The counterpart to a thin bed is a transitional- or ramp-velocity layer. This is shown in the bottom portion of Fig. 3.B.2. Its theoretical response can be derived in a fashion similar to Widess's (1973) development, or a heuristic approach can be used. When the reflectivity series for a thin bed $[\delta(t) - \delta(t-\Delta t)]$ is convolved with the reflectivity series of a ramp [unit-step function], a spike results at the top and base of the ramp. In order to achieve this, the ramp must compensate for the thin-bed effect. To do this, the ramp has an integral wavelet shape and a scalar that is inverse to the thin-bed scalar.

While the concept of amplitude associated with thin-bed effects received new attention in the mid-1970s, previous work had been published. Basically, the principles presented in Figs. 3.B.1 through 3.B.3 were elegantly developed by Sengbush et al. in 1961. However, it took the digital-recording revolution and the concepts of "true" amplitude processing to awaken our industry to these benefits.

Small-Area and Small-Volume Responses

An amplitude-interpretation falsehood of the early 1970s was put to rest by Widess's (1973) paper. No longer was it thought that thin beds were invisible to the seismic method. In a similar fashion, the argument that a geologic structure must have an areal extent of one Fresnel zone or it will be seismically invisible, still exists to some extent. In Fig. 3.B.5, the unmigrated seismic response of a small area is seen to take the same wavelet shape and scalar form as a thin bed. An example of a small-area response is a reflection from the top of a volcanic dike.

Hilterman (1982) showed that the small-area response was approximately $[\delta(t) - \delta(t-\Delta t)]$, where Δt was the two-way traveltime difference between a reflection to the center of the small area and a diffraction from the average edge. This combination of a specular reflection and diffraction from a small area has the same impulse response as a thin-bed. In short, a Fresnel zone is not necessary to support a reflection. A small area will have a seismic response that linearly decreases in amplitude as the area size decreases. The small-area response has a tuning area similar to the tuning thickness for a thin bed.

The extension to a small volume is obtained by applying a thin-bed response to a small-area response. The scalar for the small volume is the product of the small-area scalar and the thin-bed scalar. The small-volume composite shape is the derivative (thin bed) of a derivative (small area) to yield the second-derivative effect.

Amplitude, Phase, and Timing Distortions

If a geologic structure is not flat, the amplitude on unmigrated seismic data will be affected by the structure's shape. The scalar and phase introduced by geometric shapes was summarized by Hilterman (1975) and is shown in Fig. 3.B.6. The shape of a geologic surface can be approximated with two principal radii of curvature. The equations in the figure apply to one principal plane. As an example, let the structure be a 2-D anticline with a seismic line traversing the dip direction. If the top of the anticline is buried at 5000 ft (1500 m) and the anticline's radius of curvature is 3000 ft (900 m), the reflection off the top of the anticline will have an amplitude that is reduced from a flat reflection at the same depth by the factor $[1/1+5000/3000]^{1/2}$. The anticline's amplitude will be 0.6 that of an equivalent flat bed. Of course, migration will restore the anticline's reflection amplitude to 1.

However, if the geologic structure is not 2-D in shape, then the out-of-plane response is applied as indicated in the bottom of the figure. Thus, for our example, if the geologic structure is a dome with a radius of curvature of 3000 ft, the resulting amplitude off the top of the structure will be 0.36. 2-D migration will restore the amplitude to 0.60. Thus, amplitude ratios for predicting pore-fluid content that compare top of the structure reflections to downdip reflections will be biased by 3-D geometry. The problem becomes more complicated for negative structures as phase distortions and extra events (sideswipe) become involved. A couple of examples will illustrate these unwanted effects.

Seismic lines were generated across a syncline and a basin (Fig. 3.B.7). The syncline and basin have the same cross-sectional shape in the plane of the seismic lines. The syncline has 2-D curvature while the basin has 3-D. The same syncline and basin were modeled at two different depths, 1500 ft (450 m) and 7500 ft (2300 m). The seismic lines were 2-D migrated and are shown in the lower portion of the figure. For the 1500-ft depth, the migrated sections for the basin and syncline are nearly the same. However for the 7500-ft depth, the basin displays an additional reflection that is associated with the out-of-plane lip of the basin. Though it is difficult to see on these figures, the amplitude in the basin is significantly higher than it should be, due to focusing.

The next examples in Fig. 3.B.8 are even more discouraging. The previous example was modeled with a seismic line through a principal plane. A principal-plane seismic line exists if a mirror is placed vertically through the seismic line, and the mirror image is exactly what exists if the mirror is removed. Lines B and C do not go through a principal plane. The false interpretations shown on the 2-D migrated sections include extra faults, extra events, and amplitude and phase distortions.

Though basins are not favorite structures to drill, deposits on the sides of shale diapers and salt domes have "basin-type" shapes that are tilted and enjoy all the unpleasant seismic effects if 2-D seismic is used for amplitude interpretation. The warning is repeated: if 2-D processing is applied, then potential amplitude and phase distortions, extra events, and erroneous faults caused by 3-D geometry must be reconciled. That's a tough assignment.

Multi-Boundary Relationships

Often, a clue to the magnitude and polarity of a reflection event can be obtained near a geologic pinchout. As shown in Fig. 3.B.9, the reflection coefficients associated with the boundaries that meet at the truncation point are not independent. Reflection coefficient R3 is approximately equal to the algebraic sum of R1 and R2. If all the reflection coefficients are the same polarity, then R3 will be "brighter" than R1 and R2. In short, an increase in amplitude is not necessarily an indication of hydrocarbons, even though it may be appropriately situated geologically.

On the right of the figure, formations are shown encased between two beds that have the same acoustic impedance. For this situation, the reflection coefficients (R1 to R4) algebraically sum to zero (approximately). When analyzing a bright spot that is thought to be encased in shale, top and bottom reflections of equal magnitude should be observed, otherwise a derivative of the basic wavelet is expected. If this is not the case, then vertical variations in the acoustic properties of the reservoir should be suspected.

3C. Amplitude Versus Incident Angle

The normal-incident reflection coefficient equation was the mainstay for amplitude interpretation for numerous years. Now, amplitude interpretation includes AVO. In 1955, Koefoed presented five observations relating the shape of the AVO curve to changes in Poisson's ratio. These observations led Koefoed to advocate that lithology could be extracted from seismic data. His observations will be discussed later.

However, it was Ostrander's (1982) AVO verification with field data and successful exploration wells that spurred geophysicists to examine AVO. These AVO origins are captured in Fig. 3.C.1 by statements from the two pioneers.

Not listed in Fig. 3.C.1 was Koefoed's first suggestion for the practical application of AVO—that is, use AVO to improve the quality of reflections on a seismogram by a judicious choice of the distance from the shotpoint to the seismometers. With the expansion of the number of recording channels, this suggestion has had limited application. Likewise, his second comment about using AVO as a correlation tool is often underutilized by interpreters. If synthetic seismograms had been invented at the time of Koefoed's article, his statement might have read, "Whenever a 1-D synthetic doesn't correlate with the field seismic, correlate the synthetic AVO response to the migrated CDP gathers at the well location." This is especially helpful for areas with young clastic sediments at shallow depths. In these areas, the difference in Poisson's ratio between the lithologies is a more robust expression of the AVO character than the small changes in the acoustic impedances that drive the normal-incident response. An interesting note about his third statement, which relates lithology to AVO, is that Koefoed predicted this application to occur in the more "remote future." He was right ... 27 years' remote, until Ostrander's presentation.

Ostrander's statement in Fig. 3.C.1 was excellently supported in his 1984 article. The CDP gather in the figure, which shows an increase of amplitude with offset, is from the article and represents the classic signature that all interpreters hope to find over their prospects. In his paper, Ostrander presented the theoretical models, petrophysics, and the required data processing before he discussed three case histories. Likewise, he highlighted the anomalous factors that affect AVO, as warnings to the interpreter. His paper is a mini-course in AVO interpretation.

Immediately after Bill Ostrander made his presentation at the 1982 SEG Annual Convention, plans were formulated to develop his concepts into an SEG Continuing Education Short Course. These notes have their origin in this short course.

Fluid-Fluid Interfaces

It might seem a bit inappropriate to cover reflections from fluid-fluid boundaries, because our objectives of determining pore-fluid content and rock type are associated with solid-solid interfaces. However, the fluid-fluid reflection coefficient equation is an integral part in deciphering pore-fluid effects with AVO.

The fluid-fluid equation given in Fig. 3.C.2, at first glance, appears to be almost a duplicate of the normal-incident reflection coefficient equation except for the cosine terms. However, the equation, though appearing simple, covers post-critical angle reflections. The reflection amplitude for incident angle θ_1, $RC(\theta_1)$, is dependent on the transmission (refracted) angle θ_2. If the incident angle exceeds $\sin^{-1}(\alpha_1/\alpha_2)$, the reflection becomes critical. No transmitted *P*-waves exist for incident angles beyond the critical angle. The reflection coefficient past the critical angle has an imaginary part that means the waveform exhibits a phase change. Surprisingly, all this information is contained in the simple fluid-fluid equation.

The amplitude and phase spectra for a fluid-fluid interface are plotted in Fig. 3.C.3. The density contrast is zero between the two media. Past the critical angle of 33.7°, the amplitude spectrum has a value of 1 and the phase spectrum slowly changes from zero-phase at the critical angle to π (180°, a phase reversal) at the grazing incident angle of 90°.

What is not indicated on these spectral plots is the head wave (often called the refraction arrival). To observe this, a total elastic synthetic (SOLID, Sherwood et al., 1983) was generated for the same model in Fig. 3.C.3 and this is plotted in Fig. 3.C.4. The model was generated with an upper half-space medium having the same properties as the first layer. This is equivalent to having no air-water interface, or having water up to the moon and towing the source and streamer with a submarine.

The amplitude of the direct arrival in the figure is constant because a constant-velocity spherical-divergence correction was applied to the synthetic. By applying the spherical divergence correction, the amplitudes on the NMO-corrected *PP*-arrival should somewhat correspond to the amplitude spectrum in the previous plot. The NMO (normal moveout) correction is not the conventional NMO, but rather is a static correction that lines up the *PP*-reflection. Correcting the extra moveout time in this fashion does not stretch the waveform, and thus amplitude and phase relationships at various angles can easily be evaluated with respect to the zero-offset reflection. For instance, the last trace on the static shifted event has an incident angle of 63° and the phase spectrum from the previous figure indicates a phase change of approximately π/2 (90°). The waveform on the last trace has an approximately 90°-phase shift with respect to the basic wavelet at normal incidence. The wavelet on the last trace has a lower frequency content than the wavelet on the first trace, as a result of the array response used in the model. The fluid-fluid synthetic has only three events: direct arrival, *PP*-reflection, and a head wave. The amplitude associated with the head wave for this model is very small.

The shape of the AVO curve for a fluid-fluid interface is not complicated. This is illustrated by the amplitude spectra from four models in Fig. 3.C.5. The four models represent all possible shapes for fluid-fluid reflection spectra. The models were based on permutations of the velocities 5000 and 7000 ft/s (1500 and 2100 m/s) and the densities of 1.0 and 2.0 gm/cm³. There are two possible velocity ratios, 0.71 and 1.40, and two density ratios, 0.5 and 2.0. All model permutations are shown. The amplitude responses can be summarized as:

- If the lower-medium acoustic impedance is greater than the upper, the normal-incident reflection is positive, and vice versa.
- If the lower-medium velocity is greater than the upper, the reflection magnitude is one (1) for angles between the critical and grazing incidence (90°).
- If the lower-medium velocity is less than the upper, the reflection amplitude monotonically approaches −1.0 at grazing incidence.
- The amplitude spectra increase or decrease monotonically, depending on the velocity ratio.

The fluid-fluid spectra are simple to analyze. Are the solid-solid AVO curves as easy to interpret?

Solid-Solid Interfaces

With the addition of shear waves, the evaluation of all possible events generated from an incident *P*-wave source onto a single interface quickly becomes complicated. Fig. 3.C.6 illustrates all wavefronts that are generated if the source medium has a *P*-wave velocity that is less than the *S*-wave velocity of the second medium. This is equivalent to having the source in the weathered layer. There are 10 different wavefronts generated. And this is for an isotropic, elastic medium without an air interface to reflect energy downward! If anisotropy is introduced and *S*-wave splitting is allowed, there would not be enough room on the page to label all the possible wavefronts.

Concentrating on the reflected and refracted (transmitted) waves only, Fig. 3.C.7 shows the notation for the principal raypaths for the *P*- and *S*-waves. With the help of Snell's Law, the direction of all raypaths are defined. All that is needed now is to associate amplitudes with each of the four waves generated by the incident *PP* wave.

There are several textbooks that derive these amplitudes and all are prone to some printing error, including authors who note that others have published the incorrect equations. Therefore, following the precedent of assurance of accuracy by others, the equations published by Jakosky (1960) and reproduced in Fig. 3.C.8 are "correct." Once again, the amplitudes for the reflected *P*-wave, *RP*, and *S*-wave, *RS*, can be complex numbers. Computer programs to invert this matrix to yield a complex-number column solution are readily available such as the one provided by Press et al. (1996).

An excellent bible on ray-trace procedures and algorithms is the book by Cerveny and Ravindra (1971). Among other things, they provide explicit expressions for all 16 different reflection coefficients (incident direction downward and upward for *P*-wave and *S*-wave sources). No attempt has been made here to reproduce the explicit *PP* reflection-coefficient expression—it requires more than 80 multiplications and additions. However, the author has compared the matrix-inversion solution against Cerveny's explicit expression for the reflected *PP* amplitude and phase spectra. They yield identical results.

Solid-Solid Interfaces—Large Velocity Contrasts

For a *P*-wave source, there are eight possible reflected or transmitted waves that can be generated from a solid-solid interface if both the upward and downward incident waves are considered. Fig. 3.C.9 contains the eight magnitude spectra for a geologic model that is an exception for exploration seismic. The *P*-wave velocity of the lower medium is 2.5 times that of the upper *P*-wave velocity. This large *P*-wave velocity contrast creates "interesting" shapes for the reflection-coefficient curves with respect to incident angle. In fact, one of these plots could supply enough information for a PhD dissertation. The following points relate to the coefficient curves in the figure:

- At normal incidence, no shear waves are generated (panels b, d, f, and h).
- No compressional energy enters the lower medium beyond the first critical angle, a_C (panel c). No shear energy enters the lower medium beyond the second critical angle, a_S (panel d).

- When the incident direction is reversed (panels e – h), there are no critical angles and the coefficient curves are much smoother.

While there are incident angles that have near total reflection in panel (a), the associated amplitudes do not necessarily appear on the synthetic because of the contribution from head waves that are not taken into consideration on these plots. This can be observed on the total elastic synthetic plotted in Fig. 3.C.10. The same input parameters were used as in Fig. 3.C.9.

The *PP* reflection has once again been aligned using a static shift in order to observe the amplitude and phase relationships along the reflection event. A spherical divergence correction has been applied. At the critical angle of 23°, a large reflection amplitude is predicted from the amplitude spectrum. However, on the synthetic, the head wave interferes destructively with the *PP* reflection so that the high amplitude does not exist. Because $\beta_2 > \alpha_1$, a second head wave is also generated. At the very-far offsets, the *PP* reflection changes phase with respect to the normal-incident reflection. As mentioned, this large velocity contrast is an exception rather than the rule for exploration seismic. So let's examine a more realistic geologic model in Fig. 3.C.11.

Solid-Solid Interfaces—Small Velocity Contrasts

The model in this figure, with a 30% increase in velocity, has coefficient curves that are much smoother than the previous large velocity contrast model. The *S*-wave velocity of the lower medium is less than the *P*-wave velocity of the upper, so the second critical angle does not exist. The following are a few generalized points about the coefficient curves:

- Even though the *PP* reflection curve is smooth for small angles, the zero-offset amplitude is almost twice as strong as the 30° amplitude. Large velocity contrasts are not necessary to have significant amplitude variations at the small incident angles.
- The amplitude of the transmitted wave is approximately constant up to the critical angle.
- For small incident angles, the *PP* reflection from beneath the boundary has a shape similar to that of the *PP* reflection from above the boundary. However, they are opposite in polarity.

The total elastic synthetic for this model is shown in Fig. 3.C.12. Statics and a divergence correction have been applied. According to the amplitude spectrum, the reflection should exhibit large amplitude at the critical angle when compared with the normal-incident amplitude. As noted before, this large amplitude does not exist because of the head-wave interference. For postcritical analysis, there are differences between the amplitude spectrum from plane-wave theory and the amplitude response generated from the total elastic solution. For a one-on-one comparison, the amplitudes in the total elastic solution were corrected for spreading loss and direction of emergence ray to a vertical-response phone and the array effect imposed by the modeling program. The amplitude comparison is presented in Fig. 3.C.13. Well before the critical angle is reached, the ray theory and total elastic amplitudes begin to diverge. With the advent of routine nonhyperbolic NMO corrections, one has to wonder how the amplitudes associated with the very-large offsets will be interpreted. Do we have an amplitude interpretation theory that will handle the nonpredictable zone? The author doesn't have concise equations to deal with these far offsets; however, a case history will be presented later regarding how to deal with these problems using today's interpretation and modeling software.

While there are large variations in the amplitude spectrum associated with critical and postcritical reflections, most amplitude interpretations are conducted well beneath the critical angle. There were several generalized statements made concerning reflection amplitudes for small velocity contrasts, but there are still basic questions unanswered such as the one presented in Fig. 3.C.14. Seismic interpretation is interested in the change in AVO shape as a function of property changes. The property changes in Fig. 3.C.14 represent the lower medium going from a water-saturated state to a gas-saturated state. Is there any advantage in going back to the Zoeppritz matrix in Fig. 3.C.8 and asking what would happen to the *PP* reflection if the lower *P*-wave velocity and density were reduced by 10%? No interpretive insight is gained from this equation. This is why linear approximations to the Zoeppritz equation were developed.

3D. Linear Approximation of Zoeppritz's Equation

In 1961, Bortfeld derived several formulae for calculating reflection and transmission coefficients as a function of incident angle. He claimed that his approximations of Zoeppritz's equations were accurate to within a few degrees of the critical angle. His formulae for the reflected *PP* and *PS* coefficients are shown in Fig. 3.D.1. The *PP* equation has been modified to remove the natural logarithms from his original equation, but the modified equation yields essentially the same result as the original formula.

An important aspect of Bortfeld's equations is the insight that they provide the interpreter in predicting how amplitude varies with offset as a function of rock properties. The first term in Bortfeld's *PP* equation is the fluid-fluid reflection coefficient equation that was discussed earlier. The second term has been called the rigidity term because of its dependence on the *S*-wave velocity, and thus on the shear-rigidity modulus. There are three special cases to examine in the Bortfeld approximation. They are:

- If $\beta_1 = \beta_2 = 0$, the fluid-fluid case, the rigidity term goes to zero;
- If $\beta_1 = \beta_2$ and $\rho_1 = \rho_2$, then once again the rigidity term goes to zero; and
- If $\rho_1 = \rho_2$, the rigidity term factors to $2[\sin(\theta_1)/\alpha_1]^2 [\beta_1^2 - \beta_2^2]$.

In order to illustrate the interpretive benefits of Bortfeld's work and to correlate his work to petrophysics, a model based on rock properties from the Gulf of Mexico (GOM) was developed, rather than selecting arbitrary velocities and densities.

Rock-Property Model

Shale velocity and density trend curves were generated from well-log curves in the GOM. At 4000-, 9000-, and 14,000-ft depths (1200-, 3000-, and 4000-m depths), sand velocities were selected to yield shale-over-sand reflection amplitudes that are negative, near zero, and positive. As will be discussed in more detail later, these reflection amplitudes correspond to Class 3 (bright spot), 2 (phase reversal), and 1 (dim out) AVO anomalies, respectively. The density values of the sands were selected from GOM velocity-density crossplots. Gas was fluid substituted into these sands using the Greenberg-Castagna method, with fluid properties from Batzle and Wang. The water-saturated and gas-saturated rock properties for the three depth intervals are given in Fig. 3.D.2. The three models will be used throughout this book to illustrate amplitude-interpretation principles.

Analysis of Bortfeld's Equations

Bortfeld AVO responses were generated for the water-saturated and gas-saturated models at 9000 ft (3000 m). The results are plotted in Fig. 3.D.3. Each plot contains four curves. The green-triangle curve represents the rigidity term; blue plus signs, the fluid term; brown squares, the total Bortfeld response; and black line, the exact Zoeppritz solution.

For the water-saturated and gas-saturated scenarios shown in Fig. 3.D.3, the Bortfeld approximation is quite close to the exact Zoeppritz solution, which is plotted as the black curve. What is interesting is the similarity of the rigidity term for the wet and gas cases. They are almost identical. This implies that the difference between a water-saturated AVO response and the respective gas-saturated AVO response lies solely with the fluid term. Stated another way, *Only the acoustic impedance is necessary to differentiate pore-fluid content*. This is not surprising, though. The rigidity term depends mainly on the S-wave velocities, and these aren't appreciably influenced by the pore-fluid content. This emphasizes why an understanding of the shape of the reflection coefficient curve for the fluid-fluid AVO response is essential. If the pore-fluid content is determined from the fluid-fluid term in Bortfeld's equation, what is the significance of the rigidity term?

In order to gain some insight to this last question, AVO responses from the Bortfeld approximation are shown in Fig. 3.D.4 for the shallow and deep models. Once again, the rigidity curves are approximately the same for the water-saturated state and the gas-saturated state.

One conclusion can be reached when the AVO responses from the three depth models are compared: the normal-incident amplitude difference between the water-saturated state and the gas-saturated state commonly decreases with depth.

If the rigidity curves for the three depth models are compared, it is noted that the slope of the rigidity curve increases with depth. This occurs because the rock-property model was developed for a basin in which the P-wave velocity of sand becomes faster than shale as a function of depth. With sand normally having a smaller V_P/V_S ratio than shale, the difference in S-wave velocities between shale and sand increases with depth.

This also represents going from unconsolidated sands at shallow depths to more consolidated sands at deeper depths.

What is disappointing about the Bortfeld approximation is its inaccuracy for incident angles approaching 30° for the 14,000-ft depth model. The exact Zoeppritz solution (black curve) for the water-saturated model at 14,000-ft depth indicates that the amplitude at 30° would be approximately 33% of the normal-incident amplitude, while the Bortfeld approximation predicts zero amplitude at 30°. This magnitude of error is definitely within the resolution of seismic data. This suggests that the exact Zoeppritz equation should be used for ray-trace modeling—a suggestion that will be refuted later.

AVO Relationship to Rock Moduli

The significance of the fluid term in Bortfeld's equation can be related to Gassmann's equation, as depicted in Fig. 3.D.5. Gassmann's equation was previously expressed in terms of the moduli for the dry-rock components and for the pore-fluid component. Values for these moduli for the 4000-ft depth and 14,000-ft depth models are given in the figure.

For the 4000-ft model, the water-saturated pore-fluid contribution (5.4 GPa) is of the same order of magnitude as the total dry-rock modulus (4.22 GPa). When the rock is gas saturated, the pore contribution reduces to approximately 0.3 GPa. Thus, changes in the pore-fluid moduli change the total moduli by almost 100%. The rock begins to act as a suspended load (unconsolidated) and Wood's fluid equation holds. Thus, changes in the fluid factor dominate the AVO response.

At the 14,000-ft depth, the pore-fluid contribution (2.4 GPa) is insignificant when compared with the dry-rock moduli (36.85 GPa). Now, the pore fluid contributes little to the total rock moduli for either the gas- or water-saturated model; the dry-rock moduli are the dominant components.

Bortfeld's introduction of the fluid-fluid and rigidity terms provided rock-property insight on how the AVO curves change during pore-fluid substitution. However, this occurred only after the AVO curves were computer generated. The fluid-fluid and rigidity terms themselves are still a bit difficult to evaluate mentally. Yanghua Wang (1999) expressed Bortfeld's equation in a form that is quite instructive (Fig. 3.D.6). His notation, along with other authors' notations for the linear-approximation equation, is included in Table 1. Wang's expression for the fluid-fluid term indicates that only the *P*-wave velocity can change the way the amplitude increases or decreases with offset in fluid-substitution models. The density contribution is flat. In the rigidity term, $\Delta\mu$ is the same for the hydrocarbon- and water-saturated states. The term $\sin^2(\theta)/\alpha^2$ is the square of the ray parameter, p, and this basically remains the same for hydrocarbon- or water-saturated states. The only change that the rigidity term offers during fluid substitution is through the change of the average density, ρ, which is a small change.

In order to simplify Bortfeld's equation, Wang introduced the elastic constant, μ, rather than using exclusively velocity and density variables. Other authors have suggested this change in variables also. With Gardner's strong petrophysical contributions to literature, it was a natural that Gardner and Forel (1987) advocated expressing the AVO response in terms of rock moduli rather than *P*-wave and *S*-wave velocities.

Gardner and Forel's linear approximation to Zoeppritz's equation is expressed as:

$$\cos^2(\phi)\ RC(\theta) \approx \frac{1}{4}[\Delta\rho/\rho + \frac{1}{4}\Delta M/M] -$$
$$[\frac{1}{2}\Delta\rho/\rho + 2\Delta\mu/M]\sin^2(\theta) + [2\Delta\mu/M]\sin^4(\theta) \qquad [21]$$

This emphasis of expressing the reflection-coefficient equation in terms of the elastic constants has started to gain additional support with the introduction of $\lambda\rho$ and $\mu\rho$ AVO attributes by Goodway et al. (1997).

Table 1. Rock-Property Notation

$RC(\theta)$ = reflection amplitude for incident angle θ
Subscript 1 refers to upper medium, 2 to lower medium

$\Delta\alpha$ = difference in *P*-wave velocity = $\alpha_2 - \alpha_1$
$\Delta\beta$ = difference in *S*-wave velocity = $\beta_2 - \beta_1$
$\Delta\rho$ = difference in density = $\rho_2 - \rho_1$
$\Delta\sigma$ = difference in Poisson's ratio = $\sigma_2 - \sigma_1$
ΔM = difference *P*-wave modulus = $M_2 - M_1$
$\Delta\mu$ = difference *S*-wave modulus = $\mu_2 - \mu_1$

α = average *P*-wave velocity = $(\alpha_2 + \alpha_1)/2$
β = average *S*-wave velocity = $(\beta_2 + \beta_1)/2$
ρ = average density = $(\rho_2 + \rho_1)/2$
σ = average Poisson's ratio = $(\sigma_2 + \sigma_1)/2$
M = average *P*-wave modulus = $(M_1 + M_2)/2$
μ = average *S*-wave modulus = $(\mu_1 + \mu_2)/2$

$\theta = \theta_1$ = incident angle
θ_2 = refracted or transmitted angle
ϕ = average of incident and transmitted angles

In Shuey's equation:
$NI_P = \frac{1}{2}[\Delta\alpha/\alpha + \Delta\rho/\rho]$
$A_0 = B - 2(1+B)[(1-2\sigma)/(1-\sigma)]$
$B = [(\Delta\alpha/\alpha)/(\Delta\alpha/\alpha + \Delta\rho/\rho)]$

Linear Approximations of Zoeppritz's Equation

There are numerous expressions for the linear approximation of Zoeppritz's equation, each with a different emphasis. Gardner's was on rock moduli. Three others are shown in Fig. 3.D.7. Bortfeld's equation is shown in its original form with the natural logarithms along with Aki and Richards's (1980) and Shuey's (1985) equations. Although not referenced as often, Richards and Frasier in 1976 published the linear-approximation equations that appear in Aki and Richards's book.

While Bortfeld's emphasis on the fluid and rigidity terms provided insight when interpreting fluid-substitution problems, Aki and Richards's equation emphasizes the contribution of variations in the *P*- and *S*-wave velocities and density. Shuey, after learning about the contributions of Koefoed and the amplitude dependence on Poisson's ratio, decided to cast Aki and Richards's equation in terms of Poisson's ratio. In addition, he showed which combinations of rock properties were effective at successive ranges of incident angles. The Poisson's ratio dependence was introduced by replacing the variable $\Delta\beta/\beta$ with Poisson's ratio, σ. This was accomplished by taking the derivative of

$$\beta^2 = (.5 - \sigma)/(1 - \sigma)\ \alpha^2 \qquad\qquad [22]$$

to yield

$$\Delta\beta/\beta \approx \Delta\alpha/\alpha - (1/4)[\Delta\sigma/(1 - \sigma)][1/(.5 - \sigma)]. \qquad\qquad [23]$$

Replacing $\Delta\beta/\beta$ in Aki and Richards's equation and employing a little bit of algebra, Shuey's equation is derived.

All the linear approximations in Fig. 3.D.7 are based on small variations in rock properties. The three classes of AVO defined by the models in Fig. 3.D.2 offer an excellent opportunity to validate the linear approximations for real-world environments. These approximations are illustrated in Fig. 3.D.8 along with the exact Zoeppritz solution.

While Shuey claimed that the linear-approximation equations were adequate to within a few degrees of the critical angle, this is not quite true. The three linear-approximation equations expressed in Fig. 3.D.7 yield almost identical results, except Bortfeld's is slightly more accurate for the large incident angles in the 4000-ft depth response. However, these angles are seldom of interest in conventional seismic.

All three equations are inaccurate for the 14,000-ft depth model, which has a large increase of velocity (dim out or Class 1 AVO anomaly). Fig. 3.D.8 contains AVO curves from the linear-approximation (red) and exact (black) equations out to 90° incident angles. Both the gas- and water-saturation models are plotted. The three linear-approximation equations yield results that overplot one another in Fig. 3.D.8.

The approximate solution for the wet case in the 14,000-ft model predicts an amplitude of zero at 30°, while the exact Zoeppritz solution predicts zero amplitude at the same incident angle for the gas case. As will be shown by an example later, the angle at which the reflection amplitude changes polarity is a diagnostic tool for evaluating Class 1 anomalies. Once again, the approximate solutions are not appropriate for Class 1 anomalies.

Shuey's Angle Dependence

One of Shuey's main contributions is that he identified how various rock properties can be associated with near-, mid-, and far-angle ranges. On the right side of Shuey's equation in Fig. 3.D.7, the first term is the normal-incident reflectivity and this is constant across all incident angles. The second term does not start to contribute significantly until incident angles of 15° or greater are reached. The third term, Shuey argued, is insignificant and can be ignored if the incident-angle range is beneath 30°. Using only the first two terms of his equation, Shuey illustrated that Koefoed's conclusions were easy to verify. Shuey, like Koefoed, didn't offer any petrophysical evidence that Poisson's ratio was directly related to lithology. However, he did provide the incentive for the industry to use only the zero-offset and mid-angle contributions to the reflection-coefficient equation to extract estimates of Poisson's ratio. He showed how both the normal-incident coefficient, *NI*, and the change in Poisson's ratio, $\Delta\sigma$, could easily be extracted from the amplitudes in a CDP gather. Having the ability to extract these two parameters, Shuey continued by suggesting that the rock properties in an area be crossplotted in terms of $\ln(\rho\alpha)$ versus Poisson's ratio, σ. Now with the extracted *NI* and $\Delta\sigma$ from seismic and the crossplot from well-log data, an estimate of the lithology could be made. This was the first practical method suggested for extracting lithology from seismic data. Ostrander verified Koefoed's prediction, and Shuey showed how to implement Koefoed's theory. This was a major contribution to the AVO attribute era.

Both the first and second term in Shuey's equation contain the normal-incident reflection coefficient, *NI*. Verm and Hilterman (1995) rearranged Shuey's equation to emphasize the rock-property dependence on incident angle as illustrated in Fig. 3.D.9. With this new arrangement, the near-angle response is basically influenced by changes in acoustic impedance; the mid-angle response is influenced by variations in Poisson's ratio; and, the far-angle, by variations in *P*-wave velocity. Of course, there must be a variation in an individual rock-property for the contributions in a particular angle range to respond. The AVO response from this equation is the same as Shuey's original form and also Aki and Richards's.

Synthetic AVO responses (Fig. 3.D.10) were generated for each of the three rock-property terms. The left panel was generated from the first term in Fig. 3.D.9, and the main rock property contributing to this response is the acoustic impedance. The second-term response is displayed in the middle panel. This panel responds to changes in Poisson's ratio. The right panel, which is the large incident-angle response, has insignificant energy for this example.

It is interesting to note that the AVO response from Poisson's ratio is not always in phase with the acoustic-impedance contribution. Also, where there are large contributions from acoustic impedance, the Poisson's ratio contribution can be rather small, and vice versa. The question remains, "How does this relate to lithology?"

Fig. 3.D.11 is a repeat of the center panel of Fig. 3.D.10 with the well-log curves displayed next to the AVO response. The AVO response, is the Poisson's ratio contribution. The velocity and density curves are plotted to the left of the Poisson's ratio AVO response, while the resistivity curve is plotted to the right. The geology consists mainly of unconsolidated sands and shales. The resistivity curve depicts sand beds as deflections to the left (low-resistivity values). The strong correlation between the Poisson's ratio AVO response and the sand beds suggests that if Poisson's ratio can be extracted from the seismic data, an excellent sand-versus-shale discriminator would exist. This would be a lithologic AVO attribute.

There is a disclaimer that must be acknowledged for this comparison. In order to compute the AVO response, either a measured *S*-wave velocity curve is needed, or an estimate of it. For the comparison in Fig. 3.D.11, the *S*-wave curve was estimated using the Greenberg-Castagna and Batzle-Wang techniques that were described in the petro-physical section. To some extent, the conclusion might be considered biased. However, comparisons of S-wave log estimates versus logged dipole sonics in the same area have shown excellent correlations.

Modeling: Exact Versus Approximate Solutions

Several times it was mentioned that the linear-approximation equations are inadequate for large velocity contrasts, especially for high-velocity beds encased in low-velocity for-mations. Anomalous high-amplitude responses on the large offsets exist. The AVO response in Fig. 3.D.12 has two high-amplitude events annotated. When the sonic and Poisson's ratio curves are examined, there are no beds thick enough, with large rock-property contrasts, to warrant these high amplitudes on the far-offset traces.

In the computation of this AVO response, the well-log curves were depth sampled in units equivalent to 1-ms time intervals. That corresponds to sampling the depth log at approximately 5-ft intervals. This might be considered oversampling. The exact Zoeppritz solution was then employed. AVO synthetics were also generated for the same model using the linear-approximation solution and the total elastic solution. The same input logs were used for the linear-approximation, exact Zoeppritz, and total elas-tic solutions. The resulting AVO responses are shown in Fig. 3.D.13.

The total elastic solution contains all multiples, converted events, direct arrivals, head waves, etc. It is considered to be the true solution. Its response is displayed in the upper-right corner next to the ray-trace exact Zoeppritz solution with *PP* waves only. The total elastic AVO response does not exhibit the large amplitudes on the far traces. The Zoeppritz solution has inaccurate amplitudes on the far traces when applied to logs that were depth sampled equivalent to 1-ms time intervals. The linear-approximation solution for the same model is displayed in the lower-right corner. Its AVO response closely matches the total elastic model. However, when a coarser depth sampling inter-val (equivalent to 4-ms time sampling) is utilized on the initial well-log curves and the exact Zoeppritz solution is applied, the AVO response more closely matches the total elastic model. At first, this doesn't appear to be logical.

The model in Fig. 3.D.14 will assist in describing these inconsistencies. A 13,000 ft/s bed is encased between 9000 ft/s formations. The exact and linear-approximation amplitude versus incident-angle curves are plotted for both the upper and lower inter-face. If the incident angle is 30°, the refracted angle is 46°. For the top interface, the point labeled ET (a value of 0.16) indicates the exact Zoeppritz reflection coefficient. For the bottom interface, the exact Zoeppritz reflection coefficient is indicated by EB (−0.06). When the thickness of the bed approaches zero, the refracted angle does not change significantly. Thus, an amplitude of 0.16 will be added to −0.06 at the same time arrival (bed thickness ⇒ zero), leaving a residual amplitude of 0.10. This is the source of the anomalous far-offset anomaly when only *PP* waves are considered.

For the linear approximation, the incident and refracted angles are averaged. For a 30° incident angle, the computations use (30° + 46°)/2 = 38°. Likewise, when the inci-dent angle is 46° for the bottom interface, the computations use 38°. Thus, it is not sur-prising that the reflection coefficient for the upper interface at 30° incident for the lin-ear solution, ST, has the same magnitude as the bottom-interface reflection coefficient at

46° incident (SB). The sign of the amplitude curves are opposite. In short, as the thin bed approaches zero thickness, the linear-approximation solution approaches zero amplitude. The exact Zoeppritz solution with only *PP* waves included does not. Simmons and Backus (1994) noted this false anomalous amplitude for beds with large velocity contrasts. This effect is more pronounced though for high-velocity beds than low-velocity beds.

When the sampling for the input model is coarser (depth equivalent of 4 ms), the thin bed has its high-velocity values averaged with the surrounding low-velocity formations. Thus, the velocity contrast reduces and the problem solves itself—not a perfect solution, but one to try when high-velocity beds are encountered. In summary, don't use the exact Zoeppritz solution when high-velocity beds are encountered; a total elastic solution is necessary.

3E. Linear-Approximation Equation with Anisotropy

Properties of Anisotropic Media

An anisotropic rock has variations in its physical properties that depend upon the direction a property is measured. In a rock with a north-south fracture system, permeability measurements in that direction are larger than measurements in the east-west direction. Likewise, in the same rock, a *P*-wave propagating in the north-south direction has a faster velocity than one traveling in the east-west direction. However, the *S*-wave velocity in the east-west direction will be larger. This type of anisotropy is called horizontal transverse isotropy or HTI (Fig. 3.E.1).

Another anisotropic model, which is more commonly considered, is vertical transverse isotropy (VTI). Alternating thin layers that are individually isotropic but have significantly different *P*-wave velocities can induce VTI. For horizontal layering, seismic waves normally travel faster in the horizontal direction than in the vertical. This is the principal reason that depth estimates based on seismic-velocity analyses are too deep; the *rms* velocity derived from stacking analyses measures the horizontal-component of velocity and not the vertical.

A few wave-propagation effects of VTI models that will have an impact on amplitude interpretation are diagrammed in Fig. 3.E.2. The fact that the incident phase angle in an anisotropic medium is different from that in an isotropic medium influences an amplitude interpretation. For VTI media, this incident-angle difference becomes significant around 40° to 50°.

While the VTI model discussed above can be thought of as a macroscopic effect, VTI effects also exist in individual layers. Shale, because of its intrinsic nature of having a platy structure, tends to be stronger in the horizontal direction than in the vertical. Once again, the horizontal velocity is faster than the vertical velocity.

Accounting for anisotropic effects in the seismic method was greatly advanced by the pioneering work of Thomsen in 1986. Thomsen simplified the tedious math that is normally associated with anisotropic wave propagation. Two of his weak anisotropic parameters (ε and δ) are related to the wave-propagation effects mentioned, and these are defined in Fig. 3.E.3. Thomsen's third parameter, which is not discussed here, is related to *S*-wave propagation. The last term in Fig. 3.E.3, η, is dependent on Thomsen's first two parameters, and it is this term (η) that relates to NMO velocity measurements (Fig. 3.E.4).

Measurement and Application

Alkhalifah and Tsvankin (1995) published the NMO equation for anisotropic media (Fig. 3.E.4). Numerous articles authored by Tsvankin around this same time period dealt with other practical applications of anisotropy. Tsvankin and Thomsen (1994, 1995) jointly authored two of these papers. The significance of Tsvankin's work on anisotropy won him the SEG Virgil Kauffman Gold Medal in 1996.

In order to estimate Thomsen's anisotropic parameters, ε and δ, from seismic data, additional information at a well location is needed. The estimation procedures are roughly illustrated in Fig. 3.E.4. During a velocity analysis using the illustrated equation, two unknowns are required, $V_{NMO,SS}$ and η, at each two-way time, t_0. $V_{NMO,SS}$ is the short-spread velocity analysis performed by initially muting the CDP gather to offset = depth. After $V_{NMO,SS}$ is estimated, the unmuted CDP gathers are scanned for $\eta(t_0)$. Finally, adjustments to $V_{NMO,SS}$ and $\eta(t_0)$ are performed. $\eta(t_0)$ can be estimated only if energy is on the far-offset traces. Therefore, for any CDP gather, there are more velocity picks than η picks. $\eta(t_0)$, derived from the velocity analysis, is an "rms" function that must be reduced to individual layer values for subsequent modeling. Once this is done, layer values for δ and ε can be computed as indicated in the figure. Can these layer estimates of δ and ε be used to study the anisotropic effect during an amplitude interpretation? Unfortunately, the time resolutions of these δ and ε estimates are normally too coarse to assign anisotropic values to media above and below the reflection of interest. This is not a desirable situation because of the potential anisotropic effect on the reflection amplitude.

The contribution of anisotropy can be added to the isotropic linear-approximation equation as illustrated in Fig. 3.E.5. This anisotropic approximation, along with equations for other anisotropic models such as HTI, can be found in Ruger's PhD thesis (1996).

In Fig. 3.E.5, typically measured values for δ and ε were assigned only to the shale properties for the 9000-ft (3000-m) depth model (Fig. 3.D.2). The decision to assign anisotropy only to shale has been questioned by several authors. AVO responses were generated for the wet- and gas-saturated states. There are significant differences between the AVO responses with and without anisotropy. With the current trend of applying nonhyperbolic NMO corrections, the amplitude variations beyond 40° need to be reconciled by the interpreter. Are observed large amplitudes on the far-offset traces caused by lithologic, pore-fluid, or anisotropic variations? Recently, Bork et al. (1997) concluded that the unusual AVO anomalies they were observing in the Gulf of Mexico and Trinidad were directly related to VTI anisotropy. However, they also noted that much research is still necessary to make this a viable exploration tool.

Figures

Figure 3.A.1

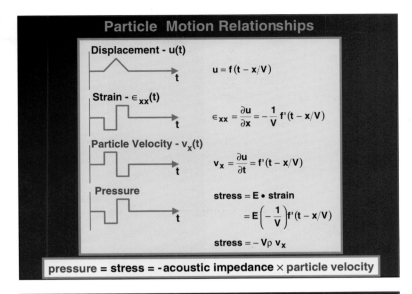

Figure 3.A.2

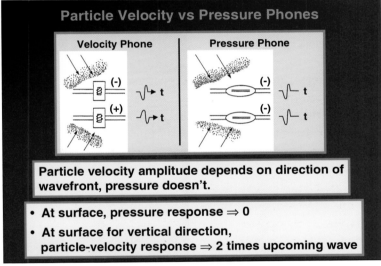

Figure 3.A.3

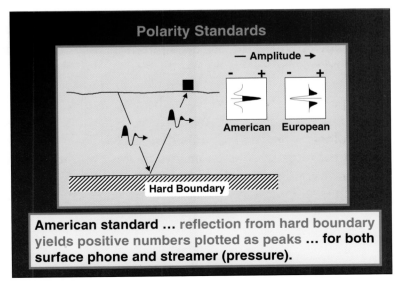

Figure 3.A.4

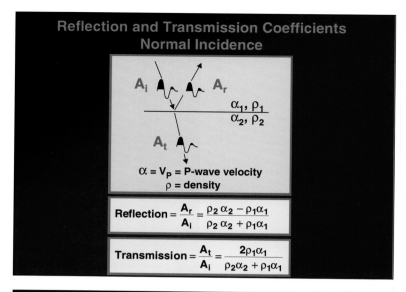

Figure 3.A.5

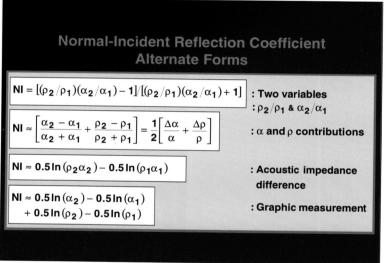

Figure 3.A.6

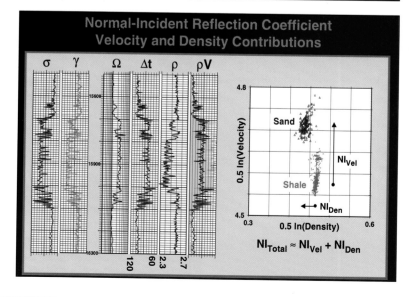

Figure 3.B.1

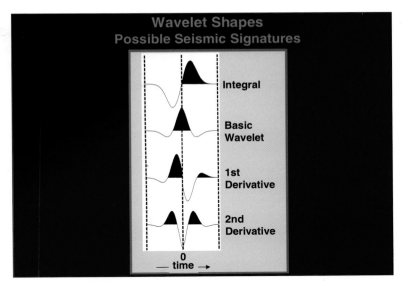

Figure 3.B.2

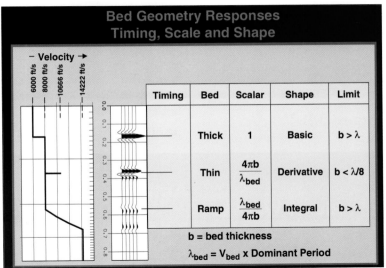

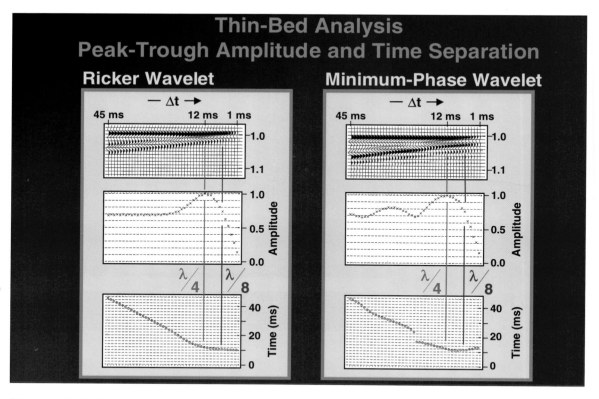

Figure 3.B.3

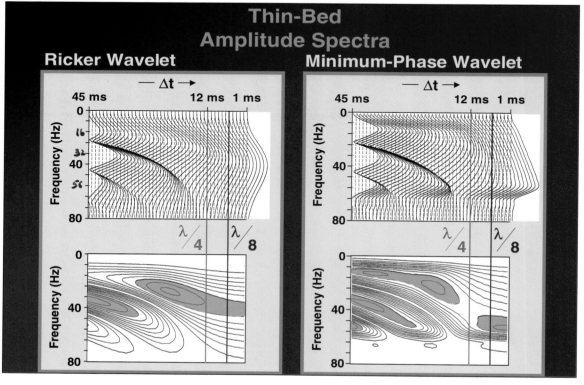

Figure 3.B.4

Figure 3.B.5

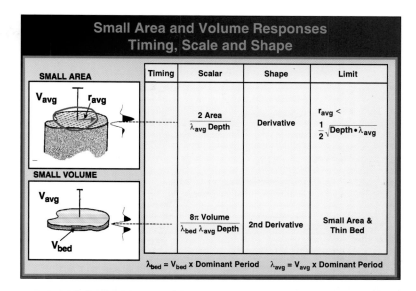

Figure 3.B.6

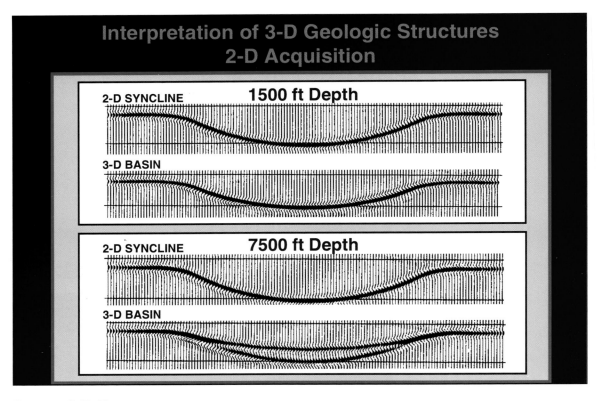

Figure 3.B.7

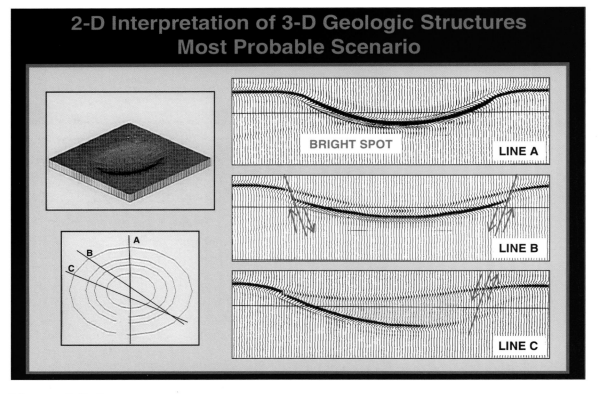

Figure 3.B.8

Figure 3.B.9

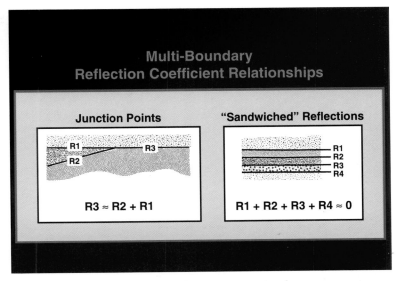

Figure 3.C.1

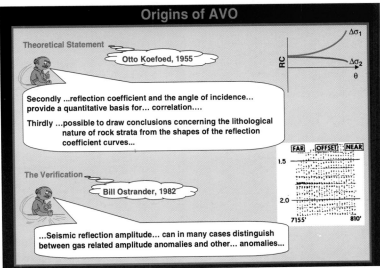

Figure 3.C.2

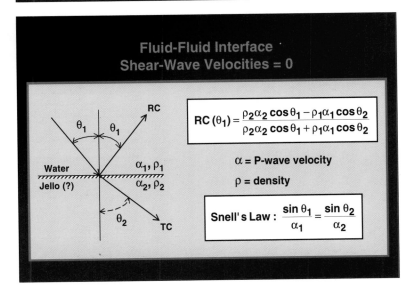

Figure 3.C.3

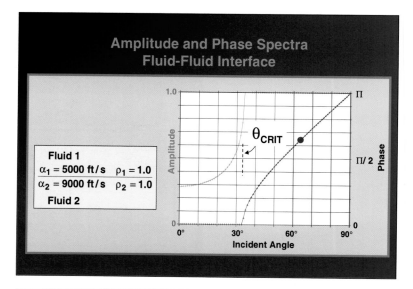

Figure 3.C.4

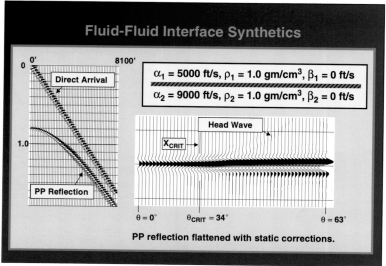

Figure 3.C.5

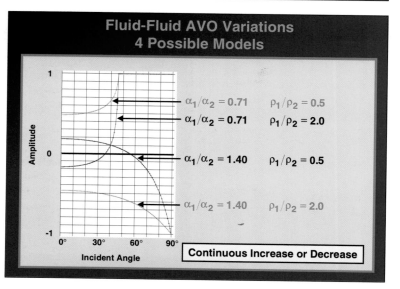

Figure 3.C.6

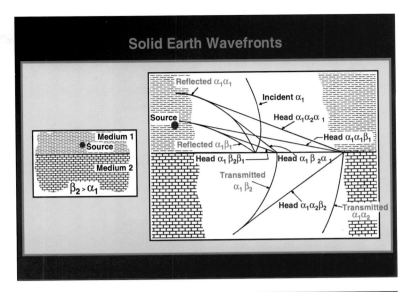

Figure 3.C.7

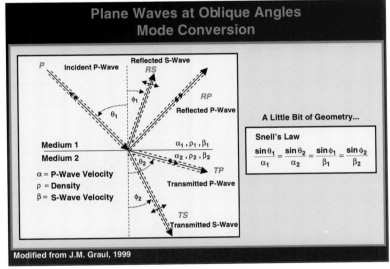

Figure 3.C.8

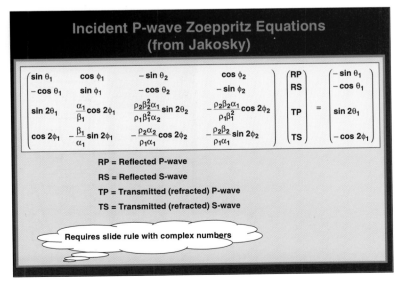

Figure 3.C.9

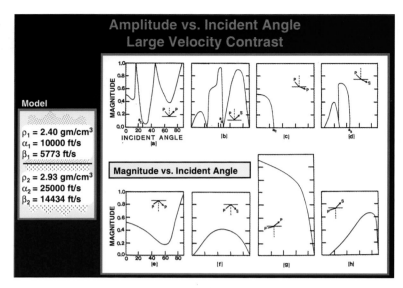

Figure 3.C.10

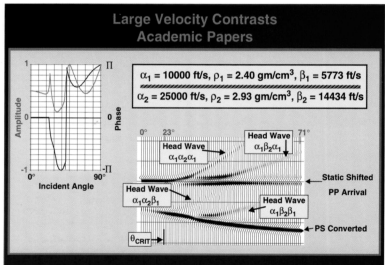

Figure 3.C.11

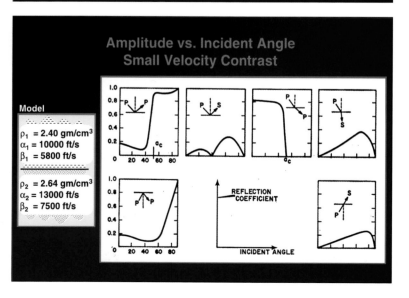

Figure 3.C.12

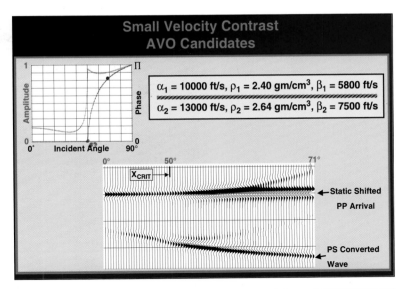

Figure 3.C.13

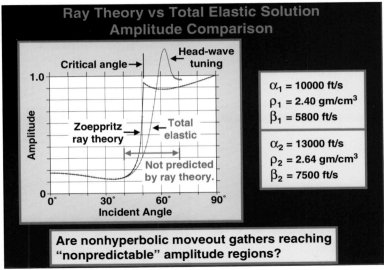

Figure 3.C.14

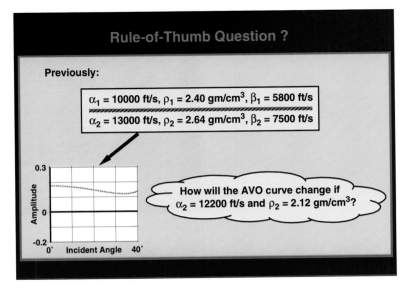

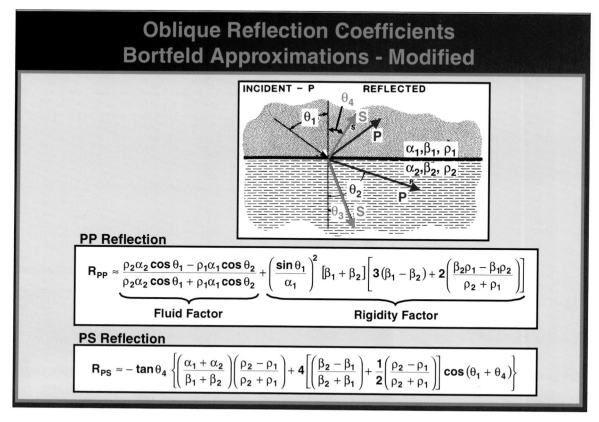

Figure 3.D.1

Figure 3.D.2

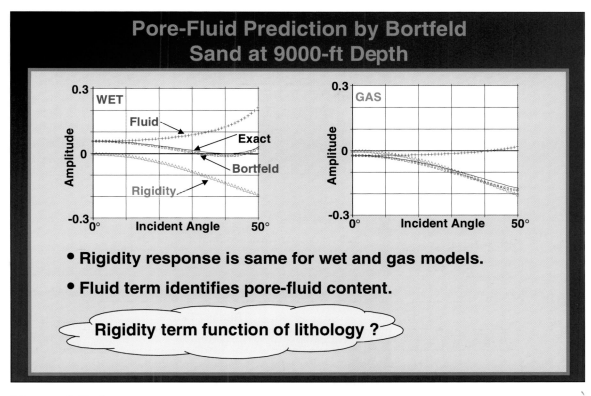

Figure 3.D.3

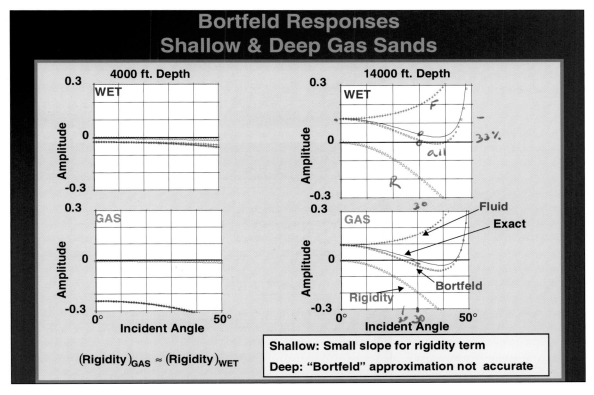

Figure 3.D.4

Figure 3.D.5

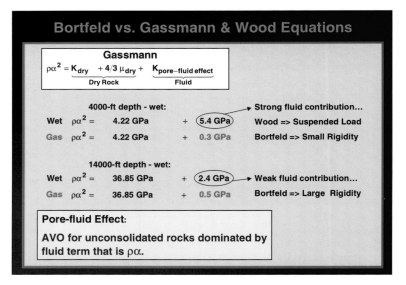

Figure 3.D.6

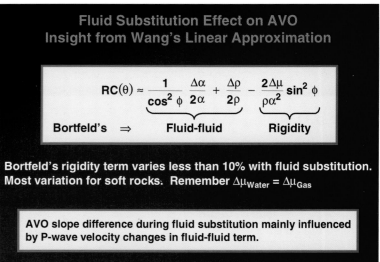

Figure 3.D.7

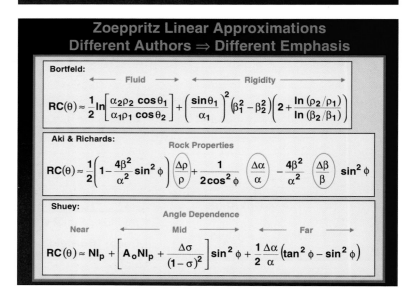

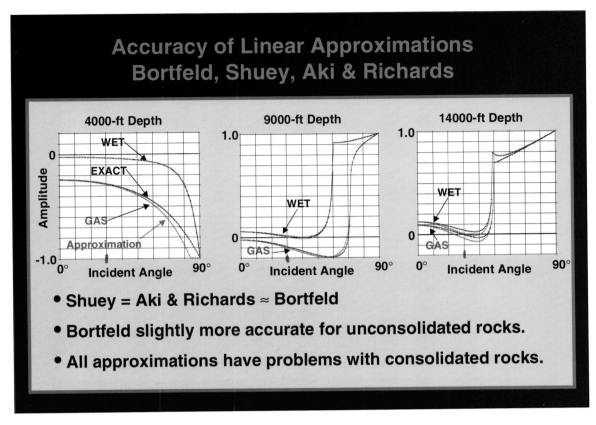

Figure 3.D.8

Figure 3.D.9

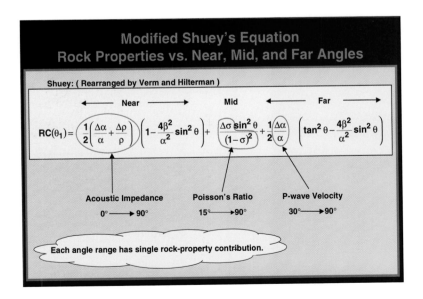

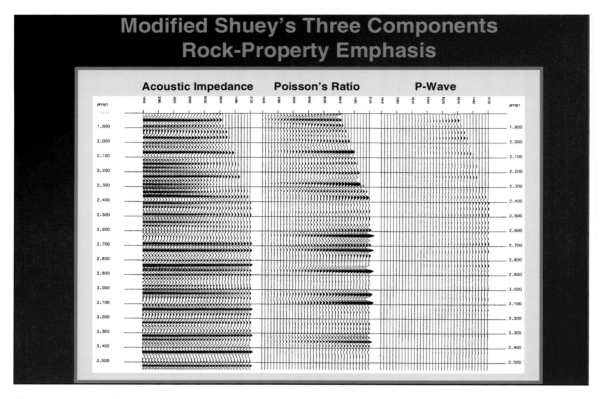

Figure 3.D.10

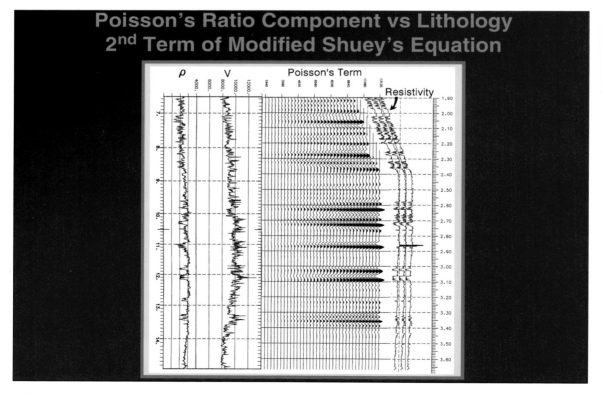

Figure 3.D.11

Figure 3.D.12

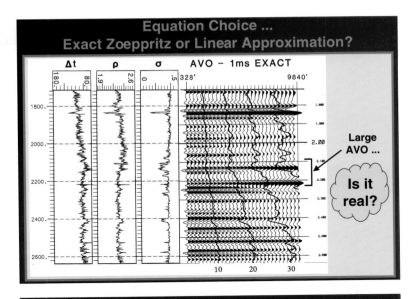

Figure 3.D.13

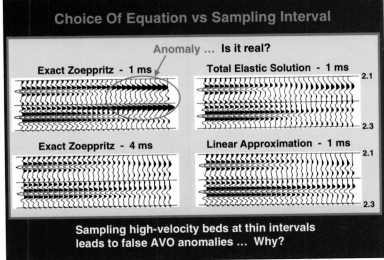

Figure 3.D.14

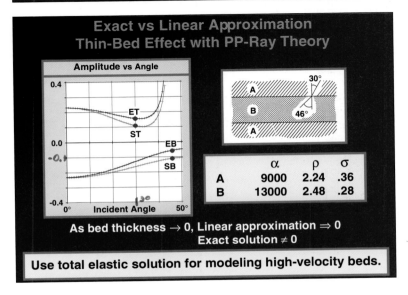

Figure 3.E.1

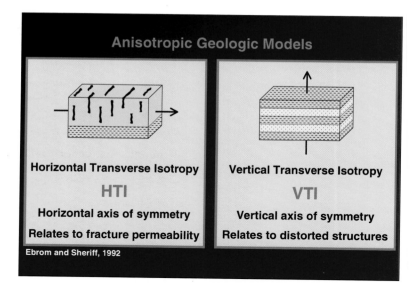

Figure 3.E.2

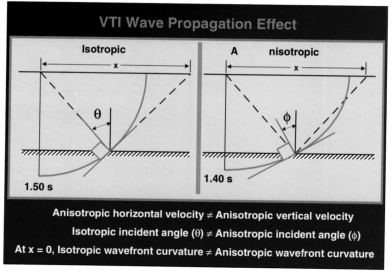

Figure 3.E.3

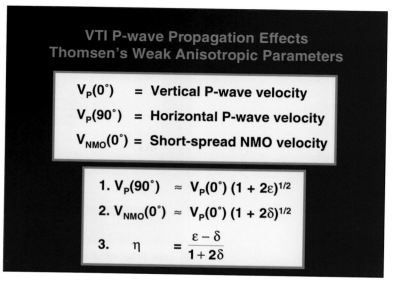

Figure 3.E.4

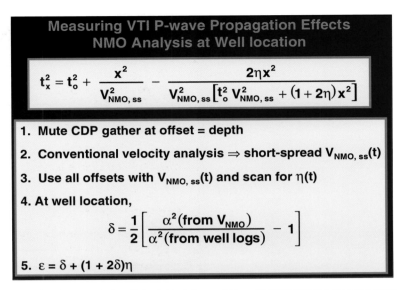

Measuring VTI P-wave Propagation Effects
NMO Analysis at Well location

$$t_x^2 = t_o^2 + \frac{x^2}{V_{NMO,\,ss}^2} - \frac{2\eta x^2}{V_{NMO,\,ss}^2 \left[t_o^2 V_{NMO,\,ss}^2 + (1+2\eta)x^2 \right]}$$

1. Mute CDP gather at offset = depth
2. Conventional velocity analysis $\Rightarrow$ short-spread $V_{NMO,\,ss}(t)$
3. Use all offsets with $V_{NMO,\,ss}(t)$ and scan for $\eta(t)$
4. At well location,

$$\delta = \frac{1}{2} \left[\frac{\alpha^2 (\text{from } V_{NMO})}{\alpha^2 (\text{from well logs})} - 1 \right]$$

5. $\varepsilon = \delta + (1 + 2\delta)\eta$

Figure 3.E.5

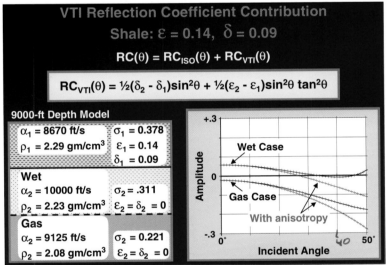

VTI Reflection Coefficient Contribution
Shale: $\varepsilon = 0.14$, $\delta = 0.09$

$$RC(\theta) = RC_{ISO}(\theta) + RC_{VTI}(\theta)$$

$$RC_{VTI}(\theta) = \tfrac{1}{2}(\delta_2 - \delta_1)\sin^2\theta + \tfrac{1}{2}(\varepsilon_2 - \varepsilon_1)\sin^2\theta \tan^2\theta$$

9000-ft Depth Model

$\alpha_1 = 8670$ ft/s	$\sigma_1 = 0.378$
$\rho_1 = 2.29$ gm/cm^3	$\varepsilon_1 = 0.14$
	$\delta_1 = 0.09$

Wet

$\alpha_2 = 10000$ ft/s	$\sigma_2 = .311$
$\rho_2 = 2.23$ gm/cm^3	$\varepsilon_2 = \delta_2 = 0$

Gas

$\alpha_2 = 9125$ ft/s	$\sigma_2 = 0.221$
$\rho_2 = 2.08$ gm/cm^3	$\varepsilon_2 = \delta_2 = 0$

Section 4. Recognizing Hydrocarbon Signatures

Objective:

1. **Develop rules-of-thumb for recognizing hydrocarbon signatures**

2. **Catalog seismic anomalies associated with hydrocarbon signatures**

In the 1970s, the realization that hydrocarbons could be directly detected by seismic data caused a major revolution in seismic processing and interpretation. The main drivers were digital recording and digital processing. The digital world led to the preservation of "true" or "relative" amplitude from acquisition through interpretation. The routine application of automatic gain control (AGC) was being reevaluated by all processing centers. Outstanding differences between processing with and without AGC were being displayed around the industry. Figure 4.A.1 contains an early 1970s example. What is surprising about this figure is that the data were acquired with a marine vibroseis source in the offshore Gulf of Mexico. One can't miss the gas anomaly at 1.6 s. Thus was bright-spot technology.

Figure 4.A.2 depicts the cry heard throughout the oil industry during the early 1970s: "Hydrocarbon reservoirs can be detected as seismic events that have significantly higher amplitude than surrounding reflections." This thesis, once realized by an oil company, became the leading-edge technology to be exploited with internal research on new interpretation applications. The economic benefits for a company that had bright-spot technology were staggering when it came to evaluating potential prospects for upcoming lease sales, farm-ins, and the like.

4A. 1970s Classification and Recognition of Hydrocarbons

Thirty years after the advent of the bright-spot technology, one has to wonder if there are any other interpretation techniques waiting to be developed that will change the oil industry as drastically as bright spots did. Probably not! However, there have been numerous incremental advances in amplitude interpretation since that time.

These incremental advances were developed as it was realized that there were other Direct Detection Indicators (DDI) or Hydrocarbon Indicators (HCI) present if a bright spot was detected. In essence, if the earth's properties changed dramatically with a change in pore fluid, then there should be additional methods for recognizing the hydrocarbons with the seismic method other than high amplitudes. Sengbush (1983) listed numerous examples and amplitude-interpretation techniques relating to this early technology. These are still relevant today and thus a brief review of them is in order.

Sengbush reprinted the seismic sections shown in Fig. 4.A.3 from the 1973 symposium *"Lithology and direct detection of hydrocarbons using geophysical methods."* The upper-right section has two high-amplitude events. These are bright spots from sands that have acoustic impedances that are significantly lower than the acoustic impedance of the encasing sediments. The bright event just beneath 1.0 s is from a thin gas-charged sand, while the event at approximately 2.0 s corresponds to a gas-charged sand with a thickness of approximately 150 ft (50 m). In addition, the deeper event has a flat reflection associated with the gas-water interface that lies near the 2.0-s timing line. The right side of the reservoir has a trapping fault, while the left side indicates an interference of the reflections from the top of the reservoir and the flat spot.

It didn't take long to realize that not all hydrocarbon reservoirs were bright. In the upper right of Fig. 4.A.3, a "dim-out" anomaly is shown for a porous limestone beneath a shale. In a dim-out anomaly, a positive reflectivity is reduced by the presence of hydrocarbons.

One of the more difficult hydrocarbon anomalies to recognize on the stack section is the phase reversal, as shown in the lower left of the figure. The polarity of the reflection changes from negative to positive, going from the hydrocarbon portion to the water-saturated portion of the reservoir. Even with the circle around the zone of interest, the polarity reversal is difficult to distinguish from what may be a small fault or possible data-processing problems.

The last section in the lower right of the figure is a dream of all geophysicists: a bright spot with an obvious flat event. The flat event is associated with a reflection from the interface of two different pore fluids. This is considered by many geophysicists to be the most diagnostic indicator of hydrocarbons. With the advent of 3-D seismic, Backus advocated that the search for flat spots is not emphasized enough in modern interpretation. His article with Chen (Backus and Chen, 1975) illustrates this philosophy.

During the 1973 symposium, many direct-detection techniques were presented for recognizing hydrocarbons. However, there was one technique shown by Paige that appears to have been forgotten by the industry. Paige (1973) suggested that a comparison of stacks with different offsets would be a diagnostic hydrocarbon-detection technique. Yes, he advocated AVO interpretation with seismic in 1973. His example is shown in Fig. 4.A.4. The far-offset section has three gas sands annotated. The gas sands are significantly "hotter" on the far-offset stack than on the near-offset stack. Unfortunately, it appears that with all the other direct-detection techniques being offered during this short time span, Paige's AVO observation was overlooked.

Qualitative Analysis of Seismic Amplitudes

The cartoon in Fig. 4.A.5 is a qualitative analysis of the bright-spot, phase-reversal, and dim-out anomalies with respect to their normal-incident reflectivity, *NI*. The models are derived for shale over sand, but other rock types are also applicable. The calibration is based on a comparison of the reflectivities derived for shale over water-saturated sand versus the shale-over-hydrocarbon-saturated sand. The water-saturated states are represented by the squares; the gas-saturated states, by circles.

For bright spots, the acoustic impedance of the overlying shale is greater than the water-saturated sand, so that when hydrocarbons are introduced the *NI* decreases from a slightly negative value to a larger negative value. This normally occurs when sands and shales are within the velocity range of 5000 ft/s to 8500 ft/s (1500 m/s to 2600 m/s).

A phase-reversal event occurs when the overlying shale has an acoustic impedance slightly less than the water-saturated sand's acoustic impedance; a small positive *NI*.

Insertion of hydrocarbons reduces the sand's acoustic impedance below that of the shale's. The resulting *NI* is slightly negative. The absolute values of the reflections from the water-saturated sand and from the hydrocarbon-saturated sand are small. Phase-reversals normally occur when sands and shales are within the velocity range of 8500 ft/s to 12,500 ft/s (2600 m/s to 3800 m/s).

Finally, a dim-out event occurs when the overlying shale has an acoustic impedance significantly less than that of the water-saturated sand—a large positive *NI*. Insertion of hydrocarbons reduces the sand's acoustic impedance, but it is still greater than the shale's. The resulting *NI* is still positive, but less than that of the water-saturated state. This normally occurs when sands have velocities greater than 12,500 ft/s.

The velocity ranges cited are rough approximations that should be verified by local rock-property measurements.

The following concepts are suggested:

• Hydrocarbon replacement always reduces *NI*.
• Unconsolidated rocks tend to exhibit bright spots, while well-consolidated rocks are candidates for dim-out events.

With the advent of AVO, Rutherford and Williams (1989) proposed a new classification to assist in the recognition of AVO anomalies.

4B. AVO Classification and Recognition of Hydrocarbons

Rutherford and Williams's classification of the reflection-coefficient curves shown in Fig. 4.B.1 has become the industry standard. The classification was developed for reflections from hydrocarbon-saturated formations. They mentioned in their article that the boundaries for Class 1, 2, and 3 should be treated as fuzzy, with the absolute boundaries determined by specific rock properties. They also included excellent seismic examples for each AVO class.

According to Rutherford and Williams's classification, the slope of the reflection-coefficient curve is negative for all classes. The reflection amplitude decreases with the angle of incidence. However, the absolute amplitude can increase with angle of incidence as depicted for Class 2 and 3 AVO gas-saturated anomalies. Castagna et al. (1998) found that certain Class 3 gas-saturated anomalies can have slowly decreasing amplitudes with offset. These were named Class 4 AVO anomalies. However, the main diagnostic feature for the Class 4 anomalies is still the large amplitude associated with the hydrocarbons.

Previously it was shown that Bortfeld's reflection-coefficient equation strongly correlated the water-saturation AVO curve to the gas-saturation AVO curve through the fluid-fluid term. Because of this relationship, Rutherford and Williams's curves are expanded to include both saturation states. The rock properties previously shown in Fig. 3.D.2 have been expanded and are given in Fig.4.B.2. These models are based on shale trend curves that vary with depth. When AVO synthetics are generated, they will be expanded to include 50-ft (15-m) sand intervals for both the water and gas-saturated states. The gas- and water-saturated sands for a particular AVO class are separated by a 500-ft (150-m) shale interval. Thus, the encasing shale properties for the top and bottom of a particular sand interval are slightly different.

Included in the table in Fig. 4.B.2 are the respective normal-incident reflectivities for the upper boundary of each of the six sand beds. For each depth range, the water- and gas-saturation NI_P's (normal-incident P-wave reflection coefficients) are given. At the 4000-ft (1200-m) depth interval, they are -0.025 and -0.256 for the water and gas-saturated states, respectively. This ten-to-one amplitude ratio corresponds to the 1970s bright spot classification or Class 3 anomaly of Rutherford and Williams. The 9000-ft and 14000-ft (3000-m and 4000-m) depth ranges are likewise related to the 1970 classification of phase reversal and dim out.

The reflection-coefficient curves for the top interface of the six sand beds are shown in Fig. 4.B.3. Once again, for a particular AVO class, the shape of the two amplitude curves (wet versus gas) are approximately the same for incident angles below 30°; the gas curve is merely shifted downward from the water-response curve. If the pore fluid were replaced with oil, the oil-response curve would fall between the water and gas curves. It would still be essentially parallel to them.

The parallel nature of the water and hydrocarbon amplitude curves is not as apparent when the synthetic AVO responses for these models are examined, in Fig. 4.B.4. For the Class 2 synthetic responses in Fig. 4.B.4, it is difficult to imagine that the gas response is the same as the wet response if a constant value is subtracted from the wet response.

For each AVO class, the respective stack traces are shown. From the stack traces, the concept of a bright spot, phase reversal, or dim out is associated respectively with Class 3, 2, and 1 AVO anomalies. From the AVO responses, it is noted that the Class 3 anomalies essentially have constant amplitude with offset. The dominant feature of the Class 2 AVO anomalies is that the gas sand has an increase of amplitude with offset. Finally, for the Class 1 AVO anomalies, the gas-sand response decreases amplitude with offset at a faster rate than its corresponding water-saturated model.

For the Class 2 AVO anomaly, Ross and Kinman (1995) suggested a subdivision to emphasize that the stack for these nonbright responses can be positive or negative. The main classification feature of the Class 2 anomaly is the small reflectivity at normal incidence.

4C. Class 1, 2, 3 AVO Field Examples

In this section, field examples will be presented in a style similar to Rutherford and Williams's work. Stack sections along with their respective range-limited angle stacks and CDP gathers will be shown for each AVO class. Reflection coefficient curves for both the in-situ and fluid-replacement properties are included.

Class 3—Bright Spot

In Fig. 4.C.1, the 2-D stack section across a deep-water field in the Gulf of Mexico depicts numerous pay zones that are classified as bright spots. The shallowest anomaly unfortunately points out an interpretation pitfall associated with low-saturated gas sands (fizz). They can appear as bright as fully saturated gas sands. Though some authors report success in differentiating low versus high gas saturation using the seismic method, this area still remains a pitfall for most interpreters.

The deeper three bright events are from high gas–oil ratio (GOR) oil sands and a gas sand. In the next figure (Fig. 4.C.2), all three angle-limited stacks for the shallow two bright spots have large amplitudes. The presence of salt was one of the main reasons for concentrating on the two shallower bright spots as an example, rather than the deeper zones. Salt affects the raypaths to the deeper horizons, thus making amplitude interpretation on the longer offsets questionable.

The broadening of the seismic wavelet from NMO stretch tends to overemphasize the increase of amplitude with incident angle. There is also more event continuity and a smaller number of reflections on the 24°–36° angle stack because the shale-upon-shale reflections tend to lose amplitude with offset.

While the reflection polarity can be determined from the color bar, for the old timers in the crowd, a wiggle variable area (WVA) equivalent is given in Fig. 4.C.3. All the pay zones are thin beds, and thus the polarity convention is a large trough followed by a large peak (the derivative of the seismic zero-phase wavelet). The trough-peak wavelet character is evident on all the angle stacks.

The large amplitude associated with these Class 3 AVO anomalies is emphasized in Fig. 4.C.4 by examining the CDP gathers at the well location and at a location downdip from the shallow hydrocarbons (see the red arrows). From the well-log data, reflection amplitude curves were derived and are shown in the bottom right of the figure. The CDP gathers and the stack indicate that the bright spots are about two to three times larger than their equivalent water-saturated responses. This is the same ratio that is predicted from the reflection amplitude curves.

In summary, Class 3 anomalies have the following properties:

- *Hydrocarbon zones are bright on the stack section and on all angle-limited stacks.* When multiples are a problem, the near-angle stacks tend to have more noise contamination than the far-angle stacks.
- *The hydrocarbon reflection amplitude, with respect to the background reflection amplitude, is constant or increases slightly with incident-angle range.* Even though the amplitude of the hydrocarbon event can decrease with angle, as suggested for the Class 4 AVO anomaly, the surrounding shale-upon-shale reflections normally decrease in amplitude with angle at a faster rate.
- *Wavelet character is trough-peak on all angle stacks.* This, of course, assumes that the dominant phase of the seismic wavelet is zero and the reservoir is below tuning thickness.
- *Hydrocarbon prediction is possible from the stack section.*

Class 2—Phase Reversal

Class 2 anomalies are the natural candidates for AVO analysis. In Fig. 4.C.5, the lower gas sand is difficult to detect on the conventional stack section. The conventional stack section normally provides good structural definition for Class 2 anomalies, but it is often difficult to recognize potential hydrocarbon pay using amplitude. However, from the three angle-limited stacks in Fig. 4.C.6, the hydrocarbon signatures become evident. Or are they?

There were two gas-sand zones encountered at the well location. Each gas zone has a significant increase in amplitude with offset angle. If increase in amplitude with offset is a criterion for hydrocarbons, then there appear to be additional hydrocarbons in the adjacent downthrown block. From other wells in the area, these downthrown events have been interpreted to be clean water-saturated formations. (These wells were drilled and logged in the late 1960s and early 1970s and there appears to be some question about this interpretation because the mud logs had gas shows.) Note that the upper clean sand signature is not evident on the near-angle stack (shown by the green arrows in the figure). The purple arrows indicate another shallower water sand that was encountered at the well location. It is dim on the near offsets, and brightens with increasing incident angle. This suggests that even if the amplitude increases with offset, some relative measurement of the degree of brightening needs to be considered for hydrocarbon prediction.

The time interval spanned by the red arrows in the figure has decreasing amplitude with offset, and this interval corresponds to a thick shale sequence. The ability to discriminate both lithology and/or pore-fluid content using AVO analysis is greatly enhanced in Class 2 environments. For this example, sand reflections increase in strength with offset compared with shale-upon-shale reflections.

For Class 2 environments, the acoustic impedances of adjacent sand-shale intervals are approximately the same, and reflection quality can be high on large offsets. Because of this, anisotropic (nonhyperbolic) NMO corrections are often applied to utilize the amplitude behavior from offsets as large as twice the depth. This was done for this data set, and angle ranges up to 50° were preserved.

In Figs. 4.C.7 and 4.C.8, an expanded version of the angle-limited stacks is displayed. The hydrocarbon signature is normally weak on the near-angle stacks and increases with incident angle. The wavelet character is normally difficult to determine on the near-angle stack, but changes to a trough-peak with increasing incident angle. This wavelet character is evident for the upper gas sand in the two figures but not for the lower. The lower zone has stacked gas intervals.

CDP gathers at the well location and at a location in the adjacent fault block are shown with the conventional stack in Fig. 4.C.9. The conventional stack exhibits the classic trough-peak wavelet character for a thin-bed gas zone at the upper gas interval (annotated with a red arrow). However, the wavelet character is not as pronounced on the stack section as is observed on the far-angle stacks in Figs. 4.C.7 or 4.C.8.

In the lower-right portion of Fig. 4.C.9, reflection-amplitude curves are shown for the gas zone, for the water-saturated equivalent, and for a clean water-saturated sand. The clean water-saturated sand is predicted to have an amplitude increase with offset, but not as much as the gas sand has. Relative measurements are necessary, to avoid interpreting clean sands as gas sands. The conventional NMO mute of 30° is depicted by the blue line on the CDP gather display. The red arrows on the CDP gathers point to the gas sand and the clean water sand in the adjacent fault block. The amplitude for the clean water-saturated sand (off-field CDP gather) is evident past the 30° mute, and appears to change phase with respect to the near offsets. This is the same response that the reflection-amplitude curves predict.

In summary, the following properties are exhibited by the Class 2 anomalies:

- *There is little indication of the gas sand on the near-angle stack.*
- *The gas sand event increases amplitude with increasing angle.* This attribute is more pronounced than anticipated because of the amplitude decrease of the shale-upon-shale reflections.
- *The gas sand event may or may not be evident on the full stack, depending on the far-angle amplitude contribution to the stack.*
- *Wavelet character on the stack may or may not be trough-peak for a hydrocarbon-charged thin bed.*
- *Wavelet character is trough-peak on the far-angle stack.*
- *Inferences about lithology are contained in the amplitude variation with incident angle.*
- *AVO alone, unless carefully calibrated, cannot unambiguously distinguish a clean wet sand from a gas sand, because both have similar (increasing) behavior with offset.*

Class 1—Dim Out

The interpretation of a Class 1 anomaly requires trust in the quality of the data acquisition and processing. The presence of hydrocarbons is recognized by amplitude dimming on the stack and amplitude dimming with offset on the CDP gathers. When dimming occurs on seismic data, one would normally question the image processing and also look for possible skips or rough terrain during data acquisition. In order to have any faith in Class 1 amplitude interpretations, the calibration of seismic to existing well data is essential.

The deep turbidite play shown in Fig. 4.C.10 is a Class 1 anomaly. In order to evaluate amplitude associated with the deep (16,000-ft [5000-m]) turbidite plays, far-offsets greater than 30,000 ft (9000 m) were needed. Angle-limited stacks are shown in Figs. 4.C.11 and 4.C.12. The upper reflection associated with this thick sand package decays in amplitude with increasing angle ranges, as depicted by the blue arrows in the figures.

Even though a conventional suite of well-log curves existed for this well, a question remains as to the actual pore-fluid content. Several interpretations favor some gas associated with the turbidite sand. This interpretation has been selected for modeling the reflection-amplitude responses in the lower right of Fig. 4.C.13. The 36° mute is shown on the CDP gathers. The CDP gathers at the well location and at a downdip location exhibit the same amplitude response as the theoretical reflection amplitude curves suggest. The downdip CDP gather has a larger positive normal-incident reflection than observed on the well-location CDP gather. Also, the CDP gather at the well location decreases in amplitude faster than observed on the downdip CDP gather.

Rutherford and Williams also presented a Class 1 anomaly that was verified by production. This is shown in Fig. 4.C.14. On the stack section, the boxed area indicates the well location and the associated dimming of reflection amplitude. The CDP gathers show a phase reversal on the event associated with hydrocarbons. While the normal-incident trace would show some dimming going from the water-saturated to the gas-saturated state, the major dimming on the stack is associated with stacking of reversed polarities in the CDP gather.

In summary, the following properties are exhibited by the Class 1 anomaly:

• *Amplitude decreases with increasing angle, and may reverse phase on the far-angle stack.*

• *Amplitude on the full stack is smaller for the hydrocarbon zone than for an equivalent wet-saturated zone.*

• *Wavelet character is peak-trough on near-angle stack.*

• *Wavelet character may or may not be peak-trough on the far-angle stack.*

4D. Summary of Hydrocarbon Indicators

During the 1973 Direct Detection Symposium in Houston, Miller Quarles from Petty-Ray Geophysical presented numerous processing schemes to enhance hydrocarbon signatures from background reflections. Miller was well known and respected for his interpretation skills. After Miller's presentation, a participant who worked for a competitor asked, "What is the scientific basis of all these attributes?" Miller, one not to miss a straight line, replied tongue-in-cheek, "We don't know yet, but remember Petty-Ray invented them."

Miller's comment was not off base. Many times, interpreters who look at massive amounts of data find high correlations between particular seismic attributes (potential HCI's of tomorrow) and hydrocarbon reserves. Yet the petrophysical basis for the attributes might still be a bit fuzzy. Today we often call this phenomenon geostatistics.

Key to Miller's presentation was his scorecard for ranking prospects with attributes measured from seismic data. The number of attributes suggested by Miller has grown tremendously with the advent of interpretation workstations. Implicit in his discussion was the suggestion of upgrading the weights assigned to each attribute in the scorecard as prospects are drilled. Nickerson and Tuttle (2000) have suggested a modern technique based on clustering for upgrading seismic attributes or quantifying risk.

Hydrocarbon Indicators

As indicated in the beginning of this section, HCI's are only significant when several indicators or attributes are present. A majority of these attributes are associated with a decrease in the formation velocity when hydrocarbons are present. If the hydrocarbons are gas, the possibility of reservoir leakage, increased attenuation, decreased energy transmission, etc. manifest themselves in other seismic measurements. Sheriff (1989) provides an explanation for numerous HCI's. Some of these HCI's are captured in the next few figures.

Of the HCI's listed under Amplitude Changes in Fig. 4.D.1, bright spots and dim outs have been discussed. If the hydrocarbon anomaly is a shallow bright spot, it is not uncommon for numerous multiple bounces from the free surface to be evident on the seismic. In addition, under a bright spot, the multiples generated above the anomaly can appear stronger because of the decrease of energy reaching the primary events beneath the bright anomaly. The multiples exist along the entire section, but beneath the anomaly the ratio of primary energy to multiple can change sufficiently to enhance the multiples.

The amplitude shadow beneath hydrocarbons can be an accumulated effect of hydrocarbon leakage above the reservoir to increased attenuation through the hydrocarbon zone. An unwanted effect of data processing is the shadow around the hydrocarbon zone that corresponds in time to the time gate of an AGC, if one is applied.

Velocity changes associated with hydrocarbons are often measured above the hydrocarbons (reservoir leakage), through the hydrocarbons, and beneath the hydrocarbons (associated with the hydrocarbon migration path). At the edge of the hydrocarbon zone, the raypaths of a CDP gather can become time distorted. For those CDP's that are just entering the hydrocarbon zone, the far traces are delayed and the stacking velocity for events beneath the hydrocarbons has an apparent lateral decrease in velocity. When the small offsets of the CDP gather traverse the hydrocarbon zone in both the downward and upward paths, a higher stacking velocity for the lower reflections is measured.

With respect to wavelet changes, if the reflections from the hydrocarbon zone are small and intermingled with reflections above and below it, it is possible for a subtle phase shift in the reflection event to occur on and off the reservoir.

In Fig. 4.D.2, various petrophysical reasons for the lower frequency content just beneath a hydrocarbon reservoir have been reported. One way to check whether there is a petrophysical link to this HCI is to remove all deconvolutions from the processing flow. Deconvolution tries to enhance the low frequency that is absent in the seismic wavelet. Thus, the deconvolution operator has a low-frequency component. If the reflection series consists of equally weighted reflections, the low-frequency component is not observed. However, a single large reflection coefficient from the hydrocarbon zone can make this low-frequency component observable. Other explanations for the low-frequency component have been assigned to attenuation.

The most diagnostic HCI is the flat spot. Flat spots are enhanced if the reservoir is thick, has sufficient dip, and is viewed on 3-D data. If there are shallow lateral velocity changes or if the hydrocarbon interval is sufficiently thick, the flat spot can be tilted on the time display.

It goes without saying that the most important aspect of an amplitude interpretation is that it should make sense geologically. Figure 4.D.3 highlights a few geologic constraints. If the structural map does not conform to an amplitude horizon map from the stack volume, try comparing amplitude maps from angle-limited volumes. In Class 2 AVO environments, the amplitudes extracted from far-angle stacks often conform to the structure more than those from the full stack do.

The final comment in this figure was overheard during a gravity course given by Tom LaFehr. When gravity interpretation was in its prime, it was common to generate numerous derivative and higher-order polynomial maps to approximate the residual gravity field. LaFehr commented that seldom does the earth satisfy a *Principle of Least*

Squares—more often, Mother Earth obeys the *Principle of Least Astonishment*. Geologic sense simply overrides the mathematics, because the physical phenomena we seek to describe mathematically are too complex for simple description. This comment is especially appropriate today with the sophisticated software and algorithms available.

Figures

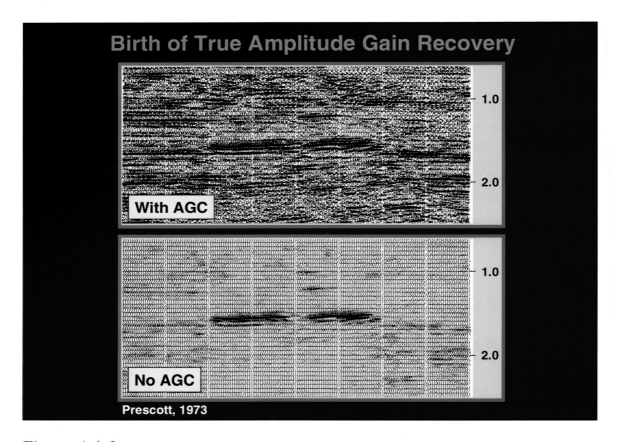

Figure 4.A.1

Figure 4.A.2

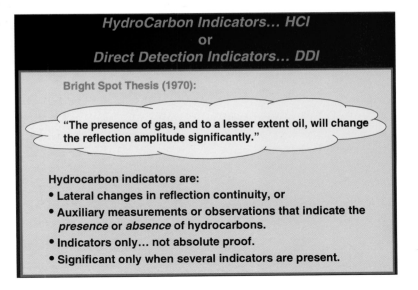

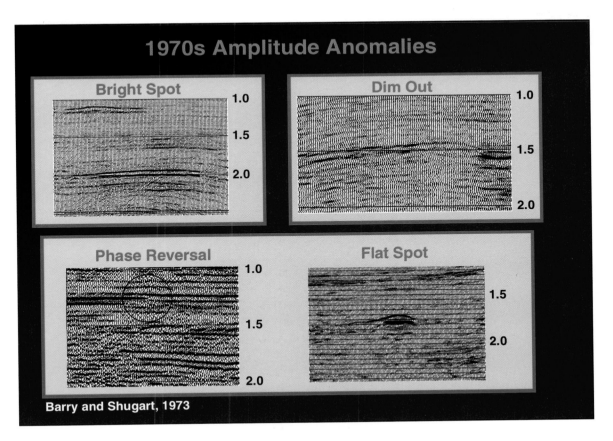

Figure 4.A.3

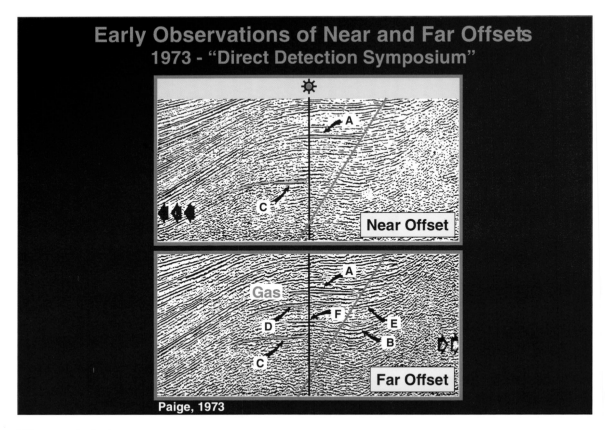

Figure 4.A.4.

Figure 4.A.5

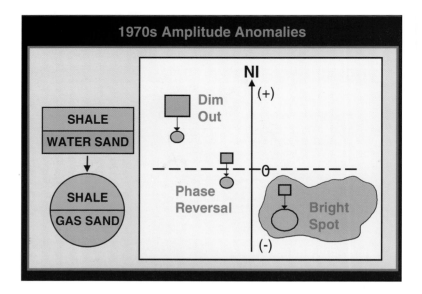

Figure 4.B.1

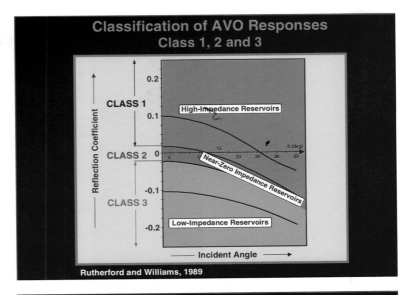

Figure 4.B.2

Model Rock Properties
Class 1, 2, and 3 AVO Anomalies

Class 3 AVO ... 4000-ft Depth - Bright spot

	α (ft/sec)	ρ (gm/cm³)	σ	β (ft/s)	φ	α/β	NI_P	NI_S	PR
Shale	7190	2.16	.419	2684	30	2.67			
Wet sand	7000	2.11	.403	2820	33	2.48	-.025	.013	-.046
Gas sand	5061	1.88	.241	2956	33	1.71	-.256	-.045	-.385
Shale	7350	2.18	.414	2813	29	2.61			

Class 2 AVO ... 9000-ft Depth - Phase reversal

	α (ft/sec)	ρ (gm/cm³)	σ	β (ft/s)	φ	α/β	NI_P	NI_S	PR
Shale	8670	2.29	.378	3828	22	2.27			
Wet sand	10000	2.23	.311	5233	25	1.91	.058	.142	-.157
Gas sand	9125	2.08	.221	5462	25	1.67	-.034	.111	-.313
Shale	8840	2.30	.375	3956	21	2.23			

Class 1 AVO ... 14000-ft Depth - Dim out

	α (ft/sec)	ρ (gm/cm³)	σ	β (ft/s)	φ	α/β	NI_P	NI_S	PR
Shale	10150	2.40	.343	4970	15	2.04			
Wet sand	13500	2.32	.224	8048	20	1.68	.124	.219	-.230
Gas sand	13288	2.21	.182	8288	20	1.60	.083	.196	-.288
Shale	10320	2.41	.339	5100	14	2.02			

Figure 4.B.3

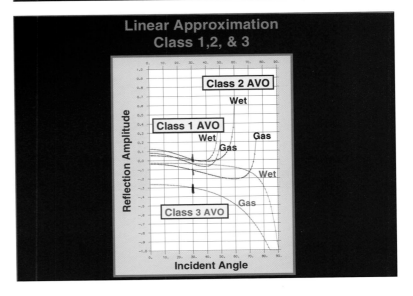

Figure 4.B.4

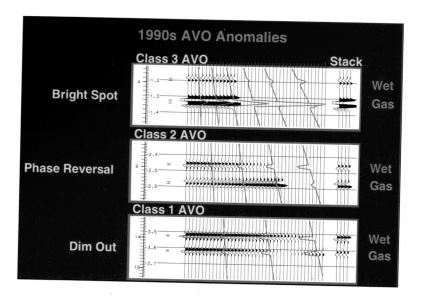

Figure 4.C.1

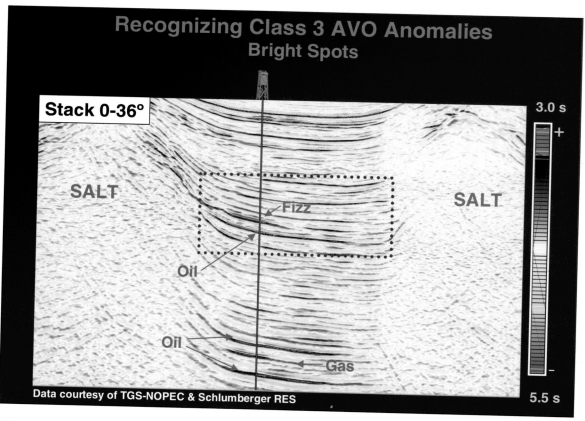

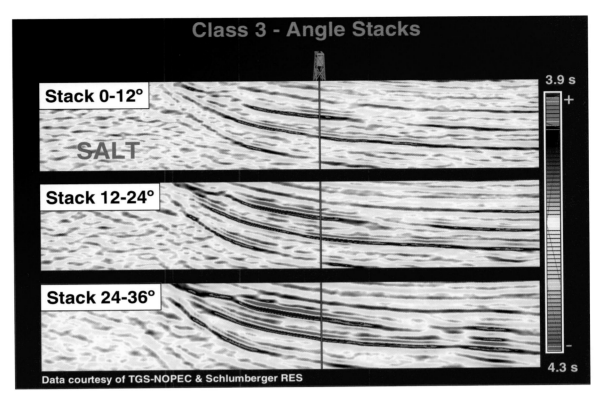

Figure 4.C.2

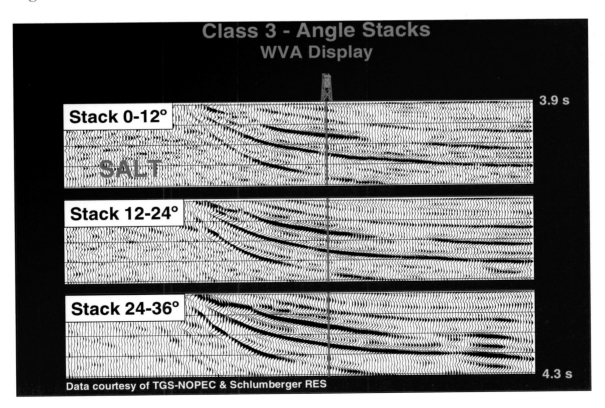

Figure 4.C.3

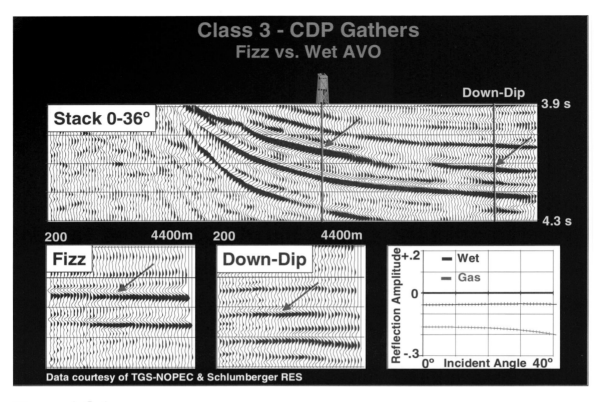

Figure 4.C.4

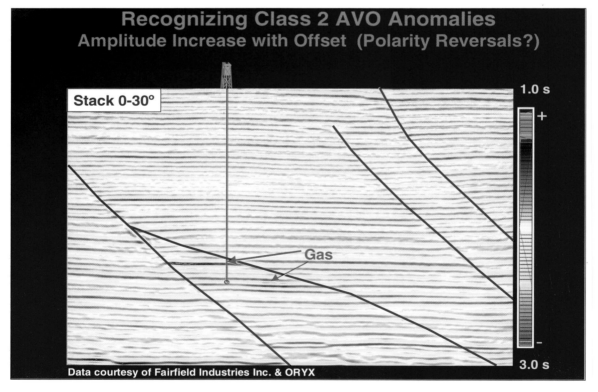

Figure 4.C.5

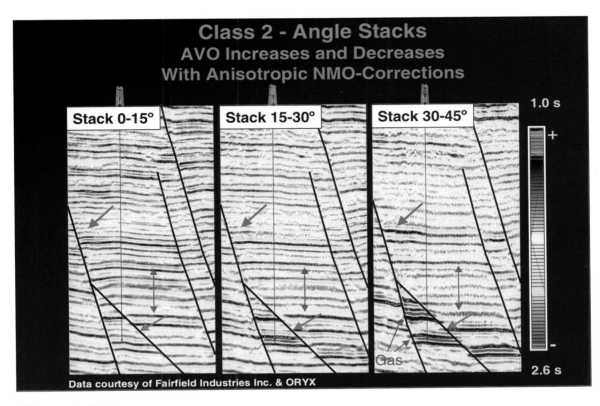

Figure 4.C.6

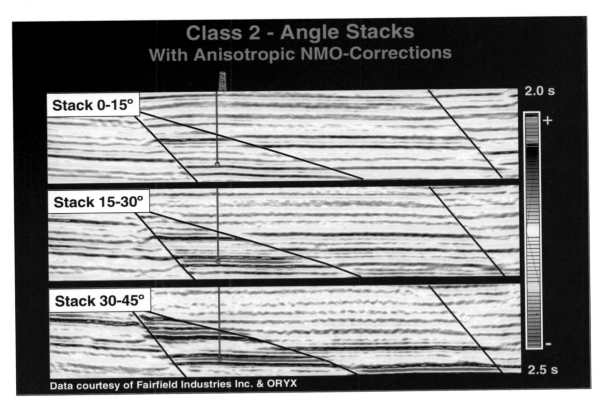

Figure 4.C.7

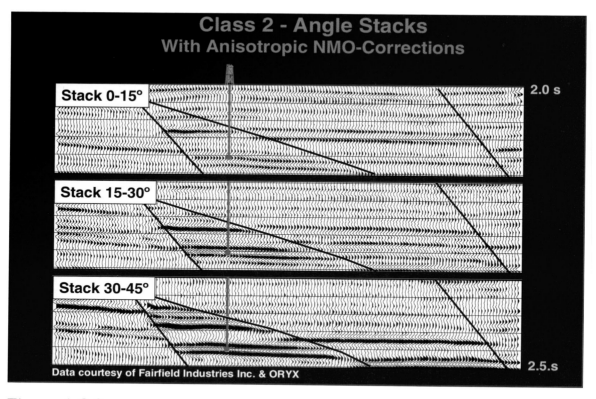

Figure 4.C.8

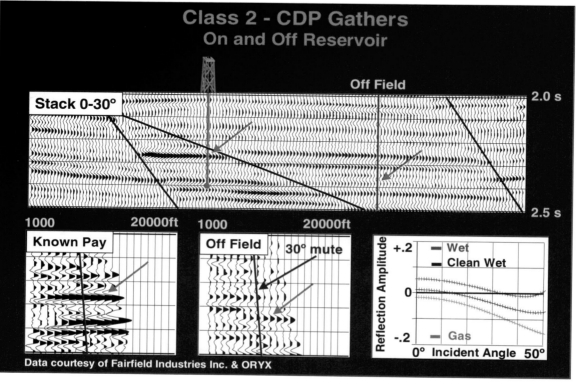

Figure 4.C.9

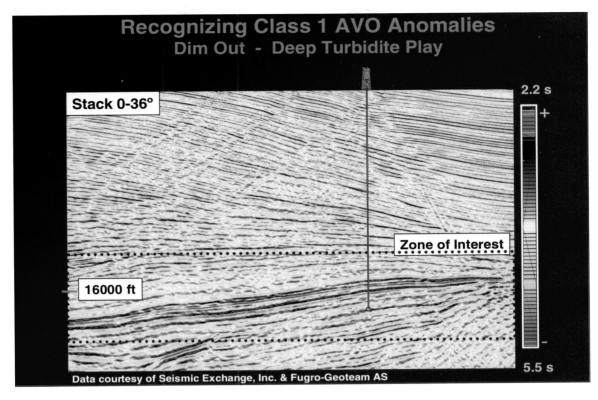

Figure 4.C.10

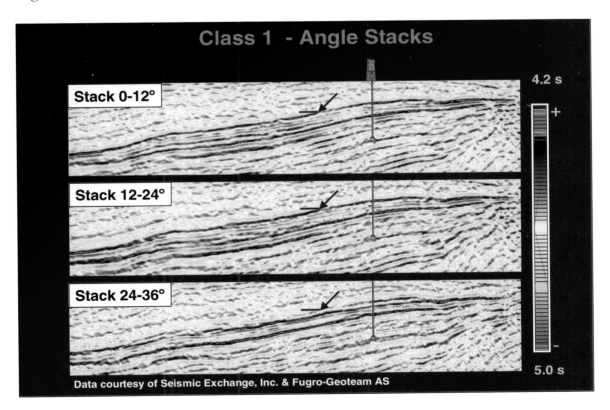

Figure 4.C.11

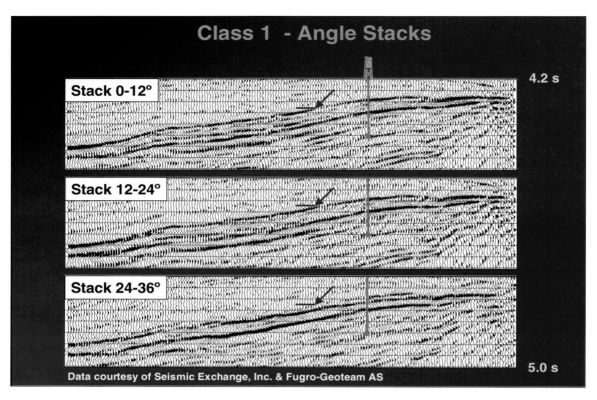

Figure 4.C.12

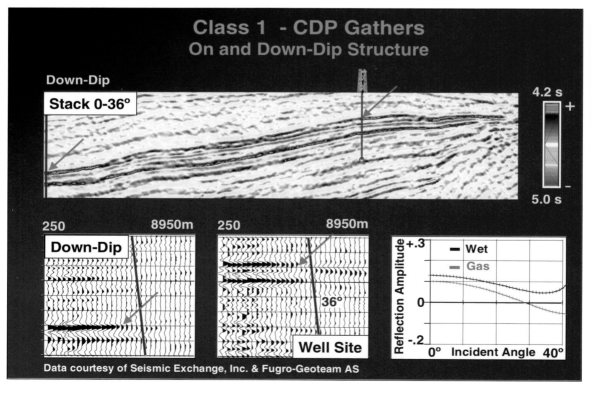

Figure 4.C.13

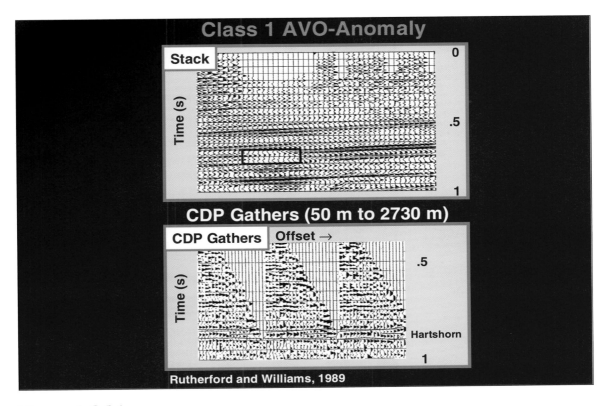

Figure 4.C.14

Figure 4.D.1

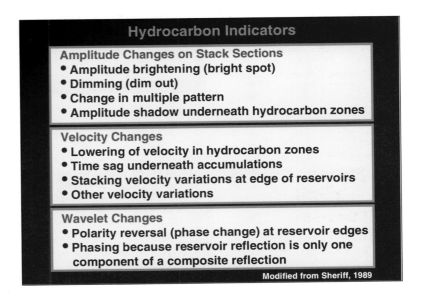

Figure 4.D.2

Hydrocarbon Indicators, Continued

Frequency Changes
- Lowering of frequency immediately beneath reservoir because of deconvolution operator
- Lowering of frequency beneath reservoir because of attenuation

Flat Spot
- Horizontal reflection where other reflections dip, produced by fluid-interface reflection

Gas Chimney Effects
- Deterioration of data quality
- Time sag
- Distortion of reflections

And, finally

Changes in Amplitude with Offset
- Gas and high GOR reservoirs may exhibit larger reflection amplitudes as the distance between source and receiver increases ... Class 2 AVO anomalies

Modified from Sheriff, 1989

Figure 4.D.3

Geological Constraints for Hydrocarbon Indicators

Structural Conformity
- HCI limits must honor trapping mechanisms such as rollover, up-dip pinch outs, trapping faults, etc.

Down-dip Limits
- The down-dip limits of HCIs are expected to exhibit a flat event if a pore-fluid interface is anticipated.
- The HCI limits must confirm to the structural down-dip contours.

Others: _____

_____

_____

Amplitude interpretation must make sense geologically.
Apply less *Principle of Least-Squares* and more *Principle of Least Astonishment.*

Modified from Sheriff, 1989

Section 5. "Quick-Look" Rules-of-Thumb

Objective: To develop rules-of-thumb to

1. Predict AVO responses from rock-property crossplots
2. Predict fluid-substitution *A/B* ratios from rock-property crossplots
3. Predict lithology from rock-property crossplots
4. Predict AVO response from well-log curves
5. Create a case-history crossplot

In the first section of this book, the philosophy of "Geophysical data can't be interpreted without knowing the answer" was introduced. If one doesn't have past experience or rules-of-thumb, the most sophisticated interpretation workstation will be of no help. A short story will illustrate the goals of this section.

You're exploring a new area. You find a bright spot and map it. The amplitude map does not conform to the structure. You don't want to condemn the prospect yet. You question the reason for the bright spot. Is it a pore-fluid effect or lithologic change? You examine available well-log curves to determine the local rock types and their properties. What curves have you selected? Most likely, you have chosen the sonic curve to determine if there are large velocity contrasts. You find one. Is the contrast at approximately the right depth? Is the high-velocity bed thick enough to yield the bright spot found on the seismic?

In this little scenario, most interpreters wouldn't stop to compute the normal-incident reflection coefficient. For now, knowing the velocity contrast is sufficient ... there is no need to include density and normalize by the sum of the acoustic impedances. Having found the depth on the log, equating the depth in meters to the time in milliseconds is adequate. There is no need to waste time with check-shot corrections. Quickly, rules-of-thumb have been applied and new avenues for explaining the bright spot are investigated.

Can this concept of rules-of thumb be expanded to AVO interpretation? Or is it necessary to rely upon time-consuming petrophysical analyses and Zoeppritz solutions? Hopefully, answers to these questions will be addressed in this section.

5A. Crossplotting Shuey's Equation

Even with the linear approximations of Zoeppritz's equation, there is still not adequate insight about the correlation of rock properties to the AVO response. In order to provide this correlation, a few approximations are made to further simplify Shuey's equation. In Fig. 5.A.1, Shuey's equation from Fig. 3.D.9 is simplified to

$$RC(\theta) \approx NI \cos^2(\theta) + [(\sigma_2 - \sigma_1)/(1 - \sigma_{\text{avg}})^2] \sin^2(\theta) \qquad [24]$$

$$RC(\theta) \approx NI \cos^2(\theta) + PR \sin^2(\theta) \qquad [25]$$

An average background α/β (V_P/V_S) ratio of 2 has been assumed. Also, the higher-order term that becomes effective beyond incident angles of 30° has been dropped. The resulting approximation now contains two reflectivities, the normal-incident reflectivity (NI_p) and the Poisson reflectivity (PR). The name Poisson reflectivity is suggested because of its similarity to NI.

Is this an adequate rule-of-thumb equation? One test to determine whether it will assist in distinguishing different lithologies is to see if it satisfies the observations that Koefoed made in 1955.

Koefoed's Observations

Koefoed made the following observations:

(a) When the underlying medium has the greater longitudinal velocity, and other relevant properties of the two strata are equal to each other, an increase of Poisson's ratio for the underlying medium causes an increase of the reflection coefficient at the larger angles of incidence.

(b) When, in the above case, Poisson's ratio for the incident medium is increased, the reflection coefficient at the larger angles of incidence is thereby decreased.

(c) When, in the above case, Poisson's ratios for both media are increased and kept equal to each other, the reflection coefficient at the larger angles of incidence is thereby increased.

(d) The effect mentioned in (a) becomes more pronounced as the velocity contrast becomes smaller.

(e) Interchange of the incident medium and the underlying medium affects the shape of the curves only slightly, at least up to values of the angle of incidence of about 30°.

These five observations were tested using the exact Zoeppritz equation out to 30°. The results are displayed in Fig. 5.A.2. The base model has upper and lower *P*-wave velocities of 7000 ft/s and 9000 ft/s (2100 m/s and 3000 m/s), respectively. The densities and Poisson's ratios of the two media are equal, as Koefoed requested in part (a).

The amplitude versus incident-angle graph labeled (a) tests Koefoed's (a) observation. The lower Poisson's ratio was increased to 0.40 and the result was an increase in amplitude with offset. The red curves in the graphs represent the response curves resulting from rock-property changes. The base model's response is plotted in black.

By increasing σ_2, the term ($\sigma_2 - \sigma_1$) goes from a value of 0 to 0.15. Now the sine-squared term adds to the amplitude with offset. The denominator associated with PR changes from 1.77 to 2.19 and only has a small effect on the amplitude with offset. Normally, the numerator term in PR has more effect than the denominator.

The second Koefoed observation, (b), should have the opposite effect because σ_1 was increased over the base model's Poisson's ratio. The resulting amplitude decrease is predicted by the simplified equation.

In test (c), the Poisson's ratios for both media are still equal but are increased from the base model of 0.25, to 0.40, as requested by Koefoed. An additional model was run where the Poisson's ratios of the upper and lower media were set to 0.15. The response from this last model is plotted in blue. This is a test where the simplified Shuey's equation fails to predict the responses in graph (c). The simplified Shuey's equation predicts no change in the amplitude response for the Poisson's ratio models of 0.40 and 0.15. The resulting error is associated with the approximation of the background velocity ratio in the first term. Without the approximation $\alpha/\beta = 2$, the first term becomes $NI\,[1 - 4(\beta/\alpha)^2 \sin^2(\theta)]$.

If $\alpha/\beta = 2$, the above reduces to $NI\cos^2(\theta)$. For other values of α/β, the following are obtained.

$$\sigma = 0.40 \quad \beta/\alpha = 0.41 \Rightarrow NI\,[1 - .67\sin^2(\theta)]$$
$$\sigma = 0.33 \quad \beta/\alpha = 0.50 \Rightarrow NI\,[1 - 1.0\sin^2(\theta)] \Rightarrow NI\cos^2(\theta)$$
$$\sigma = 0.25 \quad \beta/\alpha = 0.58 \Rightarrow NI\,[1 - 1.3\sin^2(\theta)]$$
$$\sigma = 0.15 \quad \beta/\alpha = 0.64 \Rightarrow NI\,[1 - 1.6\sin^2(\theta)]$$

The first term decreases the amplitude response at the far angles as the background Poisson's ratio decreases. As mentioned, the simplified equation fails on Koefoed's third observation, (c). The significance of this error will be evaluated in Section 6.

Test (d) involves a new base model. The new model has the same rock properties as the original model with one exception. The upper medium velocity is increased to 7500 ft/s (2300 m/s), thereby reducing the velocity contrast and consequently NI. The net effect is that NI decreases and the AVO effect is more pronounced when compared to NI. This is predicted by the simplified equation.

Finally, the simplified equation is symmetric with respect to the media properties. Thus, if the media are interchanged, only the sign changes, as is observed by graph (e) in the figure.

The simplified equation is NOT recommended as a modeling equation of choice when serious comparisons are being made between synthetics and field data. However, if the match between the synthetic and field data is poor, the simplified equation can be used as a rule-of-thumb to determine how the rock properties should be altered for a better match.

Even though the simplified equation failed to predict Koefoed's test (c), one would not normally expect to have the background velocity ratio change drastically at a particular depth. With some assurance that this simplified equation provides a rule-of-thumb for relating rock properties to AVO response, let's examine the graphical solution of this equation.

Graphical Solution of Shuey's Equation

In his 1985 article, Shuey commented that " ... crossplot of Poisson's ratio versus impedance $\rho\alpha$ on a logarithmic scale ... could be the basis of a graphic procedure to relate information about RC(θ) to information about lithology." The transformations indicated in Fig. 5.A.3 are suggested in order to evaluate Shuey's observation.

The normal-incident reflection coefficient is related to the difference of the natural logarithm of the acoustic impedances. The second term, PR, requires, as Shuey suggested, an approximation for the background V_P/V_S ratio that is contained in both σ_{avg} and in the first term. This will be area-dependent, but the former assumption of 2 will be carried forth here. The objective of these transformations is to arrive at expressions for both *NI* and *PR* that are related to differences in elastic properties. This has been done as shown in the figure.

As expressed in Fig. 5.A.3, PR includes the multiplier of 2.25. Rather than plotting 2.25σ as the elastic constant, the factor 2.25 has been incorporated into the plot scales as shown. The lengths of the axes should be the same so that the graph is square.

Shuey's equation and his suggested crossplot are now shown in Fig. 5.A.4. The three points plotted on the graph represent the rock properties of shale, water-saturated sand, and gas-saturated sand. Because *NI* and *PR* have been expressed as differences of rock properties, the *NI* and *PR* reflectivities can be measured directly from the graph as shown. For shale overlying the water-saturated sand, the vertical distance labeled NI_{WET} represents the normal-incident reflectivity, while the horizontal distance labeled PR_{WET} represents the Poisson reflectivity. The arrow points from the upper medium to the lower. The sign of the reflectivities is negative if the arrow points downward or to the left.

If the axes are scaled as shown, the measured reflectivities are in true proportion. This facilitates a quick quantification of the AVO response and pore-fluid analysis. If the measured *NI* and *PR* are equal and of the same sign, then the equation indicates that the AVO response will be constant with offset. If *NI* and *PR* have the same sign, and the magnitude of *NI* is less than *PR*, the AVO response will increase with offset. Conversely, if *NI* and *PR* have the same sign, and the magnitude of *NI* is greater than *PR*, the AVO response will decrease with offset.

With both the water- and gas-saturation states represented, the reflectivity ratios of *NI* can be compared. The ratio of the distances NI_{GAS}/NI_{WET} is the normal-incident amplitude of the anomaly divided by the amplitude of the background wet-sand reflection. This is often referred to as *A/B* (Anomaly / Background). A similar ratio for Poisson reflectivity can be captured. These "quick-look" quantification techniques are summarized in Fig. 5.A.5.

The *A/B* ratios from the rock-property crossplots provide a technique to validate the pore-fluid content of potential hydrocarbon anomalies. The .5 ln(acoustic impedance) versus Poisson's ratio crossplot also provides a method to validate the lithologies across an interface.

In Fig. 5.A.6, four traces are shown that might have been extracted from a CDP gather. The left trace has an incident angle of 0° and the amplitude of the event is labeled A_0. The right trace represents the last live trace before the NMO mute pattern is applied, that is, an incident angle of approximately 30°. The event amplitude is labeled A_{30}. From these two amplitudes a scaled estimate of *NI* and *PR* can be made. The equation $PR \approx 4A_{30} - 3A_0$ is almost the same as saying that the far-trace amplitude minus the near-trace amplitude is equivalent to *PR*. The measured *NI* and *PR* are scaled to some length, voltage, digital value, and the like. However, their ratio should represent the true *NI/PR* ratio. This ratio is exploited on the rock-property crossplot in Fig. 5.A.7.

In this figure, various lithologies have been crossplotted based on their elastic properties. Using the *NI* and *PR* measurements taken from the CDP gather, the slope as shown can be drawn. Theoretically, only those rocks that fall on this slope (or one parallel to it) are possible candidates for generating the reflection event of interest. In the scenario described in Fig. 5.A.7, the reflection would come from shale overlying an igneous rock. Obviously, if a trace inversion of *NI* to acoustic impedance (or *PR* to Poisson's ratio) is performed, then the vertical (or horizontal) position of the *NI-PR* slope could be uniquely defined.

An important aspect of these "quick-look" graphical solutions is to understand how variations in pore-fluid, porosity, and shaliness will affect the sand point in Fig. 5.A.7. This is answered with Fig. 5.A.8. The sand and shale trends are illustrated with dashed lines in the figure. Thus, if the porosity changes, the sand point will move up or down the sand trend line. The porosity arrow indicates an increase in porosity. The change in the shaliness of the sand will obviously move the sand point toward the shale trend line. In the next section, it will be shown, as is illustrated in the figure, that an increase in gas saturation will move the sand point almost perpendicular to the sand trend line.

In order to benefit from Shuey's "quick-look" crossplot, estimates of Poisson's ratio are needed, and these are not always available. Therefore, a "quick-look" method will be suggested to estimate Poisson's ratio along with AVO responses.

5B. AVO Predictions from Well-Log Curves

In Section 2, various empirical trend curves of rock properties and techniques to construct them were presented. In addition, techniques for predicting rock properties during pore-fluid substitutions were addressed. The next three graphs were generated from techniques presented in Section 2.

Graph 5.1 (Fig. 5.B.1) contains the ARCO wet-trend transforms for predicting density from *P*-wave velocity. A gas-substitution density curve is overplotted. The gas-saturated density value is read vertically beneath the equivalent water-saturated density value. Thus, for a sand that has a water-saturated V_P of 10,000 ft/s (3000 m/s), it would have an approximate density value of 2.20 gm/cm^3, and when gas-substituted, its density value would reduce to 2.02 gm/cm^3 (vertically beneath the 2.20 point). Of course, the exact equation can also be used to compute the gas-saturated sand density.

The ARCO wet-trend transforms for predicting V_S from V_P are shown in Graph 5.2 (Fig. 5.B.2). These transforms were plotted as a function of Poisson's ratio to facilitate the application of Shuey's equation. As was done in the previous graph, the gas-saturated curve is overplotted. Once again, the gas-substituted Poisson's ratio is read on the vertical line for the water-saturated velocity.

The final graph relates the water-saturated *P*-wave sand velocity to the gas-saturated velocity (Graph 5.3, Fig. 5.B.3).

In Fig. 5.B.4, hypothetical well-log values are given. An interpreter might ask two questions. "What is the AVO response for this shale overlying a wet sand? How will it change if the sand is gas charged?" If this is a preliminary investigation, only approximate solutions are required. If the simplified Shuey's equation is used, only *NI* and *PR* values are needed. A suggested procedure for finding *NI* and *PR* for the wet and gas-saturated cases is given in the next two figures.

For the wet case, Poisson's ratio is needed for both the sand and shale interval in order to estimate the AVO response. As indicated in Fig. 5.B.5, the shale and sand Poisson's ratio can be read from Graph 5.2 if the *P*-wave velocities are known, which they are for this scenario. *NI* and *PR* are computed, and the simplified Shuey's equation is used to predict the reflection amplitude at 30°.

For the gas-saturated model, besides needing Poisson's ratios for the sand and shale interval, we also need a new *P*-wave velocity and density for the gas sand. Graph 5.2 provides an estimate of the necessary Poisson's ratios. Graph 5.3 provides an estimate of the gas-saturated *P*-wave velocity. Gas-sand density is estimated from Graph 5.1. The computations for *NI*, *PR*, and *RC*(30°) are repeated. The results are graphed in Fig. 5.B.6.

The CDP-gather cartoons illustrate that the water-saturated AVO response should change polarity within the CDP gather. In essence, the far traces for reflections from the water-saturated sand have very small amplitudes. The gas-saturated AVO response has a twofold increase in amplitude from the near traces to the normal mute at offset = depth or 30° incident angle. The amplitude response generated with the exact Zoeppritz equation is shown in the bottom of the figure, with the estimated values shown as blue dots. For this particular model, the simplified Shuey's equation yielded accurate results.

As this section indicates, the key to successful application of AVO theory is the calibration of local rock properties. A case study will suggest some points to consider when developing rock-property-to-seismic calibration plots.

5C. Calibration of Rock Properties for Deep-Water Seismic

For the past decade, the hottest exploration areas have centered on worldwide deep-water plays. The following calibration study was conducted for the deep-water Gulf of Mexico (GOM) and was reported by Hilterman et al. (1999). However, the techniques and even some of the specific conclusions are applicable to other deep-water plays.

Once again, the primary objective of the study was to establish a calibration methodology for predicting pore-fluid content and lithology from seismic amplitudes. A secondary objective was to develop rules-of-thumb that were applicable under specific constraints. At the same time, an effort was made to identify unique lithologies that might yield "surprises" when verified by the drill bit. Of course, the trend curves are also applicable for predicting salt thickness from gravity data, predicting predrill pressure profiles, and converting seismic time to depth.

Available Data

The study was based on digital well-log curves from 447 GOM wells located in water depths greater than 500 ft (150 m). A well location map is shown in Fig. 5.C.1. When available, the digital curves included the sonic, density, neutron, shallow- and deep-resistivity, gamma, SP, caliper, and dipole shear-wave velocity. For each well, data files containing well-log header information, questionable logging intervals, and hydrocarbon zones, along with their pore-fluid properties, were created. The depth to the onset of abnormal pressure (referred to as geopressure) was interpreted and entered into the database. A sand-percentage curve for each well was generated. Paleontological data such as foraminifera, nannofossils, and bathymetric environment were introduced as possible classification attributes.

Velocity and Density Trends—Lithology and Pressure

With the knowledge that effective pressure is a critical parameter for predicting the properties of deep-water sediments, separate analyses were conducted for those sediments above and below the onset of abnormal pressure. The selection of the onset of abnormal pressure for each well is, in itself, highly interpretive. Criteria for predicting the onset of abnormal pressure from a suite of well-log curves are implicit in the following steps:

- Select the depth where the low-frequency "knee" of the shale resistivity trend changes from a positive slope to a negative slope.
- Select the depth where the shale velocity and density trends either flatten or decrease in value.
- Select the depth where the mud weight changes significantly.
- Look for an increase of resistivity or gamma value just above the onset of abnormal pressure.
- Look for at least 200 ft (60 m) of shale just beneath the onset of abnormal pressure.

The trends displayed in Figs. 5.C.2 and 5.C.3 consist of histogram analyses at 500-ft (150-m) intervals. Every depth point is considered a potential sample for the histogram. In addition, the histogram trends have lithologic and onset of abnormal pressure constraints applied. The lithologic constraint divides the samples in a histogram interval into either sand or shale, based on the sand-percentage curve created by the log analyst. In this example, a sample was defined as sand if it had a sand-percentage value greater than 50%. All other samples were defined as shales. Of course, salt, hydrocarbon zones, and questionable logging intervals were omitted from the histogram analyses. Likewise, the log analyst's onset of abnormal pressure was used to divide the samples into groups above and below geopressure. The depth reference was ocean bottom.

In Fig. 5.C.2, the histograms above 1000 ft (300 m) and beneath 12,000 ft (3700 m) contain a limited number of samples. This is difficult to observe from the plots because the height of the histograms is scaled to the maximum frequency mode. There are approximately ten times more shale samples than sand. Additional points worth noting from these trend curves are

- The sand velocity trend suggests the separation into two trends between 8000 ft and 12,000 ft (2400 m and 3700 m).
- The shale velocity trend flattens slightly beneath 11,000 ft (3400 m). This suggests a different environment from the shallower data, and thus additional constraints are necessary.
- Shallow sand and shale average-velocity trends have similar values.
- Sand and shale density trends (Fig. 5.C.3) are essentially the same down to 5000 ft (1500 m) and then the sand trend flattens to approximately 2.23 gm/cm³.
- Salt density nil zone (2.16 gm/cm³) occurs between 4000 ft and 5000 ft (1200 m

and 1500 m). In the nil zone, salt and clastic sediments have the same density value.

The trend curves in Figs. 5.C.2 and 5.C.3 were fitted to several mathematical expressions in order to compare the variations between lithologies. The least-squares fit was based on one sample (the average value) per depth interval. The following mathematical expressions had small standard deviations.

Velocity

$V(z) = V_0 (1 + kz)^{1/3}$	V_0 (ft/s)	k	Std Deviation (ft/s)
Shale	4903	.000566	179
Sand	5037	.000502	149

Density

$D(Z) = D_0 + kz^{1/2}$	D_0 (gm/cm^3)	k	Std Deviation (gm/cm^3)
Shale	1.88	.00424	.0133
Sand	1.95	.00272	.0131

The bimodal distribution in the sand velocity trend (left portion of Fig. 5.C.2) suggests that other constraints are necessary before these trends can be used to calibrate rock properties to seismic amplitude. Likewise, the large standard deviations of the histograms suggest that reflections from shale-upon-shale are significant enough to invalidate seismic amplitude analyses that are based on the shale-upon-sand model. However, if trend analyses such as these are localized, then there are interpretational benefits that might be drawn. For example:

- The shale density trend above geopressure can be used in gravity modeling of salt-thickness predictions for prestack depth imaging. However, the density trend beneath geopressure would be questionable in gravity modeling because the deeper density profile at a specific location is highly dependent on the onset depth of abnormal pressure.

- The shale velocity trend above geopressure could be used as a guide for depth conversion in a local area. However, like the density trend, the velocity trend beneath geopressure is dependent on the onset depth of abnormal pressure, making depth conversion questionable.

- Sand density has little variation at depths greater than 5000 ft (1500 m) beneath ocean bottom.

Velocity and Density Trends—End-Member Lithologies

In an effort to reduce the standard deviation in the rock-property trends, additional constraints were introduced. It was suspected that wells located in areas where the ocean bottom was less than 1500 ft (450 m) deep might be contaminated with both shelf and slope deposits that didn't represent deep-water or turbidite environments. To test this hypothesis, 16 wells were selected in water depths greater than 4000 ft (1200 m).

Drilling depths greater than 20,000 ft (6000 m) from sea level were reached. Thirteen of the sixteen wells had mud weights that did not exceed 13 lbs/gal.

Normal-Compaction Shale Trends—The first end-member lithology investigated for this subset of 16 wells was the normal-compaction shale. This is defined to create the "pure" shale velocity and density trends above geopressure. However, this end-member lithology had to be more specifically defined because of the influence of marl. Lithologic logs developed from sample cuttings were not available; thus some other method of discriminating mixed lithologies was needed. In order to omit the sediments with marl, only those sediments that had resistivity values below 1.0 ohm-m were selected. With the resistivity constraint to omit the marls, both the velocity and density profiles in Fig. 5.C.4 approach linear depth trends. Also, the standard deviations of the end-member trends are reduced relative to the previous trends.

A problem that was mentioned earlier was the interpretative aspect of picking the onset of abnormal pressure. As a guide, the normal-compaction curve displayed in Fig. 5.C.4 was overplotted on the velocity curves from individual wells with the intention of re-picking the onset of abnormal pressure for each well. In addition, paleo data were superimposed as a function of depth for each of the wells. At the depth where the individual well velocity curve deviated from the normal-compaction velocity curve, a significant time hiatus was also observed with the paleo data. This depth appeared to be a better estimate of the "soft" onset of abnormal pressure.

Clay-Rich Pressured-Shale Trends—The next shale end-member trend investigated was that for the clay-rich shales in abnormal pressure. Because the 16 wells that had water depths greater than 4000 ft (1200 m) showed few signs of abnormal pressure, all 447 deep-water wells were selected for this analysis. However, in order to ensure that the sediments were essentially clay-rich, each sample was restricted to resistivity values below 0.35 ohm-m. These results are shown in Fig. 5.C.5 with the average values of the normal-compaction trends overplotted. Both velocity and density trends for shale in abnormal pressure have appreciably smaller values than the normal-compaction trends above geopressure.

Clean-Sand Trends—When the sand properties were investigated, it was found that the depositional environment influenced the velocity and density values. For instance, a laminated sand package that might be found in levee or overbank deposits has variable velocity and density values. When crossplotted, the laminated sand values fell in between the clean sand and shale values. Thus, the best that could be determined were the end-member components of sand as a function of depth.

Several methods were evaluated to extract the clean-sand properties. It was found that by constraining the sand resistivity values to be below 0.35 ohm-m, the same clean sands were chosen as those selected by the log analysts. The results from the 16 wells with water depths greater than 4000 ft are shown in Fig. 5.C.6 for above geopressure. The clean sand trends beneath geopressure are shown in Fig. 5.C.7.

The average density profile for the clean sands is not affected by geopressure. The clean sands have average density values between 2.15–2.25 gm/cm^3 (30–27% porosity).

A few general conclusions with respect to predicting seismic amplitudes can be drawn from the end-member trends. Figs. 5.C.8 and 5.C.9 and the following comments summarize these conclusions.

Above Geopressure
Clean Sand Velocity ≈ Normal-compaction Shale Velocity
Clean Sand Density << Normal-compaction Shale Density
∴ Density variations dominate the normal-incident reflection coefficient

Below Geopressure
Clean Sand Velocity > Mud-rich Shale Velocity
Clean Sand Density ≈ Mud-rich Shale Density
∴ Velocity variations dominate the normal-incident reflection coefficient

∴ Top of geopressure horizon is essential in predicting lithologies from seismic.

Rock-Property Crossplot of End-Member Lithologies

A rock-property crossplot as suggested by Shuey was developed for the normal-compaction shale against clean sand for above the onset of abnormal pressure. Both water-saturated and hydrocarbon-saturated sand properties are desired. The hydrocarbon-saturated sand properties are determined by fluid substitution of hydrocarbons into the clean sand. For fluid substitution, the pore-fluid properties need to be defined. Typical mud weight, temperature, and GOR trends from the deep-water wells are illustrated in Fig. 5.C.10. Also shown are the average velocity and density trends for the end-member lithologies of clean sand and normal-compaction shale. The sands are represented as 50-ft (15-m) beds at 500-ft (150-m) depth intervals.

The resulting crossplot of ln(acoustic impedance) versus Poisson's ratio is shown in Fig. 5.C.11. In order to facilitate the interpretation, various depths are annotated. From this chart, both the *NI* and AVO responses (up to 30° incident angle) can be predicted, as discussed earlier. Likewise the *A/B* ratios for different pore-fluids can be estimated as a function of depth.

The salt point is included on the graph. From this graph, one would predict that shale over <u>salt</u> at a 4000-ft (1200-m) depth has a positive *NI* and a negative *PR*. Thus the bright amplitude on the near traces will decrease quickly with offset. However, at a 19,000-ft (6000-m) depth, shale over salt will have a near-zero *NI* and negative *PR*. An increase of amplitude with offset is expected.

Although numerous guidelines can be formulated for the seismic response from end-member lithologies, one must remember that the *rock-property variations within a particular lithology are often larger than variations between end-member lithologies,* for a given depth interval.

Anomalous Lithologies

One of the goals of all geoscientists is to be able to predict anomalous lithologies that might be encountered in an exploration area. In the above section, three end-member lithologies were investigated, and a few generic seismic amplitude conclusions were generated. These conclusions were generated based on the average histogram values and did not consider the intra-well variations of rock properties. These conclusions can be misleading, and a few examples will illustrate this statement.

Variations in Poisson's Ratio—As discussed previously, the average velocity trends for sand and shale are not substantially different from one another. However, when a large velocity contrast does occur between sand and shale, the AVO response can differ from the expected and thus be anomalous. This is easy to substantiate by examining the simplified Shuey's equation. In Fig. 5.C.11, the Poisson's ratio for sand at all depth levels was predicted to be less than the corresponding shale Poisson's ratio.

If sand and shale have approximately the same P-wave velocity, sand will have a smaller Poisson's ratio. This Poisson's ratio relationship between sand and shale is so often expected that Poisson's ratio curve is sometimes thought of as a substitute for the SP curve in sand/shale sequences. This observation can be seen in the upper part of Fig. 5.C.12. The Poisson's ratios in this figure were derived from the ARCO transforms. In the upper portion of Fig. 5.C.12, the sonic values for sand and shale are approximately the same. This sonic relationship yields a Poisson's ratio curve that resembles the SP curve. *NI* for the upper shale/sand boundary is slightly positive, while the *PR* is negative. This will lead to a phase reversal with offset and then an increase of amplitude with offset. However, in the lower part of the figure, the sonic curve depicts a significantly smaller sand P-wave velocity than the surrounding shale. Because of this, sand and shale have approximately the same Poisson's ratio value. *NI* will be negative at the top of the sand package and amplitude will decrease as a function of approximately $\cos^2(\theta)$.

Pyroclastics—Besides salt, marl, and occasional high-velocity (density) shale, pyroclastic sediments are encountered in the GOM deep-water wells. The most dramatic observation on the logs is the reduced density values. Density readings as low as 2.00 gm/cm³ (sandstone matrix equivalent to 39% porosity) have been recorded.

Summary

There were numerous observations and conclusions developed in this section about the GOM deep-water rock properties. A few are reiterated, while some of the others can be inferred from the included figures.

- Rock-property predictions and statistics should be referenced to ocean bottom and separated into groups above and below onset of abnormal pressure.
- Multi-well trend statistics for data below geopressure should be used with caution. Effective pressure does not necessarily increase linearly beneath the onset of abnormal pressure.
- Trend analyses require effective pressure and lithologic constraints in order to reduce the standard deviation.

- End-member lithologies of clean sand and normal-compaction shale yield small background reflection coefficients.

- The density trend of clean sand is not influenced by abnormal pressure. All other trends are.

- Because sand and shale velocities are similar, predictions based on "average" rock-property trends can be misleading.

- High-velocity shales, pyroclastics, and similar sand/shale Poisson's ratios caused by low-velocity sands represent a few anomalous sediments in the GOM deep-water.

- The top of abnormal pressure should be incorporated into one's amplitude interpretation if lithology prediction is a goal.

- Clean wet sands and oil sands may require detailed AVO analyses to discriminate one from the other. Oil sands are similar to clean wet sands at very shallow and very deep depths.

- Realistic predictions of hydrocarbon-saturated rock properties are accomplished by fluid substitution into water-saturated sands rather than by hydrocarbon trend curves.

- The large water column and abnormal pressure reduce the desired changes in compressibility of hydrocarbon fluids. This effect reduces the standout between wet and hydrocarbon-saturated sediments.

- Knowledge of pore pressure, temperature, GOR, and expected API is needed for evaluating potential oil sands.

Figures

Figure 5.A.1

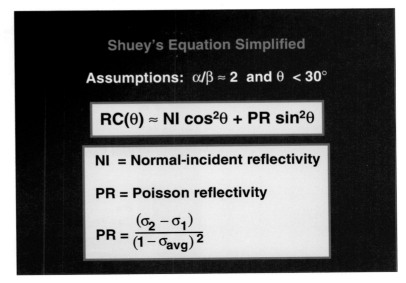

Figure 5.A.2

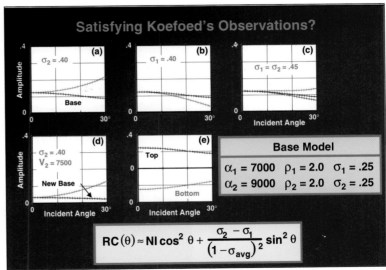

Figure 5.A.3

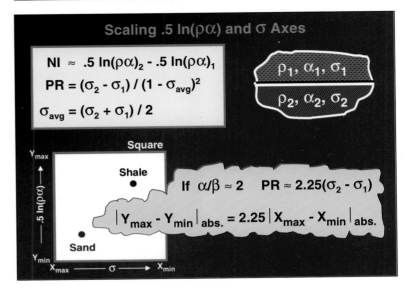

Figure 5.A.4

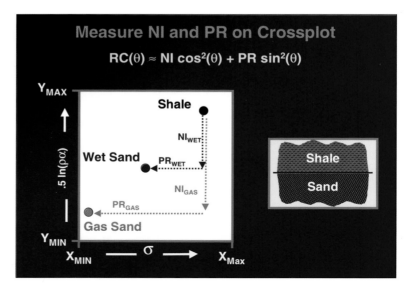

Figure 5.A.5

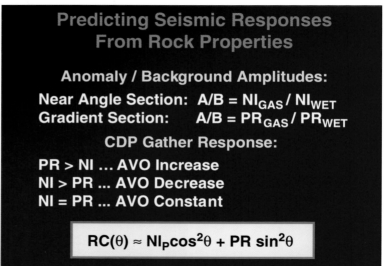

Figure 5.A.6

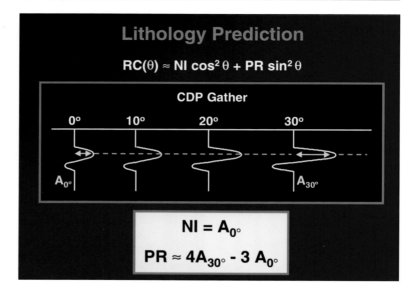

Figure 5.A.7

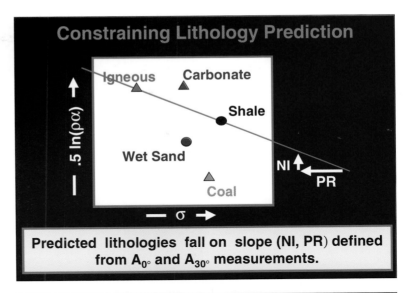

Figure 5.A.8

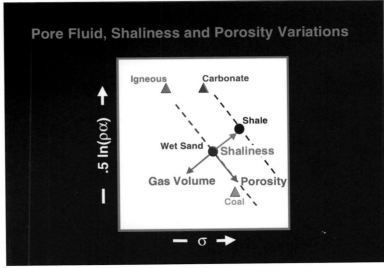

Figure 5.B.1

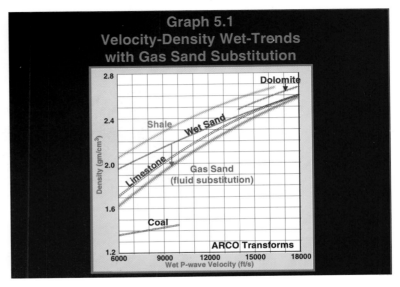

Figure 5.B.2

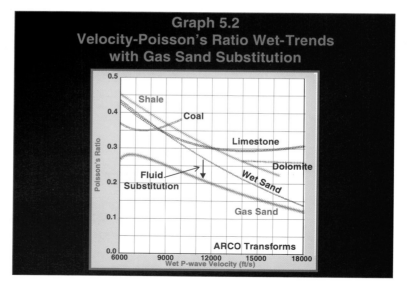

Figure 5.B.3

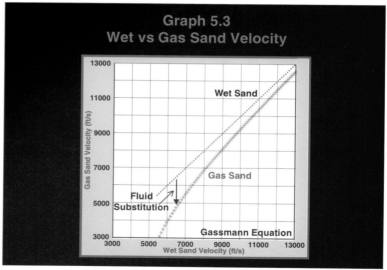

Figure 5.B.4

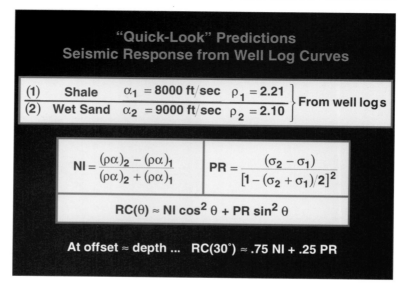

Figure 5.B.5

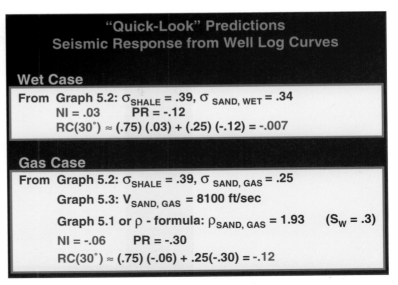

Figure 5.B.6

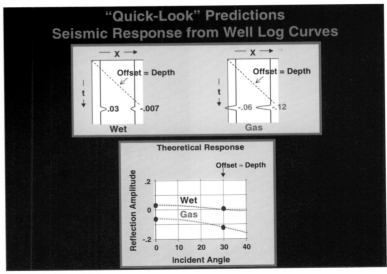

Figure 5.C.1

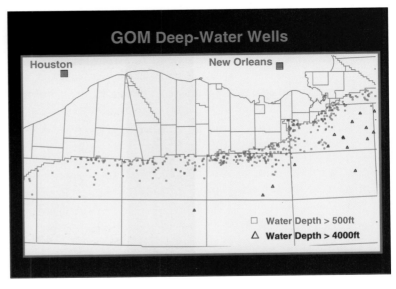

Figure 5.C.2

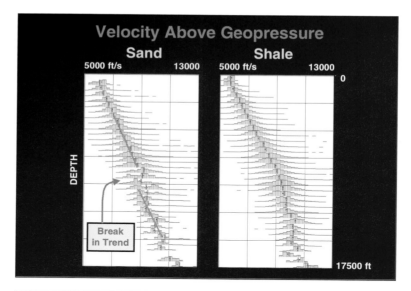

Figure 5.C.3

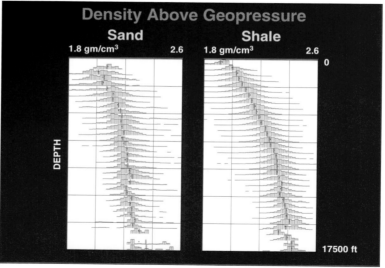

Figure 5.C.4

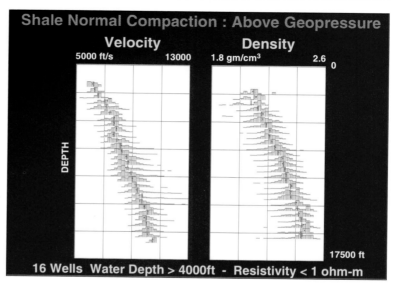

Figure 5.C.5

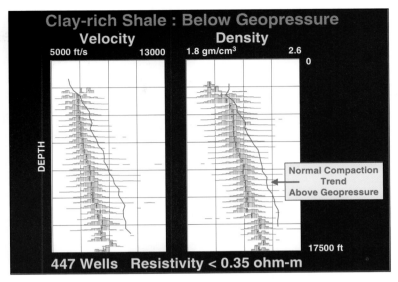

Figure 5.C.6

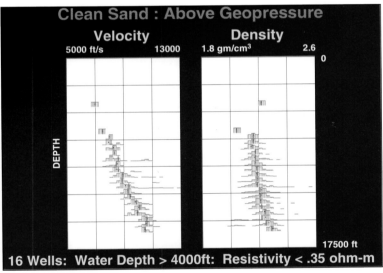

Figure 5.C.7

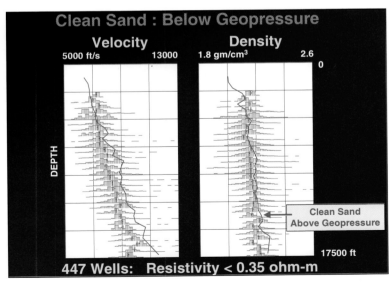

Figure 5.C.8

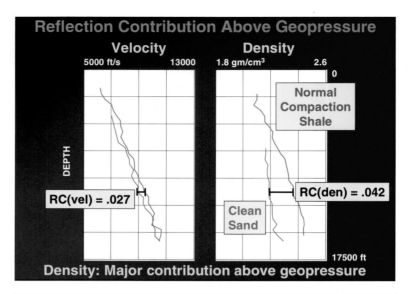

Figure 5.C.9

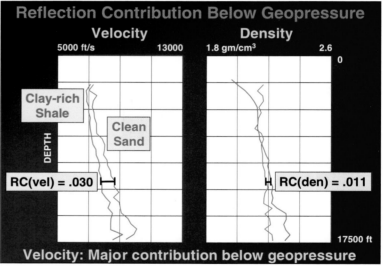

Figure 5.C.10

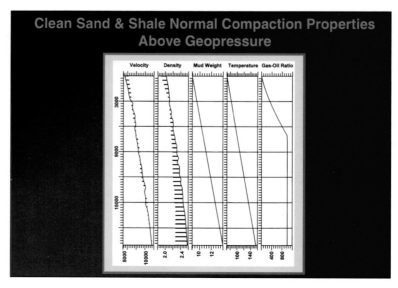

Figure 5.C.11

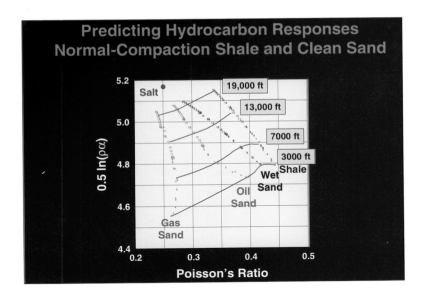

Figure 5.C.12

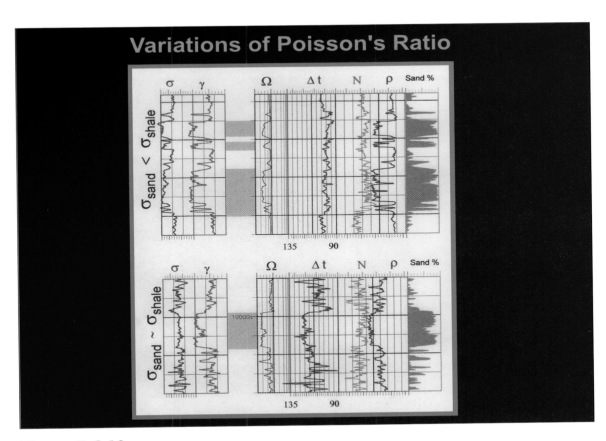

Section 6. AVO Slope and Intercept Attributes

Objective:

1. Compare rock-property variables in standard AVO equations

2. Evaluate pore-fluid and lithology discrimination from rock-property crossplots

3. Extend rock-property crossplots to seismic crossplots

6A. Pore-Fluid Discrimination from Reflectivities

Three linear approximations of Zoeppritz's equation (Fig. 6.A.1) are commonly applied in AVO modeling. They have similar if not identical information content. However, the arrangement of terms in each equation emphasizes different AVO attributes as a function of incident angle. By making a few approximations, the interrelationship of the three equations is easy to visualize, and interpretational insight is gained.

The Shuey equation in Fig. 6.A.1 was discussed earlier. In 1987 Smith and Gidlow (and Gidlow et al., in 1992) introduced the linear-approximation equation shown in the middle of the figure. With this arrangement, Smith and Gidlow proposed a new attribute called the fluid factor that enhanced the visibility of hydrocarbon-saturated rocks. The lower equation is the more conventional one seen in the literature (Wiggins et al., 1983).

If the rock properties in Fig. 6.A.1 are replaced with the normal-incident reflection coefficient NI_P, the variable B, and the last term in each equation is designated as a higher-order (H.O.) term, then the equations in Fig. 6.A.2 result. The similarity between the equations now becomes more obvious. The first term of each equation contains the normal-incident reflectivity modified by a different power of cosine-squared. The second term contains rock properties identified as the B reflectivities, which are modified by sine-squared. It should be noted that, unlike the other two, Shuey's equation already has the assumption that background $\alpha/\beta = 2$. This was necessary to obtain the cosine-squared term.

The normal-incident, NI_P, is referred to as the *intercept* because of its relationship to the straight-line equation ($y = b + mx$). The B's are referred to as the *slope* or *gradient*. In AVO articles, NI_P is often labeled as A, especially when the conventional equation is being employed.

If the background α/β is set to 2 for all three equations, they reduce to the equations shown in Fig. 6.A.3. Now, the AVO dependence on rock properties is reduced to two reflectivities: the normal-incident P-wave reflectivity (NI_P) and a term identified as the S-wave normal-incident reflectivity (NI_S). In Shuey's equation, the slope reflectivity is normally expressed as PR, while in the conventional equation the values A and B are used for the reflectivities. This notation leads to the following relationships

$$2(NI_P - NI_S) = PR = (A + B). \tag{26}$$

With this simplification shown in Fig. 6.A.3, each reflectivity in the three equations can be examined with respect to its sensitivity to pore-fluid variations (Fig. 6.A.4).

Slope and Intercept Sensitivity to Pore-Fluid Variations

In the top of Fig. 6.A.4, the normal-incident difference between a gas-saturated response and a water-saturated response is considered in terms of the individual density ($\Delta\rho/\rho$) and velocity ($\Delta\alpha/\alpha$) contributions. The amplitude change going from the water-saturated state to the gas-saturated state that is associated with velocity is defined as $\Delta\alpha_{GW}$, while that associated with density is defined as $\Delta\rho_{GW}$. As defined, $\Delta\alpha_{GW}$ and $\Delta\rho_{GW}$ are always negative. By definition, the sum of these two terms is $[NI_{GAS} - NI_{WET}]$, as indicated in the figure.

From previous observations using Bortfeld's equation in fluid-substitution models, this reflectivity difference is essentially the maximum pore-fluid discriminator. Bortfeld's rigidity term contains insignificant pore-fluid information. For this reason, the difference $[NI_{GAS} - NI_{WET}]$ has been assigned the top ranking for determining pore-fluid.

How much pore-fluid information is contained in the slope terms of the equations shown Fig. 6.A.3? If values for the slope terms are examined on and off a prospect, will the difference in the slope amplitudes assist in determining pore-fluid content for the prospect? For the slope analysis, the additional assumption is made that the *S*-wave velocity is the same for the gas and water-saturated states.

The slope difference for Shuey's equation contains only the contribution from reflectivity changes in the *P*-wave velocity. It doesn't have contributions from the density. This suggests that the slope term from Shuey's equation should be ranked as less than the *NI* differences. The density contribution for pore-fluid identification is normally smaller than the velocity contribution.

For the conventional AVO equation, the slope-reflectivity difference between gas and water states has the density contribution being subtracted from the velocity contribution. Because $\Delta\alpha_{GW}$ and $\Delta\rho_{GW}$ are always negative, this inherent subtraction reduces the effectiveness of the conventional equation to determine pore-fluid content using the slope term. If the normal-incident and slope terms from the conventional equation are added, the net effect is the same as Shuey's. Finally, the pore-fluid information from the Smith and Gidlow slope is ranked as the poorest because it depends mainly on density variations. However, as will be shown, their intent was not to use the slope term by itself.

As stated before, the pore-fluid effect is contained only in the first term of Bortfeld's equation, and the Bortfeld equation yields AVO responses similar to those from the linear-approximation equations. This implies that information about the pore-fluid content has "leaked" from the first term of the linear-approximation equations into the second term associated with the sine-squared. The "leakage" of pore-fluid information is summarized in Fig. 6.A.4.

In summary, *The slope reflectivities yield no additional information about the pore-fluid content beyond that given by the normal-incident reflectivity.* Hendrickson (1999) presented this same conclusion in a recent excellent article. In addition, he warned that slope estimates should be used with discretion because of errors in measuring the slope.

Smith and Gidlow's Fluid Factor

Let's return to Smith and Gidlow's work in Fig. 6.A.5. They suggested a clever way to maximize the discrimination of pore fluids using the intercept and slope reflectivities. First, they generated NI_P and NI_S sections using their derivation of the linear-approximation equation. Then noting that NI_P and NI_S have similar character, they estimate the ratio γ, $(NI_P/NI_S)_{WET}$, in a seismic window that contained no hydrocarbons (Step 2). The factor γ is designed to be a slowly varying function both in time and space. Next, they defined the fluid-factor trace, $\Delta F(t)$, as the subtraction of the weighted $NI_S(t)$ trace from the $NI_P(t)$ trace. In the analysis of Step 4, those zones that had no hydrocarbons would have amplitudes that approached zero, while those zones that contained hydrocarbons would have an approximate amplitude of $(NI_{GAS} - NI_{WET})$. This is the maximum pore-fluid discrimination that was observed from the Bortfeld equation. The beauty of the fluid-factor trace is that the maximum pore-fluid effect is obtained while setting the nonhydrocarbon reflection background amplitudes to near-zero levels.

Like many interpretation techniques, the Smith and Gidlow approach requires several assumptions. One assumption is that the S-wave normal-incident reflectivity for the gas-saturated state is the same as for the water-saturated state. If S-wave reflectivities for the AVO models (Fig. 4.B.2) are examined, it will be noticed that this assumption becomes questionable for Class 3 environments. However, Class 3 environments normally don't require the additional discrimination offered by the fluid factor to recognize and/or validate the presence of hydrocarbons.

Smith and Sutherland (1996) examined a worldwide data set of rock properties and found that a γ value of 0.63 gave the best fluid factor. For the three models used in these notes, the γ factors are -1.92 for Class 3, 0.41 for Class 2, and 0.57 for Class 1. The last two γ values are close to Smith and Sutherland's observation.

Lambda-Rho Pore-Fluid Discriminant

Lambda-rho ($\lambda\rho$) is a pore-fluid discriminator that has its origins in the hard-rock exploration areas of Canada (Goodway et al., 1997). Fig. 6.A.6 relates $\lambda\rho$ to Gassmann's fluid substitution term. Goodway et al. defined their pore-fluid discriminator as

$$\lambda\rho = (\alpha\rho)^2 - 2(\beta\rho)^2 . \qquad [27]$$

Let's investigate how this relates to the fluid-substitution term in Gassmann's equation. In Fig. 3.D.5, it was shown that the values for the dry-rock moduli of Gassmann's equation are the same before and after fluid substitution. In addition, it was shown that the dry-rock moduli dominate the elastic-constant values in Gassmann's equation for Class 1, hard-rock environments. In Fig. 3.D.5, only the bulk modulus with the subscript pore-fluid effect contains information about the pore fluid. This is the term that is desired for amplitude interpretation of pore fluid. With this intent, the variable "G" in Fig. 6.A.6 is defined to yield a fluid discriminator that produces Gassmann's fluid effect. This results in the relationship

$$G \equiv K_{dry}/ \mu_{dry} + 4/3. \qquad [28]$$

As suggested from literature in Fig. 2.E.4, $K_{dry} \approx \mu_{dry}$, or $\sigma_{dry} \approx .125$. This yields a value of 2.33 for G in Fig. 6.A.6. In the Goodway et al. approach, the value of $G = 2$ is suggested and this leads to $\sigma_{dry} = 0$. Thus, the lambda-rho attribute is a good approximation for Gassmann's bulk modulus of the pore-fluid effect, especially for consolidated rocks.

There is an interesting processing scheme that results by defining G as the factor that yields Gassmann's discriminator. A deterministic search of the seismic data can be performed to stabilize the results of the AVO inversion and the subsequent integration to yield the P-wave and S-wave impedances. Similar to Smith and Gidlow's suggestion of defining a background window to determine γ in Fig. 6.A.5, a window can be defined to determine G in Fig. 6.A.6. For water-saturated rocks, a background estimate of Gassmann's pore-fluid bulk modulus can be developed for an area. This background estimate provides a mechanism for constraining the AVO attributes $\alpha\rho$ and $\beta\rho$ after they are extracted from the seismic data. In essence, data scaling provides a means of relating Smith and Gidlow's fluid-factor term to the lambda-rho technique suggested by Goodway et al.

Other Reflectivity Relationships

Fig. 6.A.7 illustrates the pore-fluid effect with respect to the AVO responses from the Class 1, 2, and 3 models. The AVO response curves from the top interface of the six sands defined in Fig. 4.B.2 are plotted again. By starting with the modified Shuey's equation, it is easy to obtain the approximation shown in the bottom of the figure. Again, the pore-fluid effect is strongly related to the normal-incident reflectivity. Why use AVO if the normal-incident term is all that is needed to evaluate the pore-fluid content?

The above discussion suggests that measuring an anomaly's amplitude and comparing it to a nonhydrocarbon reflection would be a satisfactory solution for predicting pore-fluid type. However, seismic provides only relative amplitude, and normalization is needed if a quantitative amplitude interpretation is desired. Ross and Beale (1994), Chiburis (1993), and Resnick (1993) have described normalization techniques for both processing and interpretation.

A/B Analysis

A version of the *A/B* normalization technique is cartooned in Fig. 6.A.8. The stacked seismic section has a bright-spot anomaly in the middle portion of the line. Amplitudes associated with the seismic times defined by the blue line are cartooned in the bottom of the figure. The blue line is assumed to capture not only the productive portion of the prospect but also downdip limits that are water saturated. As suggested by Pan in the Introduction, the average amplitude for the water-saturated formation downdip can be found. This amplitude is defined as *B*. As an alternate, computing an *rms* amplitude over numerous traces with a long time window can approximate the background amplitude, *B*. With the time-window approach, individual *B* values can be obtained for each trace.

Let's assume *B* was obtained from a reflection off the downdip water-saturated portion of the formation. As the cartoon in the figure suggests, the *A/B* ratio would be near one (1) for the downdip limits, and would exhibit higher values across the bright-spot anomaly. If trend curves for nearby wells are available, then theoretical A/B ratios can be developed for different pore-fluid saturants, as is suggested by the *Gas* and *Oil* lines in the figure.

If the thickness on and off the prospect is assumed to be the same and the formation is in the thin-bed range, then an additional factor besides the change in reflectivities should be considered. The zones that have hydrocarbons will have a lower interval velocity than the downdip water-saturated portions. Because the formation was assumed to have constant thickness, the time separation between top and bottom reflections will be larger on the prospect than off. The prospect amplitude will be magnified because of the thin-bed effect. The reflection magnification is (water-sand velocity / gas-sand velocity). This factor is often incorporated in the normalization factor *B*.

A/B for Class 1, 2, and 3

The A/B technique presented was based on the stacked section. Also, the amplitude was a bright spot. What happens if the prospect is in a phase-reversal (Class 2) or dim-out (Class 1) regime? This question is evaluated with the assistance of Fig. 6.A.9. In this figure, the normal-incident reflectivities for the six sand models (Fig. 4.B.2) are graphed. The *NI*'s associated with the water-saturated sands are labeled *B Wet* in the figure, while the gas sands are labeled *A Gas*. For the Class 3 environment, A/B will be a large number for hydrocarbon prospects. The Class 3 sand model has A/B = 10. Normally, event amplitudes that are twice the background amplitudes will be recognized as anomalous. If B is slightly positive rather than negative, the magnitude will still be large.

However, for a Class 2 environment, the A/B technique is not as successful. With the normal-incident reflection coefficients for both the water-saturated and hydrocarbon-saturated states hovering around zero, A/B results can be quite ambiguous. The Class 2 model from Fig. 4.B.2 has A/B = 0.6.

For Class 1 environments, A/B will be less than 1. The model has A/B = 0.7. The A/B ratio for the Class 1 model is greater than the Class 2 A/B. The phase reversal of *NI*, which occurs from the wet state to the hydrocarbon state, accounts for Class 2 having a smaller A/B than Class 1. However, the magnitude of the difference [$NI_{GAS} - NI_{WET}$] is greater for Class 2 than for Class 1.

When a hydrocarbon indicator decreases in value instead of increasing, the validity of the HCI becomes questionable. Other factors, such as poor imaging over the prospect, acquisition problems, etc., then need to be reevaluated. In short, A/B using *NI* works best for bright-spot regimes, and becomes questionable for the other two regimes.

However, the story changes slightly when the amplitudes from slope reflectivities are examined as A/B ratios. Remember that A/B amplitude measurement for the Poisson reflectivity, *PR*, is similar to an *NI* A/B measurement. The amplitude of the slope reflectivity from the gas-sand reflection is divided by the corresponding *PR* value for the water-saturated zone.

Using the same sand model, the six Poisson reflectivities are plotted in Fig. 6.A.10. With *PR*, all A/B ratios are typically greater than one (1) for hydrocarbon-saturated sands. The Class 3 case maintains a high *A/B* ratio of 8. The Class 2 *A/B* ratio approaches an acceptable value for recognizing and possibly validating pore-fluid variations. However, the *A/B* for Class 1 is not much greater than 1. For the rock-property model data, *A/B* for Class 1 is 1.2. This suggests that more robust techniques are required for validating Class 1 anomalies with reflectivities, such as the fluid-factor suggested by Smith and Gidlow (1987). Alternately, increased resolution for discriminating pore-fluid could be obtained by evaluating elastic constants rather than reflectivities. This has been advocated by Goodway et al. (1997).

One final AVO relationship worth noting is the reflection from a fluid interface. Wright (1986) published the expression in Fig. 6.A.11. The encouraging feature of the fluid-interface reflection is that it is positive and increases in amplitude with offset for all AVO classes.

The emphasis so far has been on determining how sensitive the AVO reflectivities are for pore-fluid determination. While Shuey advocated crossplotting $\ln(\rho\alpha)$ versus σ for lithology discrimination, other AVO attributes might have better discrimination power for determining pore-fluid content and/or lithology, the subject of the next topic.

6B. Crossplots for Pore-Fluid and Lithology Prediction

Today's literature and software brochures abound with crossplots that are available for viewing rock properties, reflectivities, seismic data, and seismic *attributes*. As an interpreter examines these various options, it can be his dream or nightmare. Fig. 6.B.1 captures a few of the crossplots that can disrupt an interpreter's sleep patterns.

Rock-Property Crossplots

Can six elastic parameters be extracted from an amplitude inversion of a CDP gather? The inversion considered here is restricted to reflection amplitudes only, and no explicit traveltime information is available. Unless some additional information is provided, only four independent parameters can be extracted. The possible four parameters are the *P*-wave velocity ratio, the density ratio, and the two Poisson's ratios of the bounding media. If six parameters are requested from the inversion, then normally high-resolution interval-velocity analyses or rock-property transforms are included to constrain the solution. Which of these four parameters or pairs of parameters best isolate lithology and pore-fluid content?

Fig. 6.B.1 contains four crossplots that were suggested for lithology and pore-fluid discrimination (Castagna, 1993, Pickett, 1963). The crossplots in the figure indicate that they can differentiate one lithology from another and, likewise, can differentiate water saturant from gas. Which rock-property crossplot has the best sensitivity for differentiating pore-fluid content? Which rock-property pair is best for lithology prediction? Let's examine different rock-property pairs with respect to the Class 1, 2, and 3 models that have been used throughout these notes.

In Fig. 6.B.2, rock-property pairs for the six different sand models are displayed in four different crossplots. Black circles represent shale values; blue squares, wet sands; and red triangles, gas sands. Trend curves within a crossplot can be established by connecting the respective lithologic symbols (circles, squares, or triangles).

The groupings by the numbers 1, 2, and 3 refer to the AVO classes. When evaluating a rock property's potential for differentiating pore-fluid content or lithology (sand versus shale), the analysis is normally done within a class.

Because the units are different for the various rock properties, the minimum and maximum values from each data set were selected for scaling the crossplots. This can be deceiving in some instances when the minimum and maximum values of a rock property are close to one another but the crossplot shows them with a large separation.

Several of the crossplots in Fig. 6.B.2 illustrate features that should be evident already. As expected, the S-wave velocity offers little discrimination of the pore-fluid content. For pore-fluid discrimination, the amount of separation between a triangle and square for a particular class is compared. For instance, in the upper-right crossplot, there is little x-axis separation between a triangle and square for a particular class. Density appears to be a good discriminant for pore-fluid, but check the resolution required for the density values. For instance, in the upper-left crossplot, density appears to be a better Class 2 discriminator between a wet and gas sand than velocity is. The density distance separation is twice that of the velocity for the Class 2 blue square to red triangle. However, the wet-sand density changes approximately 7% going to gas sand, while the velocity changes 9%.

While these rock-property crossplots offer encouragement for discriminating pore-fluid content and lithology, a problem remains. As noted by Rosa (1976) and others, density and velocity are closely coupled in the AVO equation and the separation of either one from the acoustic impedance term is not a robust procedure. Thus, rock properties that are more robustly extracted are examined, such as the various impedances or Poisson's ratio. Using these rock properties, crossplots were generated, and the results are illustrated in Fig. 6.B.3.

As noted with S-wave velocity, shear impedance is poorer at discriminating pore-fluid than Poisson's ratio or the other impedances that are crossplotted in Fig. 6.B.3. In practice, in order to derive the rock properties displayed in Fig. 6.B.3, reflectivities estimated from the AVO inversion must be integrated, and this requires a low-frequency trend for the desired rock property. The low-frequency trend is often derived from the seismic stacking velocity and an empirical relationship such as Gardner's equation. In areas where sufficient well control is available and specific target zones are specified, the necessary low-frequency control of the impedance is available.

The lower two crossplots in Fig. 6.B.3 use the rock-property pairs of ρK and $\rho \lambda$ versus $\rho \mu$. This rock-property selection follows the suggestion by Gardner and Forel (1987) to express the AVO equation in terms of the elastic constants rather than velocities and density variations. The generation of these impedances from seismic data requires the subtraction of the integrated slope from the integrated intercept values (Goodway et al., 1997).

If the low-frequency background trends for ρK, $\rho \lambda$, and $\rho \mu$ are adequately chosen for the trace integration of the reflectivities to yield these density-times-modulus values, then the potential for pore-fluid discrimination by ρK and $\rho \lambda$ is encouraging for all AVO classes. This is represented by the separation of the gas-sand triangles from the wet-sand squares along the x-axis in the lower two crossplots. If the best pore-fluid discriminator is based on the percentage of rock-property change, then the $\rho \lambda$ rock property is the best discriminator for Class 1 rocks. The change between the Class 1 wet sand and gas sand is 40% for $\rho\lambda$, while the next best discriminator would be Poisson's ratio at a 20% change. The *P*-wave acoustic impedance only has a 6% change.

However, a warning should be mentioned when percentage changes are used for evaluating a rock property's ability to discriminate one pore fluid from another. Take, for example, a formation that has an acoustic impedance of 2 when wet, and 4 when gas saturated. This is a 100% change. Acoustic impedance is related to (density × modulus) as $(\rho\alpha)^2 = \rho(\text{modulus})$. The (density × modulus) value for the same rock when it is wet is 4, and 16 when gas saturated. This is a 300% change. In this example, no additional discrimination between pore-fluid states is available just because the rock-property values were squared. The error that is inherent in the acoustic impedance measurements will be magnified by the square, and the uncertainty is the same with acoustic-impedance measurements as it is with (density × modulus) measurements.

Amplitude interpretations based on impedances from reflectivity inversions, and (density × modulus) interpretations based on the difference of reflectivity inversions, have made tremendous gains in the last few years. These new interpretation techniques are especially popular in the "hard-rock" environments.

Reflectivity Crossplots

Using the known rock properties from the test sand model, the slope and intercept reflectivities associated with the three equations displayed in Fig. 6.A.2 were computed and are displayed in Fig. 6.B.4. These were computed from the model rock properties and not extracted by an AVO inversion. The intercept reflectivities, NI_P, are plotted along the *x*-axis in each of the three crossplots. The blue squares represent reflections from the shale/wet-sand interface, while the red triangles represent reflections from the shale/gas-sand interface. Reflections from both the top and bottom interfaces are plotted. Also shown are shale/shale reflections (green) that fall along a diagonal that strikes approximately −45°. The shale/shale interfaces were constructed by mixing the depth intervals of the shale trend curves. For instance, a shale interval from 5000–5050 ft (1525–1540 m) was switched with an interval from 7000–7050 ft (2135–2150 m) to generate a reflection point on the green shale background trend curve, and so forth.

As before, connecting the lithologic symbols (squares or triangles) on one side of the shale/shale reflection diagonal provides trend curves for the shale/wet-sand and shale/gas-sand reflections. Only the background trend for the shale/shale reflections passes through the origin. This is anticipated because only the shale/shale interfaces were defined to have $NI_S = 0$ when $NI_P = 0$. This is not the usual case for interfaces that separate shale from sand. In other words, when sand and shale have the same acoustic impedance ($NI_P = 0$), the slope term will be non-zero because sand and shale have different *P*-wave to *S*-wave velocity transforms. This is implied by the empirical ARCO transforms.

One way to quantify the discrimination of an AVO attribute is to compare the amplitude ratio of the gas-sand anomaly to the wet-sand background (*A/B*) for a particular class. If a Class 3 gas-sand reflection is to be differentiated from its respective wet-sand reflection, the normal-incident reflection from any of the three inversion equations offers sufficient discrimination. For Class 3, the top of the gas sand has an NI_P equal to –0.26, while the wet sand NI_P is –0.025, a ten-to-one ratio. However, for the Class 2 model, the gas sand has an NI_P of –0.034 while the wet-sand reflection is 0.058. A phase reversal occurs, but the magnitude of the two reflections would be difficult to differentiate. Finally, the Class 1 NI_P ratio between a gas and wet sand is almost one (1), thus making it the most difficult class in which to differentiate pore-fluid content.

If the A/B ratio for the AVO slope is used for pore-fluid discrimination, the Poisson reflectivity attribute is the best of the three considered in Fig. 6.B.4. The Smith and Gidlow slope, B_{SG}, is essentially a weighted NI_S reflectivity and, as discussed above, the S-wave acoustic impedance has small changes between the wet and gas-saturated states. The slope term, B, from the conventional inversion equation does provide discrimination, but not as much as the Poisson reflectivity provides.

The reflectivities most often crossplotted in the literature are the intercept and gradient from the conventional AVO equation. Examples from Castagna et al. (1998) are shown in Fig. 6.B.5. These reflectivities were derived both from model data and field data. In the left crossplot, the intercept and gradient reflectivities were generated for shale over wet-sand and shale over gas-sand. The wet-reflectivity trend passes through the origin because the same V_S from V_P transform was used for sand and shale. An important point emphasized by Castagna et al. for this plot is that both the intercept and gradient values decrease in going from the wet to gas states. This can also be noted for the intercept-gradient crossplot in the upper right of Fig. 6.B.4. As a verification of their theoretical observations, Castagna et al. examined intercept and gradient values computed from V_P and V_S measurements on real data. Once again, wet and gas-saturated states were considered. The results are shown in the right of Fig. 6.B.5. For the majority of the real-data cases, the intercept and gradient decrease when brine is replaced with gas.

So far, the crossplotted elastic constants and reflectivities have been derived from the actual rock-property values of the model. It is also instructive to investigate how reflectivities, intercept, and slope estimates, derived from bandlimited seismic traces, can be treated in similar crossplots. Ross (2000) provides a nice tutorial on this subject.

6C. Crossplotting Seismic AVO Attributes

Extracting Intercept and Slope Traces

A couple of cartoons will illustrate AVO inversion for intercept and slope reflectivity traces. One of the three linear-approximation equations is usually selected. In Fig. 6.C.1, the modified Shuey equation was chosen. A division by $\cos^2(\theta)$ was performed so that Shuey's equation resembles a straight-line equation.

For a specific time, t_0, on the cartoon of the NMO-corrected CDP gather, the amplitudes at various offsets represent the true reflectivities modified by a scalar k. From the stacking velocity, an average velocity and depth function can be obtained. From depth and offset, a straight-ray estimate of the incident angle is derived. This method of estimating the incident angle guarantees smooth variations with offset and time, but lacks accuracy. There are more accurate methods, such as those proposed by Ostrander

(1984) and Connolly (1999). However, some smoothing of the derived incident angles is suggested, or rapid variations in the intercept and slope estimates result.

In the 4th step, in order to illustrate the procedure, the amplitudes are plotted for a specified t_0. A linear fit of these points yields estimates of the normal-incident and Poisson reflectivities. *NI* is the y-intercept and *PR* is the slope. The CDP-gather amplitudes for the next t_0 are selected, and the procedure is repeated until estimates for the complete *NI* and *PR* traces are obtained. Remember that the absolute values of the reflection amplitudes were not known, so that *NI* and *PR* are relative values at best.

As an example, *NI* and *PR* traces extracted from AVO responses over a 70-ft (20-m) water-saturated sand and a 70-ft gas-saturated sand are illustrated in Fig. 6.C.2. Four t_0 times are annotated at 1.015, 1.030, 1.122, and 1.129 s. These times represent the trough and peak for the gas and water events in the CDP gather. The amplitudes for the four events are plotted to illustrate the polarity of the slope (*PR*) and intercept (*NI*) for each t_0. The message that this figure conveys is that the *PR* trace is opposite in polarity to the *NI* trace if the amplitude decreases with offset (water-sand event), and vice versa. Specific details were given in Fig. 5.A.5.

It is not immediately obvious, by examining the *NI* and *PR* traces individually, whether there are hydrocarbons present. However, positive events on $NI \times PR$ are sometimes useful for detecting hydrocarbons if the *NI* and *PR* values happen to fall in the 1st and 3rd quadrants. This will be examined later.

Accuracy of AVO Inversions for Intercept and Slope

Of the three commonly used linear-approximation equations, is one better than the other? If an accurate estimate of the rock properties is desired from the slope and intercept values, then it is important that these equations are based on realistic assumptions with respect to the model. In review, the following assumptions were made in deriving the equations in Fig. 6.B.4:

- Linear approximation of Zoeppritz's equation is adequate to 30°,
- Incident and transmitted angles are equal, and
- Third-order terms in each of the three linear-approximation equations are insignificant out to 30°.

An additional assumption for the modified Shuey equation is

$$\beta/\alpha = {}^1\!/_2.$$

To test these assumptions, intercept and slope reflectivities derived with a least-squares solution based on the three equations were compared with the exact reflectivities derived from the known rock properties. For the inversions, reflection amplitudes at increments of 1° from 0°–30° were generated using the exact Zoeppritz equation for the upper interface of the six sand beds. A least-squares fit was employed. The results are given in Fig. 6.C.3.

For all three equations, the intercept, NI_P, was estimated within 2% of the true value for the six interfaces. However, each inversion equation had significantly more error for the slope estimate. If related to routine AVO inversion, this test started with the assumption that true amplitude processing was conducted and absolute reflection coefficients were recovered. This is more than can ever be expected. There are some surprising results displayed in Fig. 6.C.3. The errors associated with the slope estimate from Shuey's simplified equation that had the approximation $\alpha/\beta = 2$ are in the same order of magnitude as the errors from the other two equations.

In short, there is definitely a warning that emerges from these results. Estimates of NI_P are robust and thus are strong candidates for amplitude ratio A/B interpretations, but care must be exercised when amplitude interpretations are derived from slope estimates.

Crossplotting Band-limited Seismic AVO Attributes

As mentioned earlier, each of the three AVO class models was made with water-saturated and gas-saturated sands. The thickness of each bed was 50 ft (15 m), and a 25-Hz Ricker wavelet was employed in the AVO modeling. As a first approximation, the amplitude of the AVO responses from these models can be thought of as being modified by a thin-bed response (Widess, 1973) and by the cosine of the incident angle at the lower boundary (Lin and Phair, 1993). Because the interval velocity of the six sand beds varied, a correction for the (wet-sand/gas-sand) velocities can also be included. In short, without these corrections, the extracted slopes and intercepts will not be the same as the exact or inversion reflectivities listed in Fig.6.C.3. The inversion reflectivities given in Fig. 6.C.3 were derived for a single interface.

The estimated NI_P and PR traces along with the AVO synthetics and other AVO attributes are shown in Fig. 6.C.4. For the Class 3 anomaly, either NI or PR easily differentiates the gas sand from the wet sand. For Class 2, the gas sand is best seen on the PR trace. As before, the recognition of hydrocarbons is difficult for the Class 1 anomaly. The product trace $NI \times PR$ differentiates gas from wet sands for Class 3, but is not very diagnostic for the other two classes. The traces labeled as *gradient* in the figure are slope measurements taken on the envelope of the CDP traces. The envelope gradient estimate is often substituted for PR when the S/N ratio is poor. As a pore-fluid discriminator, the envelope gradient trace works for Class 3 and sometimes for Class 2.

Using the AVO responses from Fig. 6.C.4, intercept and slope traces based on each of the three linear equations are shown in Fig. 6.C.5. The first set of traces on the left, NI and PR, was derived from Shuey's equation. The next set, A and B, was derived from the conventional equation, while NI and B_{SG} were derived from Smith and Gidlow, 1987). The following is noted:

- The relative amplitude ratio of NI to PR for the wet cases is the same for Class 3 to Class 1 AVO anomalies. This relationship provides a robust method to stabilize NI and PR traces during inversion. This relationship does not exist for A, B and NI, B_{SG} inversions.

- For the Class 3 gas anomaly, the estimates of B and B_{SG} are distorted while PR is not. This occurs because more weight is assigned to PR than to B and B_{SG} in the linear equations. In fact, the distortion of B_{SG} is quite significant. The distortion is reduced if a damping term is included in the inversion.

• The *PR* derived from the inversion of Shuey's equation is essentially equivalent to the sum of *A* and *B* extracted from the conventional equation (far right traces in figure).

The AVO attributes from Shuey's equation were chosen to illustrate the various crossplots that might be selected for pore-fluid and lithology identification. In Fig. 6.C.6, NI_P versus *PR* crossplots from the CDP gathers in Fig. 6.C.4 were generated for each AVO class. For reference, the exact NI_P and *PR* crossplot developed from the known rock properties is also displayed in the upper left. Once again, the gas zones are colored red while the wet zones are blue. This holds for the seismic trace crossplots also.

Because a band-limited pulse was used rather than a spike for the source wavelet, the extracted NI_P and *PR* traces, when crossplotted, intersect the origin. In the Class 3 crossplot (upper right), the crossplot points for the gas zone touch the left and right borders of the graph. These end points relate to the upper and lower reflections for the true values depicted for the Class 3 anomaly in the upper left crossplot. In essence, if the inversion results are correct, the band-limited response should oscillate between the upper and lower interface points, as given in the upper left graph. In general, the estimated NI_P and *PR* traces from the AVO inversion are in excellent agreement with the theoretical model. The seismic trace crossplots for wet sand over shale and gas sand over shale do not align with the shale-over-shale background that trends along the $-45°$ line. Note, shale-over-shale crossplot points have been called the background trend line, while wet sand over shale is often labeled the background trend by other authors.

For the Class 3 model, the gas-sand crossplot is distorted from a straight line. This distortion occurs because the slope estimate is affected by NMO wavelet stretch at large incident angles. The distortion from a straight line decreases with depth.

If the AVO model assumed in this study were taken from a field well, slope and intercept trace crossplots from an AVO inversion of the seismic field data at the well location would be expected to respond as shown in the figure. For Class 3 anomalies, discrimination of wet sand from gas sand reflections is based on the length of the cross-plot vectors. The rotation angle of the vectors is not a determining factor for discrimina-tion; rather, the magnitude of the reflection is. However, for Class 2 anomalies, the gas- and wet-sand events have different crossplot amplitudes and also exhibit an angle sepa-ration. For Class 1 anomalies, the vector amplitudes and angles are similar. Once again, pore-fluid content is difficult to distinguish for Class 1 anomalies.

As an option, traces derived from angle-limited stacks can be crossplotted. Angle stacks from the model CDP gathers in Fig. 6.C.4 were created. Angle crossplots for the Class 3, 2, and 1 anomalies are shown in Figs. 6.C.7 – 6.C.9. For the Class 3 anomaly in Fig. 6.C.7, the gas sand and wet sand have *NI* and *PR* values that plot along the 45° axis because both reflection events essentially have constant amplitude with offset. This is also verified by the crossplots of the 10°, 20°, and 30° angle stacks against the near trace. Again in all the crossplots, the amplitude vector discriminates wet-sand reflections from gas-sand reflections.

For the Class 2 anomaly in Fig. 6.C.8, the trends for the three angle stacks crossplotted against the near trace are quite different. The 10°-angle stack versus the near trace exhibits 45° slopes for both the wet- and gas-sand events. However, as the angle increases, the trends for the gas sand and wet sand become orthogonal for this Class 2 anomaly. The change in slope appears to distinguish the gas from the wet sand. The wet sand has almost zero amplitude at a 30° incident angle.

Finally, for Class 1 anomalies, little discrimination between the gas and wet sand is found on the various angle crossplots (Fig. 6.C.9) or the *NI, PR* crossplot.

Often, the differences of angle-limited stacks are examined. Fig. 6.C.10 illustrates a (far minus near) angle stack versus a near-angle stack. Once again, because of the near-zero amplitude at 30° for the wet sand, the bottom-left plot discriminates wet sands from gas sands. The bottom-right crossplot is presented to illustrate that the *PR* reflectivity, as well as the other slope reflectivities, can be estimated from weighted sums of the angle-limited stacks. The weighted sum of the near and far traces is very similar to *PR*. The weights were computed with knowledge of the model's rock properties.

There are several reasons for using range-limited angle stacks. Three-dimensional horizon slices derived from different angle stacks can be time-adjusted for NMO errors before they are transformed into AVO attributes. This eliminates a major problem inherent with AVO inversion of CDP gathers where the slope estimate is based on nonflat events in the CDP gather. Also, errors in the estimated slope that are introduced by noise events on CDP gathers are reduced, as stacking reduces the noise effects. The strong correlation between the intercept and slope is reduced.

While these crossplots may provide insight for discriminating wet from hydrocarbon sands, it is not convenient to examine all events at all CDP locations with crossplots such as these. An alternative method is needed.

Crossplotting Seismic Sections

A convenient method to continue this calibration away from a control well is to color crossplot the seismic AVO attributes, as described by Verm and Hilterman (1995). To facilitate this, a two-dimensional color lookup table is necessary. In Fig. 6.C.11, the mechanics of converting information contained in two traces into one color trace is diagramed. Of course, the colors are not randomly assigned, but are grouped into calibration areas. Calibration would come from examining crossplots of either the rock properties or reflectivities generated from the rock properties (Verm and Hilterman, 1995, Ross, 2000). If the area being investigated were similar to the model used in this book, then the reflectivity crossplot in the upper-left of Fig. 6.C.6 would assist in the grouping of colors. However, that same information could be obtained from the rock-property crossplot of ln(acoustic impedance) versus Poisson's ratio in the upper left of Fig. 6.B.3. The vertical and horizontal distances between shale and sand points relate NI_P and *PR* directly.

Fig. 6.C.12 illustrates the assignment of calibration colors for the AVO classes used in these notes. The upper-left crossplot of Fig. 6.C.6 is the basis for the 2-D color matrix table used in Fig. 6.C.12. The 2-D color table was designed so that a reflection from a gas sand associated with a particular AVO class has a distinct color, while the wet sands have the same color, blue. For each AVO class, the wet- and gas-sand intervals from the *NI* and *PR* traces are crossplotted on the color tables. The extracted NI_P trace is plotted on the right in the color tables. The same scale factors for the 2-D color table were used for all panels. With one 2-D color table, it is possible to distinguish the wet sands of each AVO class from the respective gas sands. In short, the pore-fluid content for each AVO class is differentiated, and the different lithologies associated with the AVO classes are differentiated from one another.

The sensitivity of the color-table crossplotting method to distinguish different pore fluids decreases from Class 3 to Class 1 AVO environments. It was possible to distinguish the Class 1 gas sand from the wet sand in the right side of the lower panel because the data were noise free. The position of the colors in the 2-D color table that are associated with the wet-sand response for the Class 1 model are right next to the gas-sand colors.

In general, a preset 2-D color table, such as the one displayed, is adequate for pore-fluid and lithologic discrimination of Class 1, 2, and 3 AVO anomalies in most sand/shale environments. However, do not assume that Class 1 pore-fluid content is easily differentiated using color crossplots, based on this noise-free example.

In order to compensate for errors inherent in the estimation of the slope term, the min-max scales for the NI_P and *PR* axes need to be normalized. A rough rule-of-thumb is to set the min-max color-table scales of a particular attribute equal to 3–4 times the background *rms* value of the attribute. Gas sands that are Class 3 will normally be pegged against the min-max scale values in the first and third quadrants.

Obviously, color crossplotting can be applied to the slope/intercept values from the other two inversion equations with the same general results expected. Also, angle-stack traces or any two attribute traces can be crossplotted.

Comments about Seismic Crossplotting

There are six reservoir properties that geophysicists have endeavored to extract from seismic data. They are pore-fluid content, water saturation, permeability, porosity, lithology, and thickness. Of these, pore-fluid content, porosity, lithology, and thickness have the highest probability of being extracted. Water saturation and permeability have been extracted from seismic properties in a few test studies. If the pore-fluid content, porosity, lithology, and thickness are to be extracted, then the seismic field data acquisition and processing must meet certain criteria. At the front end of the planning, the rock properties of the geologic targets should be characterized with respect to the expected seismic signature, so that an adequate data-acquisition program is designed.

One method for quantifying the rock properties with respect to their expected seismic signature has been discussed in this section and is summarized in Fig. 6.C.13. Seismic signature types are calibrated to the rock properties and are illustrated as Class 1, 2, and 3, or respectively, dim out, phase reversal, and bright spot. From available well-log data, a geologic target can be related to one of these types of expected reflections. Each of these classes falls into a different area of the 2-D matrix of NI_P versus *PR*. The left side of the matrix indicates reflections from the upper interface of the reservoir, while the right side indicates the base.

The most significant aspect of the color crossplot is its ability to associate the variations in the NI_P and PR traces with respect to changes in stratigraphy and pore fill. With color as a potential identifier of pore-fluid and lithology changes, the association of lithologic or pore-fluid changes can be related to the trapping geometry. For instance, the downdip limits of color can easily be related to the structural contours or trapping faults. It is not uncommon to observe a consistent color horizontally traverse adjacent fault blocks, indicating a common fluid interface.

Rocks with small values for NI_P have stack responses that are dominated by both the NI_P and PR reflectivities (Class 2). It is essential in these data areas that the maximum offset for the source and receivers is at least 1.5 times the expected depth of the target geologic horizons if lithostratigraphic information is desired.

In those areas where NI_P is strongly positive (Class 1), the lithostratigraphic sections tend to correlate very strongly to the chronostratigraphic sections, and the effects of fluid replacement are not as pronounced as changes in the porosity of the reservoir rock. Recent work in crossplotting NI_P, PR has succeeded in defining both lithology and porosity in target intervals. However, inversion to acoustic impedance and Poisson's ratio greatly assists the interpretation (DiSiena et al., 1995). In these areas, multiples and mode-converted waves tend to dominate the seismic, and reliance on noise rejection schemes in the CDP domain is essential. This requires consistent offset spacing within the CDP gathers from near offset to offsets at least equal to the geologic target depth. More recent work (Kozman and Hilterman, 2000) indicates that offsets that are twice the target depth are necessary to distinguish pore-fluid content in Class 1 AVO environments.

In bright-spot areas, the NI_P reflectivity dominates the stack section, and pore-fluid properties rather than porosity vary the rock properties the most in these areas. Very clean water-wet sands have an abnormally low Poisson's ratio compared with slightly shaly sands. Because of this and the tendency for clean sands to have sharp boundaries, false interpretations of the fluid content in clean sands are still common.

So far, sunshine and roses have been promised for discriminating pore-fluid and lithology from seismic crossplots. Surely, there should be some pitfalls. In Fig. 6.C.6, the crossplot of the Class 3 gas-sand reflection deviated from a straight line because of NMO stretch on the far traces. And, this was for noise-free data! Are there other pitfalls associated with AVO inversion and color crossplotting?

6D. Errors in Slope and Intercept Estimates

Statistical Correlation of Intercept and Gradient

Swan (1993) did considerable work in quantifying the robustness associated with various AVO attributes for "direct detection" of hydrocarbons. Cambois (1998) expanded the concepts introduced by Swan with real field data. Cambois noted that well-log calibration of rock properties to A, B crossplots (intercept, gradient crossplots) suggested that B values should be the same order of magnitude as A values. However, B values 10 times larger than A values are routinely measured on real field data. Why? To illustrate the discrepancy, he presented the results displayed in the left of Fig. 6.D.1. The stack section was derived from CDP gathers consisting of random noise. A least-squares AVO inversion of the CDP gathers yielded intercept, A, and slope, B, traces. The intercept amplitudes should have had the same range as the stack, but they were about twice as large. The slope had amplitudes about 16 times larger than the stack. The reason was that the least-squares estimates of the intercept and slope become statistically correlated in the presence of noise. The green points in the crossplot of Fig. 6.D.1 are from the A and B traces computed from the noise data. The two red slopes in the figure were theoretically derived using the data-acquisition parameters and the assumption that the data were random noise. The actual data values were not used to compute the intercept and gradient for the red lines. The green points are near the theoretical slope of -1. The position of the noise and the theoretical slope are very close to where actual rock-property values for A and B should plot. In short, with the strong correlation of the attributes A and B to the random-noise slope, real rock-property variations, such as pore-fluid variations, can be obscured.

Both Cambois (1998) and Hendrickson (1999) suggested using stacks rather than least-squares-computed intercept traces for crossplotting. Stacks do not exhibit the strong correlation that gradient traces have with intercept traces. Figure 6.D.2 illustrates the correlation between A and B in the left crossplot. The red points are associated with a known gas field, while the green points that exhibit a negative slope are associated with the background reflections. The red points still stand out from the green. However, in order to verify that the red points are not statistical correlations, Cambois plotted the slope (gradient) against the stack as shown in the right crossplot. Because the red points continue to be distinguished from the background green, the gas trend is validated as being a lithologic or pore-fluid effect and not a statistical artifact.

Residual NMO Effects on Intercept and Gradient Estimates

Besides the statistical correlation between intersect and slope, AVO inversion is very sensitive to residual NMO errors. Spratt (1987) demonstrated these effects with an inversion for NI_P and NI_S. In his figure on the left of Fig. 6.D.3, R_P and R_S refer to NI_P and NI_S, respectively. For the input model to the AVO response, NI_S was set to zero. However, after introducing 4 ms residual NMO error in the synthetic AVO response and then solving for NI_P and NI_S from the AVO response, significant non-zero values were obtained for NI_S.

If there are residual NMO errors and the estimated A and B traces are crossplotted, erroneous trends develop, as illustrated by the crossplot in the right of Fig. 6.D.3. As the residual error increases, the crossplot trend moves away from the true trend (rock-property trend) in the figure.

If residual NMO distorts the (A,B) crossplot, what distortions can be expected if the seismic wavelet deviates from zero phase? The plots in Fig. 6.D.4 address this question. AVO responses for the gas sand in the Class 2 model were generated with zero-, minimum-, and 90°-phase wavelets. The amplitude spectrum is the same for all three phase spectra. NI and PR reflectivity traces were extracted and their respective crossplots are shown in the figure. The lengths of the crossplot vectors differ slightly, but the orientations of the crossplots for the gas and wet sands are essentially the same. The gas-sand crossplot for the minimum-phase wavelet has a broader trend than the ones exhibited by the corresponding crossplot for the zero-phase or 90°-phase seismic wavelets. This is actually related to residual NMO error from the NMO stretch.

The purple lines on the AVO responses depict the actual reflection time for the gas sand. The NMO corrections for these synthetic models were based on ray-trace arrival times. For the zero-phase and 90°-phase wavelets, the majority of the reflection energy centers on the true arrival time. However, the energy for the minimum-phase wavelet arrives after the true reflection time, and this energy is NMO corrected based on a velocity function beneath the gas sand onset. In normal processing, this would not occur. However, it does emphasize that if a wavelet has a long time duration, then it will exhibit significant NMO stretch with the result that A and B crossplots will be distorted. This occurs frequently for Class 3 anomalies. One good conclusion that can be drawn from this figure is that the crossplot trends for the various pore-fluid and lithology models are not very sensitive to the wavelet phase.

In addition to the problems of statistical correlation between A and B and residual NMO errors, strong noise trends on the near traces also cause problems. In some parts of the North Sea, the near traces are so highly contaminated with noise that estimates of the normal-incident intercept are difficult. In order to capture potential AVO effects, Connolly (1999) and colleagues invented the elastic impedance trace for pore-fluid and lithologic identification. This was the birth of elastic impedance, *EI*.

Elastic Impedance

The derivation of *EI* is given in Fig. 6.D.5. Starting with Aki and Richards's (1980) linear-approximation equation, Connolly wanted to synthesize a rock-property function for nonzero incident angles that behaved similarly to the acoustic impedance at normal incidence. At incident angles that have a value of zero, the difference in the natural log of the acoustic impedance between the lower medium and the upper medium yields the normal-incident reflection coefficient. This natural log requirement for *EI* is expressed in the middle of the figure. The solution that satisfies this requirement for nonnormal incident angles is expressed in the figure. Connolly (1999) wrote an excellent tutorial on *EI* in THE LEADING EDGE that is well worth reviewing.

With this definition of *EI*, stacks at different incident angles can be calibrated to known well-log control. The angle stacks from field data are integrated to yield estimated elastic impedances in a fashion similar to integrating a near trace to yield acoustic impedance. For best results, angle stacks are calibrated to well control, so that separate seismic wavelets can be extracted for different angle stacks. NMO stretch lowers the effective seismic frequency as the incident angle increases. The inverted angle stacks are estimated *EI* functions. The *EI* traces can now be crossplotted to detect variations caused by lithology or pore-fluid variations. An *EI* calibration and crossplot will illustrate this technique.

The benefits of *EI* calibration are best displayed for Class 2 AVO anomalies such as the one shown in Fig. 6.D.6. There are two hydrocarbon packages located between the 8000- and 9000-ft (2400- and 3000-m) depths. These zones are associated with large variations in Poisson's ratio, σ. Both hydrocarbon zones exhibit strong AVO anomalies. Obviously, angle stacks centered at 30° or 40° will highlight the hydrocarbons when compared with the near-trace stack.

If the near trace in Fig. 6.D.6 is integrated and the low-frequency trend of acoustic impedance is added, an estimate of the well-log acoustic impedance is obtained. In a similar fashion, integration of the seismic trace associated with a 40° incident angle yields an estimate of $EI(40°)$. The calibration of the angle-trace inversions to the well-log data is accomplished by generating EI curves. Fig. 6.D.7 illustrates the EI curves at 0°, 20°, and 40° incident angles for the well-log curves in Fig. 6.D.6. For Class 2 anomalies, the EI values increase as a function of incident angle. There is little to no indication of the hydrocarbon zones on the AI [$EI(0°)$] trace in Fig. 6.D. 7, while the $EI(40°)$ has a significant variation in the hydrocarbon zones.

Figure 6.D.8 compares a synthetic seismic trace generated from the $EI(40°)$ depth curve to the 35°–45° angle stack from the CDP gather of Fig. 6.D.6. The PR and NI traces extracted from the CDP gather are also plotted in Fig. 6.D.8. The NI traces are plotted in blue in the middle three plots. As expected from theory, the EI synthetic is almost a duplicate of the angle stack that has the same incident angle. However, the frequency content of the wavelet for the EI synthetic was reduced by the factor (t_0/t_x) to account for NMO stretch, where t_0 is the two-way zero-offset traveltime and t_x is the two-way traveltime to offset x. The EI synthetic is quite similar to the PR trace, also. This similarity between the EI synthetic and PR trace is illustrated in Fig.6.D.9 by the crossplot of $0.5 \ln[AI]$ and $0.5 \ln[EI(40°)]$ and the crossplot of $0.5 \ln[AI]$ and Poisson's ratio.

The natural logarithm was taken of AI and EI in the crossplots so that reflectivities could be measured as they were previously described in Fig. 5.A.4.

An interesting twist in the derivation of EI is to allow the k factor $[(\beta/\alpha)^2]$ in Fig. 6.D.5 to vary at every depth point rather than selecting a constant as suggested by Connolly. If k is varied, then $0.5 \ln[EI(45°)]$ closely resembles Poisson's ratio, and with a scale adjustment, they crossplot on a 45° line. The similarity of these two curves is depicted in Fig. 6.D.10.

Figures

Figure 6.A.1

Zoeppritz Linear Approximations
Angle Dependence

Shuey: (Rearranged)

$$RC(\theta) \approx \frac{1}{2}\left(\frac{\Delta\alpha}{\alpha} + \frac{\Delta\rho}{\rho}\right)\left(1 - \frac{4\beta^2}{\alpha^2}\sin^2\theta\right) + \frac{\Delta\sigma\sin^2\theta}{(1-\sigma)^2} + \frac{1}{2}\frac{\Delta\alpha}{\alpha}\left(\tan^2\theta - \frac{4\beta^2}{\alpha^2}\sin^2\theta\right)$$

Smith et al.

$$RC(\theta) \approx \frac{1}{2}\left(\frac{\Delta\alpha}{\alpha} + \frac{\Delta\rho}{\rho}\right)\frac{1}{\cos^2\theta} - \frac{4\beta^2}{\alpha^2}\left(\frac{\Delta\beta}{\beta} + \frac{\Delta\rho}{\rho}\right)\sin^2\theta - \frac{1}{2}\frac{\Delta\rho}{\rho}\left(\tan^2\theta - \frac{4\beta^2}{\alpha^2}\sin^2\theta\right)$$

Conventional:

$$RC(\theta) \approx \frac{1}{2}\left(\frac{\Delta\alpha}{\alpha} + \frac{\Delta\rho}{\rho}\right) + \left[\frac{1}{2}\frac{\Delta\alpha}{\alpha} - 2\left(\frac{\beta}{\alpha}\right)^2\left(\frac{2\Delta\beta}{\beta} + \frac{\Delta\rho}{\rho}\right)\right]\sin^2\theta + \frac{1}{2}\frac{\Delta\alpha}{\alpha}\left(\sin^2\theta\tan^2\theta\right)$$

Figure 6.A.2

Zoeppritz Linear Approximations
Angle Dependence

$$RC(\theta) \approx NI_P\cos^2\theta^* + B_1\sin^2\theta + \text{H.O. (P-wave)} \quad \text{[Shuey]}$$

$$RC(\theta) \approx NI_P \qquad\quad + B_2\sin^2\theta + \text{H.O. (P-wave)} \quad \text{[Conventional]}$$

$$RC(\theta) \approx NI_P/\cos^2\theta + B_3\sin^2\theta + \text{H.O. (density)} \quad \text{[Smith]}$$

- NI_P = Normal-incident reflection coefficient (P-wave)
- Bs $\Rightarrow$ f(P-wave, S-wave and density)
- H.O. $\Rightarrow$ Higher-order terms

* **Assumption background $\alpha/\beta = 2$ already made**

Figure 6.A.3

Relationship Between Linear Approximations

- Assume $\alpha = 2\beta$
- Drop higher-order terms

$$RC(\theta) \approx NI_P\cos^2\theta + 2(NI_P - NI_S)\sin^2\theta \quad \text{[Shuey]}$$

$$RC(\theta) \approx NI_P \qquad\quad + (NI_P - 2NI_S)\sin^2\theta \quad \text{[Conventional]}$$

$$RC(\theta) \approx NI_P/\cos^2\theta - \qquad 2NI_S\sin^2\theta \quad \text{[Smith]}$$

$$NI_P = \frac{(\rho\alpha)_2 - (\rho\alpha)_1}{(\rho\alpha)_2 + (\rho\alpha)_1}$$

$$NI_S = \frac{(\rho\beta)_2 - (\rho\beta)_1}{(\rho\beta)_2 + (\rho\beta)_1}$$

Figure 6.A.4

Pore-Fluid Discrimination of Reflectivities

$$\Delta\alpha_{GW} \equiv 1/2\left[(\Delta\alpha/\alpha)_{GAS} - (\Delta\alpha/\alpha)_{WET}\right] < 0$$
$$\Delta\rho_{GW} \equiv 1/2\left[(\Delta\rho/\rho)_{GAS} - (\Delta\rho/\rho)_{WET}\right] < 0$$

Ranking

1	Normal Incident	$[NI_{GAS} - NI_{WET}]$	$= [\Delta\alpha_{GW} + \Delta\rho_{GW}]$
2	Shuey	$[B_{1,GAS} - B_{1,WET}]$	$= [2\Delta\alpha_{GW}]$
3	Conventional	$[B_{2,GAS} - B_{2,WET}]$	$= [\Delta\alpha_{GW} - \Delta\rho_{GW}]$
4	Smith ...	$[B_{3,GAS} - B_{3,WET}]$	$= [-2\Delta\rho_{GW}]$

Slope reflectivities have no additional information about pore-fluid content than normal-incident reflectivities.

Figure 6.A.5

Smith & Gidlow's Fluid-Factor

Step 1. **Generate NI_P and NI_S sections**

Step 2. **Over non-hydrocarbon background window, estimate**
$$\gamma = (NI_P/NI_S)_{WET}$$

Step 3. **Estimate fluid factor at each time sample**
$$\Delta F(t) = NI_P(t) - \gamma\, NI_S(t)$$

Step 4. **Analyze**
For non-hydrocarbon zones $\Delta F \Rightarrow 0$
For hydrocarbon zones $\Delta F \approx NI_{P,GAS} - NI_{P,WET}$

With valid assumptions, the fluid factor theoretically provides maximum discrimination of pore-fluid content from reflectivity traces.

Figure 6.A.6

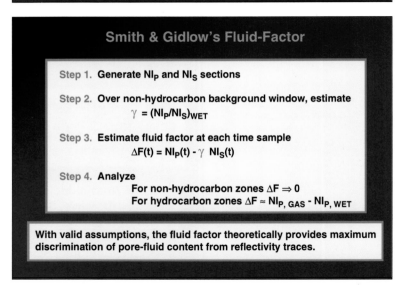

Goodway et al. $\lambda\rho$ and $\mu\rho$
$$\lambda\rho = (\alpha\rho)^2 - 2(\beta\rho)^2$$

Gassmann: $(\alpha\rho)^2 = \rho(K_{dry} + 4/3\mu_{dry} + K_{pore\text{-}fluid\ effect})$
$(\rho\beta)^2 = \rho(\mu_{dry})$

FD $\equiv$ **Fluid Discriminant** = $K_{pore\text{-}fluid\ effect}$
FD $= (\alpha\rho)^2 - G(\beta\rho)^2$
FD $= \rho(K_{dry} + 4/3\mu_{dry} + K_{pore\text{-}fluid\ effect} - G\mu_{dry})$

$$G \equiv (K_{dry}/\mu_{dry}) + 4/3$$

if $\sigma_{dry} = .125$, $K_{dry} = \mu_{dry}$, G = 2.33
for $\lambda\rho$, G = 2.0, $K_{dry}/\mu_{dry} = 2/3 \Rightarrow \sigma_{dry} = 0$

$\lambda\rho = (\alpha\rho)^2 - 2(\beta\rho)^2 \approx$ **Gassmann's fluid discriminant**

Figure 6.A.7

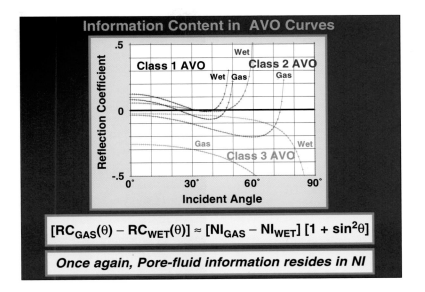

Figure 6.A.8

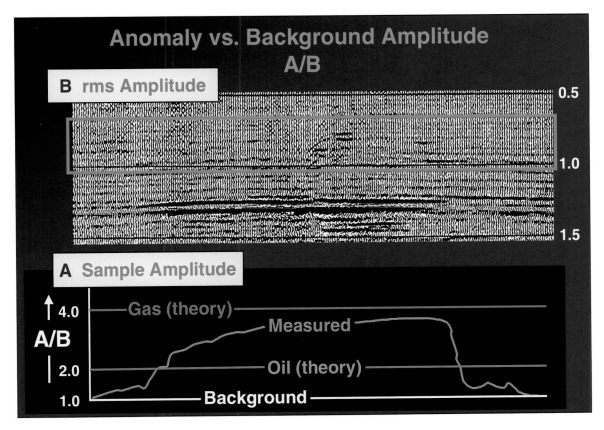

Figure 6.A.9

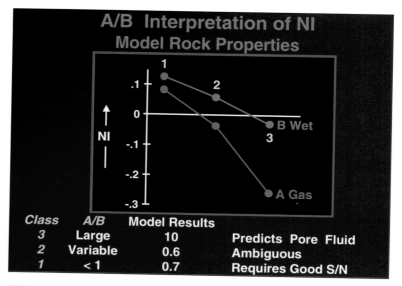

Figure 6.A.10

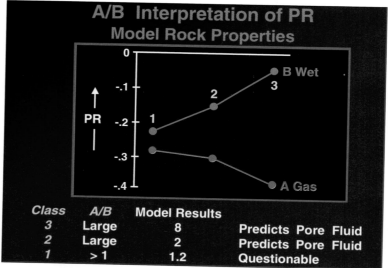

Figure 6.A.11

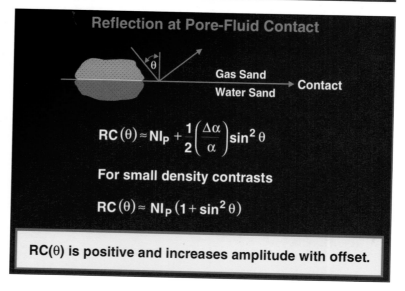

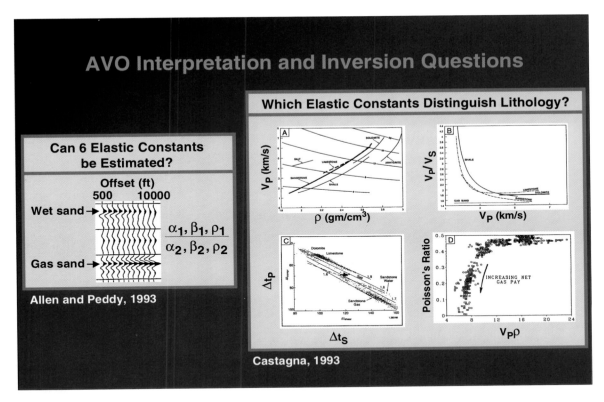

Figure 6.B.1

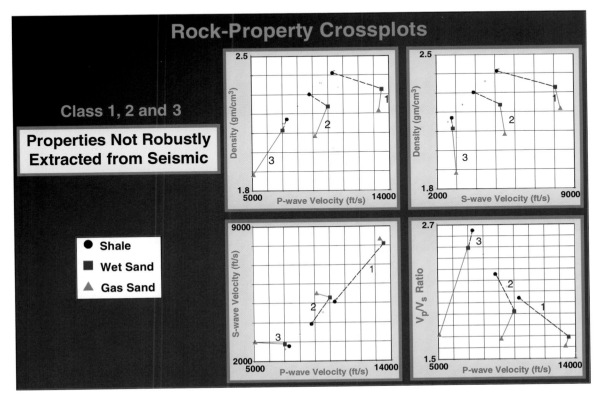

Figure 6.B.2

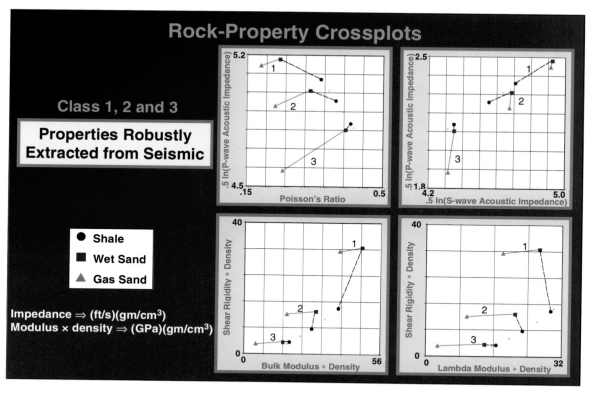

Figure 6.B.3

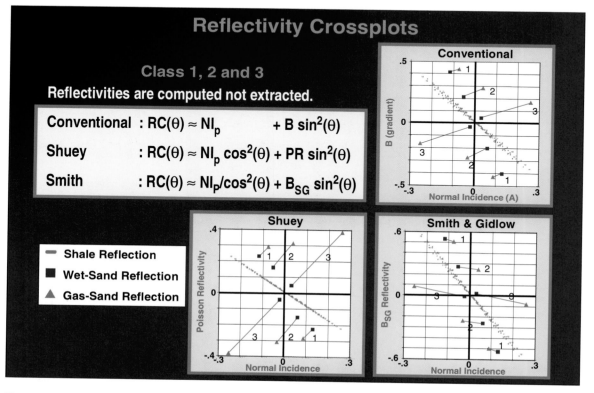

Figure 6.B.4

Figure 6.B.5

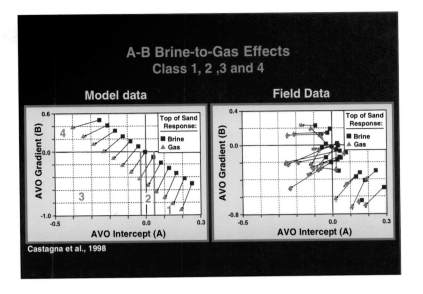

Figure 6.C.1

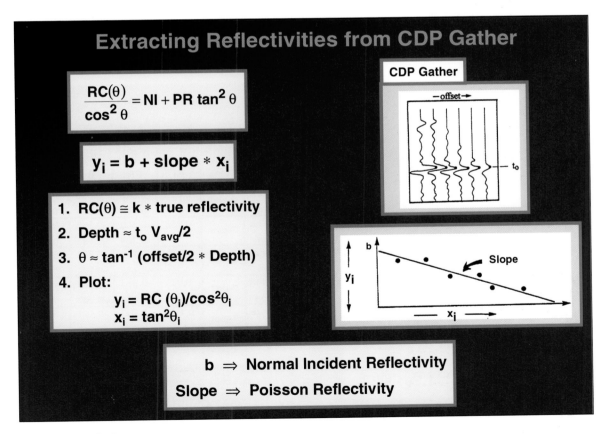

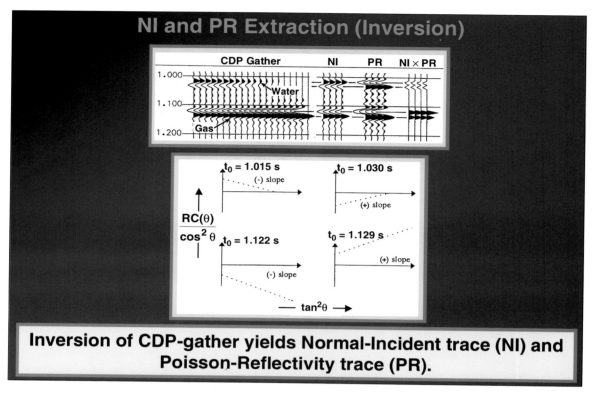

Figure 6.C.2

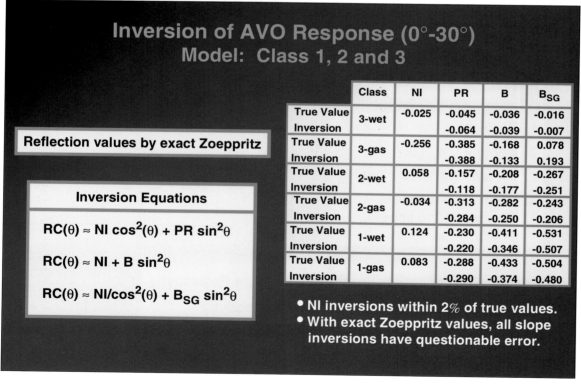

Figure 6.C.3

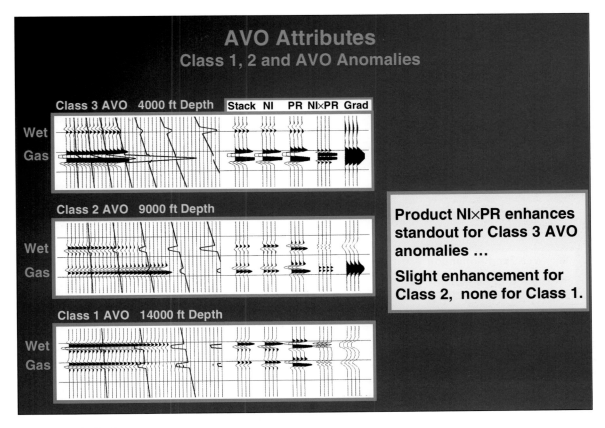

Figure 6.C.4

Figure 6.C.5

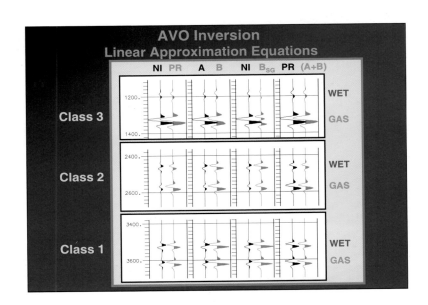

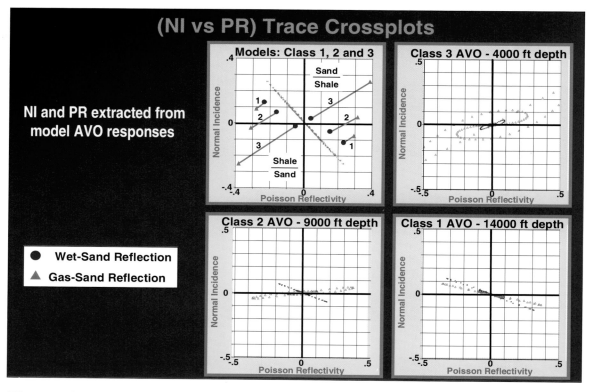

Figure 6.C.6

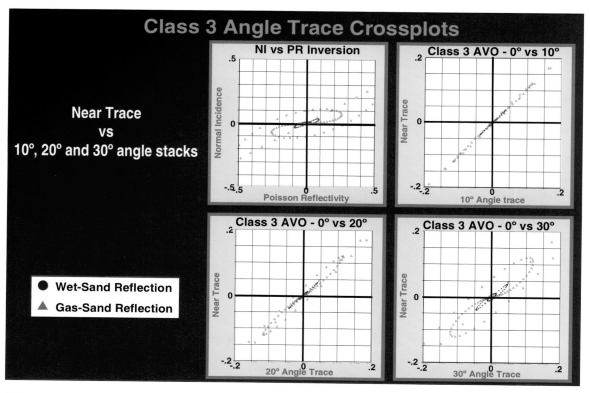

Figure 6.C.7

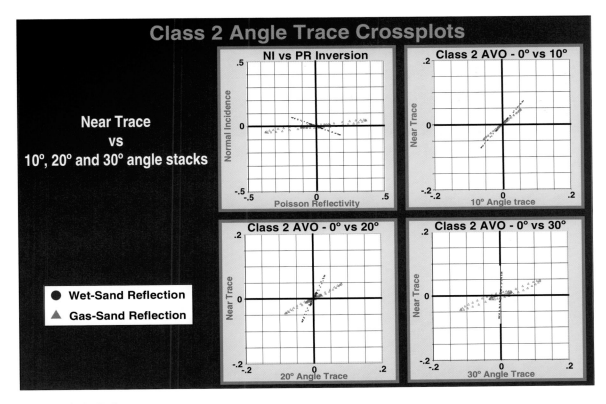

Figure 6.C.8

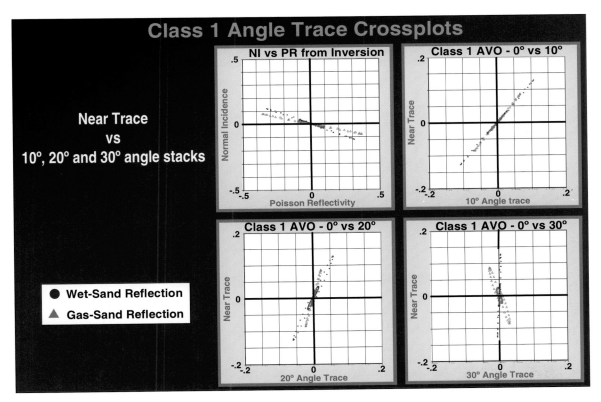

Figure 6.C.9

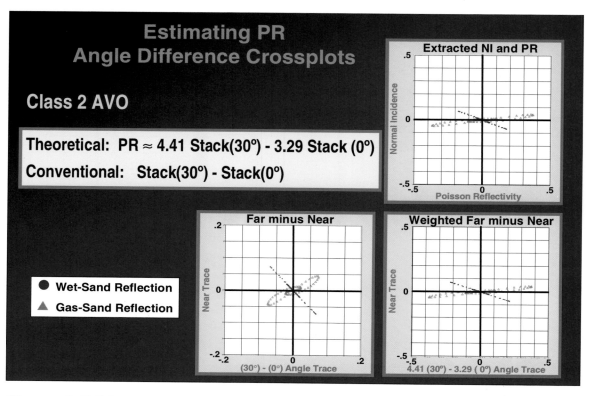

Figure 6.C.10

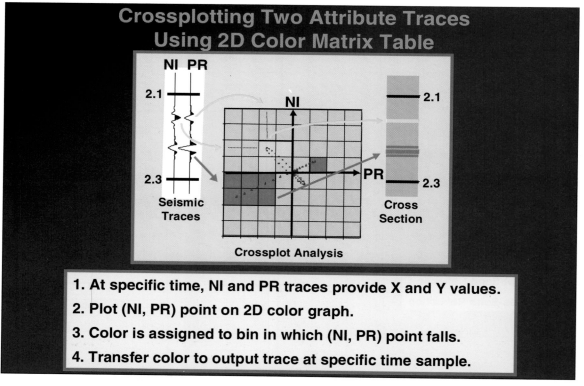

Figure 6.C.11

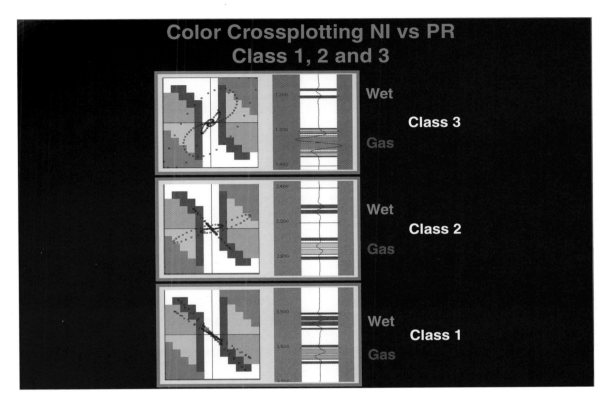

Figure 6.C.12

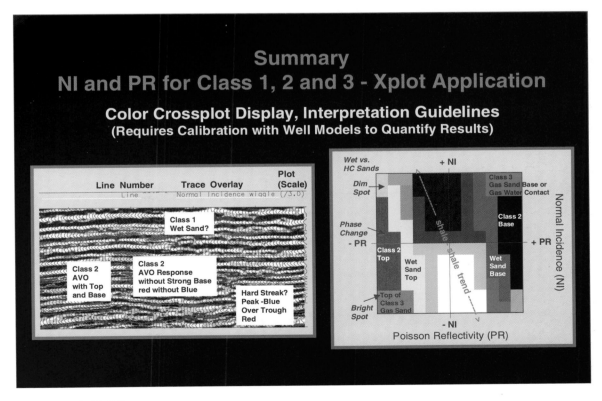

Figure 6.C.13

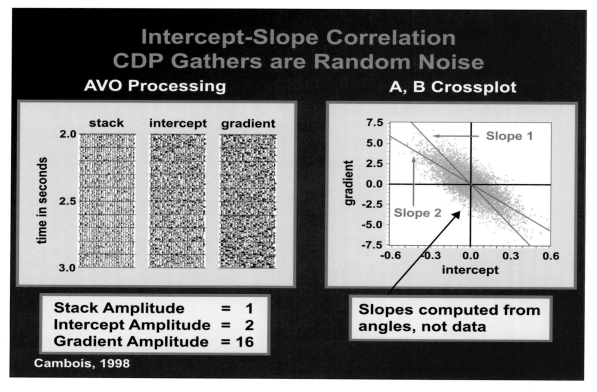

Figure 6.D.1

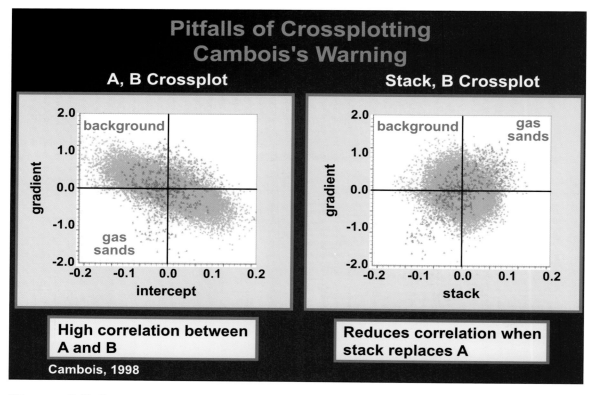

Figure 6.D.2

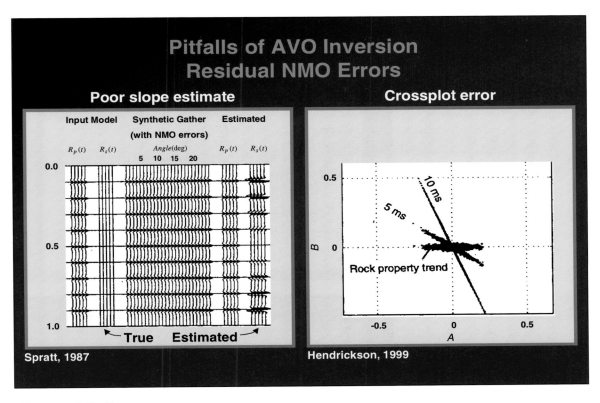

Figure 6.D.3

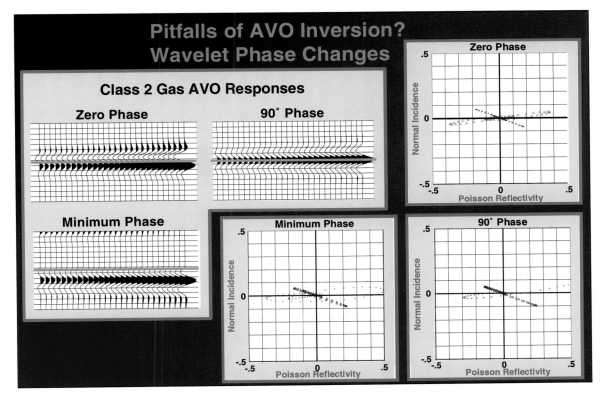

Figure 6.D.4

Figure 6.D.5

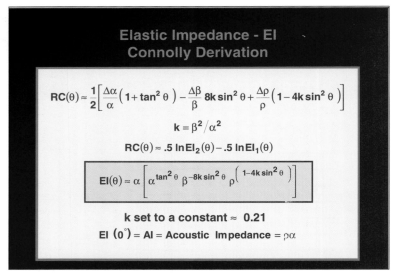

Figure 6.D.6

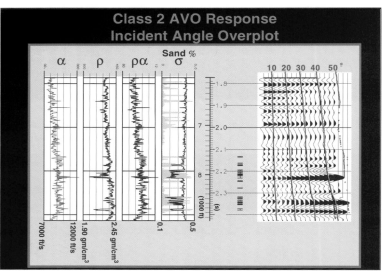

Figure 6.D.7

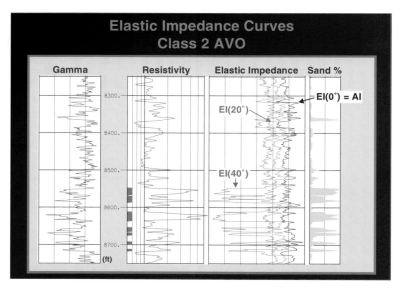

Figure 6.D.8

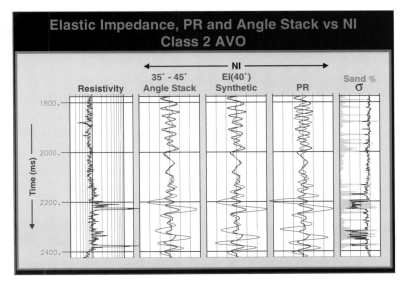

Figure 6.D.9

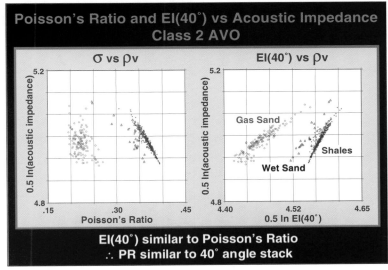

Figure 6.D.10

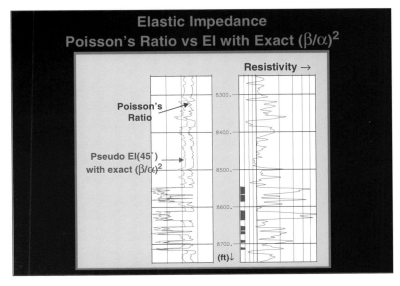

Section 7. Case Histories

Objective:

1. Illustrate Class 1, 2, and 3 AVO case histories

2. Evaluate various amplitude attributes for solving exploration problems

3. Extend interpretation with new amplitude attributes

7A. Class 3—Lithologic Identification

At Big Sky, Montana, in 1992, the SEG/EAEG Joint Research Committee held the summer workshop, "How useful is amplitude-versus-offset (AVO) analysis?" From the worldwide exploration examples shown during this six-day conference, the answer could clearly be stated that AVO was an integral part of recognizing and high-grading prospects and well locations.

During the Big Sky Conference, Revoir et al. (1992) and Russell et al. (1992) presented evaluations of AVO through seismic processing, modeling, and inversion utilizing the same data set from a Pliocene-trend gas field in the Gulf of Mexico. The field is located offshore in a fault basin bounded by major growth faults, and is near several salt and shale diapirs. The structure is broken up into several reservoirs by small (50–150-ft) (15–50-m) faults (Fig. 7.A.1). A 2-D amplitude analysis was performed from a 3-D seismic data sail line. A directional well that was parallel to the 2-D line provided borehole control.

The expanded sedimentary section consists of regressive sequences of deep marine deposits (including slope fans) overlain by shallower deltaic deposits (shelf, delta front and lower delta-plain deposits). The major productive sands are between 5000 and 12,000 ft (1500 and 3700 m) in depth and range in thickness from 20 to 180 ft (6 to 50 m) (Fig. 7.A.2). The high amplitudes in the figure characterize the major sand pays. In addition, flat spots and phase reversals were dominant HCI's for recognizing the gas/water contacts. Overall, the amplitude anomalies from the three productive sands showed excellent fit to structure.

With the amplitude matching the structure map and fluid contacts present on the seismic data, what else is needed for the prospect evaluation? One of the objectives was to determine if the quality of the reservoir sands could be predicted from AVO analysis. Although this objective might not have been totally resolved, an interesting sidelight did appear. After evaluating numerous wells in the area, it was noticed that the products of NI (normal-incident reflectivity) and PR (Poisson reflectivity) from AVO modeling were highly correlated to lithology. In Fig. 7.A.3, intervals that contain alternating thin layers of sand and shale are identified as "ratty" sands and the $NI \times PR$ response is slightly negative. These amplitude values were assigned a blue color. Shale intervals have near-zero $NI \times PR$ values (green). The top and base of thick blocky clean-sand intervals have large $NI \times PR$ values (yellow). Because the environment is predominantly Class 3 (bright spot), gas intervals are expected to have very large $NI \times PR$ values (red). This correlation from the synthetic AVO models was tested with the $NI \times PR$ extracted from the 2-D seismic line. In Fig. 7.A.4, the gamma log from the directional well is plotted on the $NI \times PR$ section for verification that $NI \times PR$ is a lithologic identifier in this area. There is excellent correlation. However, caution should be exercised because $NI \times PR$ is not a universal lithologic attribute.

7B. Class 3—Ursa: Gulf of Mexico Deep-Water Field

Ursa is typical of many deep-water plays in the Gulf of Mexico where young lowstand reservoirs of Pliocene–Miocene age are situated in structural and/or stratigraphic traps. These traps are often stacked pinchout reservoirs against salt-bounded mini-basin flanks. Fig. 7.B.1 illustrates a 2-D line across the Ursa field in Mississippi Canyon Block 809. The water depth is approximately 4000 ft. Hydrocarbons occur around the 12,000-ft (3700-m) depth and from the 17,000- to 20,000-ft (5200- to 6000-m) depth.

The 2-D data were acquired with a 6000-m (20,000-ft) marine streamer. Even though the reservoirs, as imaged by this 2-D line, are not beneath the salt, one can immediately observe that an AVO imaging problem is still present. With a streamer length that is almost the same length as the section shown in the figure, the reflections from the deeper reservoirs will have contamination from the salt mass on the far-offset traces. This geometric influence must be reconciled when an amplitude interpretation is considered.

There are also potential near-surface transmission problems. Channel margin slumping is observed around 2 s in Fig. 7.B.1. Slumping can adversely affect both the transmitted amplitude and event timing of deeper reflections. In fact, reflections from shallow distortion zones often are not recognized. Hatchell (2000) presented an excellent analysis of this transmission phenomenon for the Mars field, which is located two blocks west of the Ursa field. Fig. 7.B.2 (from Hatchell) illustrates amplitude and timing distortions within migrated CDP gathers across the Mars field. The red line in the figure tracks a low-amplitude anomaly across the CDP gathers. Amplitude variations as large as 25% are present. The timing and amplitude variations within the CDP gathers were verified to have originated from shallow slumping.

While the misalignment of the events can be addressed with processing, attempts to correct the amplitude variations with depth migration often result in two amplitude anomalies: the original anomaly and the one introduced by "true-amplitude" depth migration. When shallow distortion zones exist, It is not surprising that horizon amplitude maps from the near-, mid-, and far- angle volumes are often quite different and do not perfectly correlate to the structure map.

Well Tie

One of the first tasks when conducting an amplitude analysis in an area that has well control is to develop rock-property trends for the expected lithologies. Besides the obvious application of tying the seismic reflection amplitude to predictions from borehole measurements, trend curves are useful for quality control and editing well-log curves. Figure 7.B.3 contains trend curves from wells in the Ursa field. Only the wet sand and shale properties were extracted from the well-log curves. Also, depth intervals of questionable logging quality were omitted.

In hydrocarbon zones, invasion problems often prohibit the logging tools from recording the same rock-property values that surface seismic methods "see." Thus, logged values from the sonic and density tool in hydrocarbon zones are not included in trend curves. Velocity and density values are derived by fluid-substitution for sands saturated with dead oil, live oil, gas, and fizz.

In Fig. 7.B.3, note that the velocity in fizz sand is less than that in live-oil sand, but the density of fizz sand is greater. This relationship will be important when the acoustic-impedance curves are examined for predicting pore-fluid content.

There are two high-amplitude events observed at 4.0 s (approximately 12,400 ft [3800 m]) on the seismic section (Fig. 7.B.1). However, when the original well-log curves were examined (Fig. 7.B.4), only one hydrocarbon zone was recognized initially. The oil zone at 12,470 ft has a high resistivity value, indicating the presence of hydrocarbons. The upper zone labeled as fizz is a sand interval that has a slightly raised resistivity value that is too high for a water-saturated sand in this depth interval. The original sonic values in this interval didn't indicate the presence of hydrocarbons. This zone was interpreted to be fizz-charged, and the sonic curve was interpreted to have invasion problems. Thus, sonic corrections based on the trend curves from Fig. 7.B.3 were applied.

As mentioned earlier, the seismic data were 2-D, and an exact synthetic match is not expected for several reasons. First, the seismic line does not exactly traverse the well location. Even if it did, the 3-D effect of the structure would not be truly represented by the migrated 2-D data. Second, the amplitude of the reflections will not be truly reconstructed with a 2-D migration over a 3-D structure. Furthermore, to get an exact match one must assume that the well and the seismic waves traversed the same identical path into the earth, which is often not the case. In an effort to correct for these differences, the well-log curves were stretched and squeezed slightly. However, this was accomplished by altering the depth-sampling interval so that the interval velocities were not distorted.

After the sonic corrections in the fizz sand and the slight alteration of the depth intervals were made, obvious washout zones between the shallow and deep hydrocarbon zones were edited. No additional editing of the well-log curves in the hydrocarbon zones was performed. With this editing, the 1-D synthetic tie as shown in Fig. 7.B.5 was obtained. In general, the synthetic tie is good given the problems mentioned above.

With the color bar selected for amplitude, all the hydrocarbon zones in Fig. 7.B.5 appear as bright spots with trough-peak signatures. There are a couple of nonhydrocarbon events that have amplitudes approaching those of the hydrocarbon zones. These are associated with clean sands, but their amplitudes are less than those from the hydrocarbon intervals with the exception of the deepest pay zone.

With a good 1-D tie, a synthetic AVO response was generated (Fig. 7.B.6). The amplitude responses of the hydrocarbon events are essentially constant with offset, thus confirming that this is basically a bright spot, or Class 3, environment. The distortion effects caused by salt are evident on the field CDP gather below 5 s. Besides these distortions, the large amplitude of the hydrocarbon zones correlates from the synthetic to the field gather.

As a means of checking for anomalous lithologies that might be influencing the high-amplitude hydrocarbon signatures, all hydrocarbon zones were replaced with brine and an AVO synthetic was generated (Fig. 7.B.7). The water-saturated AVO synthetic has small amplitudes associated with the previously hydrocarbon-charged zones. This confirms that no anomalous lithologies are influencing the hydrocarbon signatures, and the large amplitudes are directly related to pore-fluid effects.

Amplitude Analyses

In all amplitude interpretations, we wish to compare the amplitudes predicted from borehole measurements with those observed on field seismic. If there is no correlation between the predicted and observed amplitudes, the interpreter is forced to reconcile these differences. Fig. 7.B.8 contains 0.5 ln(acoustic impedance) curves for the various lithologies and pore-fluid states anticipated in this area. These trend curves were generated from the velocity and density profiles shown in Fig. 7.B.3. Besides wet sand and shale, sands with four different hydrocarbon saturants were considered. An interesting feature is that the predicted acoustic impedance curves for sands with fizz gas and live oil are essentially the same beneath 9000 ft (3000 m), where 9000-ft depth is 5000 ft (1500 m) beneath the mud line. An enlargement of the zone that includes the shallower hydrocarbons is shown on the right.

When analyzing normal-incident amplitude trends, there are two methods of displaying borehole data. One is with normal-incident reflectivities, and the other is with acoustic impedance (*AI*) curves. With ln(*AI*) curves, the distance between curves is directly proportional to the normal-incident reflection coefficient (*NI*). In the bottom of the figure, normal-incident reflectivities associated with shale over three different pore-fluid states of sand are drawn. The distance on the ln(*AI*) plot between shale and wet-sand responses represents the background (*B*) amplitude. The distance between shale and hydrocarbon-saturated sand represents the anomaly (*A*) amplitude. As an example, the distance *B* (shale over wet sand reflection) is compared with the distance *A* (shale over live-oil sand reflection) to come up with the *A/B* ratio 3.5.

This quick analysis indicates that reflections off the top of thick live-oil sands will be 3.5 times the magnitude of reflections off the top of thick wet sands. The same *A/B* ratio exists for shale over fizz sand. For beds less than the thin-bed thickness, additional factors will be considered.

An offset amplitude map of the shallow fizz sand is shown in Fig. 7.B.9. The peak event of the fizz sand was snapped from the stack section, and these times were used as guides in the CDP gathers. Once in the CDP gather domain, the time picks were realigned to compensate for slight NMO and near-surface distortions. The CDP amplitude map has fairly consistent, high amplitudes across all offsets for the anomaly toward the left. Toward the right side, a small amplitude anomaly is indicated. This was one of the more consistent amplitude maps generated from the hydrocarbon zones. This result is expected in light of the noise and subsequent amplitude variations on the deeper hydrocarbon zones (Fig. 7.B.6).

A more quantitative analysis of amplitude is to compare the *A/B* measurements from the field data to those derived from well control. Fig. 7.B.10 illustrates *A/B* measurements for the two shallow-hydrocarbon events. The background amplitude (*B*) was generated from a trace-by-trace rms window of 500 ms situated above the fizz sand.

Anomaly amplitudes (*A*) were measured for the peak event of the fizz sand and the peak event of the oil sand. The two anomaly amplitude events were normalized on a trace-by-trace basis with the background amplitudes from the rms window. For illustrative purposes, a very subjective value of 8 was selected to represent the *A/B* for the fizz sand, and 4.5 for the oil sand. These two *A/B* ratios of 8 and 4.5 have a ratio themselves of 8/4.5, or 1.77.

As mentioned, *A/B* ratios are also dependent on the thickness of the beds. The dominant wavelength for the signal is approximately 250 ft (75 m). A bed that has $1/8^{th}$ the dominant wavelength is considered a thin bed. Both the fizz sand with a thickness of 37 ft, and the oil sand with 19 ft, can be considered thin beds. That means that seismic amplitude should be proportional to thickness. The fizz sand and oil sand have approximately the same interval velocity, so that adjustments for interval velocity do not have to be considered when their *A/B* ratios are compared. If two thin beds have the same velocity and density values, then their *A/B* ratios are related to their thickness ratio. The fizz sand is 1.95 times thicker than the oil sand, and this value is close to the *A/B* ratio of 1.77 that was derived above.

The individual *A/B* ratios observed for the fizz sand (8) and live-oil sand (4.5) from the field data are larger than those predicted from the well-log acoustic impedance trends (3.5) in Fig. 7.B.8. One explanation for this discrepancy is that the 500-ms background window contains significantly more shale than wet-sand intervals, and thus *rms* averaging lowers the background value for a wet-sand reflection. The number of wet-sand intervals and the thickness of these intervals are major factors for consideration when rms windows are used to determine *A/B*.

Another factor to consider when measuring background amplitudes is the variation of acoustic impedance within the shale beds. Hilterman (1990) noted large variations for shales deposited on slope environments. There were 25% variations of shale acoustic impedances within 200-ft (60-m) intervals. These large variations, if not accounted for, can drastically alter a pore-fluid or thickness prediction based on *A/B*.

One method used to visualize the effect of shale variations and predict the resulting amplitudes is to use trend analyses that indicate standard deviations. This can be accomplished with a histogram trend analysis, as displayed in Fig. 7.B.11. To generate this plot, well-log acoustic impedance and volumetric curves are converted to time. Histograms are generated at 20-ms intervals, based on lithology and pore fluid. The histogram frequency values for each component are then contoured. In Fig. 7.B.11, the black curves represent shale; red, hydrocarbon intervals; blue, wet sands; and, light blue, hydrocarbon sands that have been fluid substituted with brine. A 20-ms interval is selected because this represents a reflection package for the dominant wavelet.

Once again, by plotting .5 ln (acoustic impedance), reflection amplitudes between the various lithologies can be measured from the graph and *A/B* ratios computed. Likewise, reflection amplitudes from shale variations can be predicted. Large shale variations are not unusual, especially when a shale member is associated with a condensed section. The AVO synthetic in Fig. 7.B.12 was generated from a deep-water well, and it illustrates the signature from a large variation in shale properties. The well-log curves are plotted similarly to what was displayed in Fig. 3.D.10 in order to convey the AVO contributions for the near, mid, and far angles. The highlighted areas are two shales with a large velocity contrast. At the interface between the two shales, the acoustic impedance contrast gives rise to a positive reflection for the near traces. Because both lithologies are shale, the Poisson's ratio decreases as velocity increases, and thus the middle angles have a negative contribution at the interface. The large velocity contrast produces a positive contribution on the far angles. The total response starts out strong on the near traces, decreases amplitude on the mid traces, and increases on the far traces. This AVO response in the deep-water area is normally associated with non-hydrocarbon zones. This is an important observation for the interpreter and can be a pitfall for the uninitiated, especially if far-angle stacks are compared with near-angle stacks and mid-angle stacks are ignored.

7C. Class 2—Axis Rotation and Crossplotting

The amplitude analysis of bright spots (Class 3 anomalies) can lead to the successful prediction of lithology, pore-fluid content, and in some instances, reservoir thickness. Amplitude interpretation of phase reversals (Class 2 anomalies), on the other hand, is difficult or impossible using only conventional stack data. In this section, two interpretation tools will be introduced and applied to model and field data. Verm and Hilterman (1995) published the majority of the following material.

Stratigraphic Model

Figure 7.C.1 shows stack sections for a Class 2 AVO model. The upper section depicts the wet-sand response; the lower section, the gas response. Amplitudes for the shale/wet sand boundary are smaller than the amplitudes associated with shale/shale boundaries in this model. In the bottom portion of the figure, the corresponding gas response is even weaker than the wet-sand response. In fact, the reflection event disappears. This prospect would be difficult to promote with the lithologic rejoinder, "Drill when the reflection disappears!"

The red middle trace in Fig. 7.C.1 is at the well location for the model. AVO responses for both the wet sand and gas sand were generated for this location (Fig. 7.C.2). The AVO responses are only slightly better than the stack sections in Fig. 7.C.1 for lithology and pore-fluid identification. In the water-wet case, there is a positive *NI* response that decays quickly with offset. When the sand contains gas, the event amplitude decreases with offset much faster than the wet case event. More importantly, at the 8500-ft (2600-m) offset (where offset equals depth in this model), the reflection amplitude has completely changed polarity. If the CDP gathers were muted at this offset or if the acquisition was offset limited, would the gas-sand response be recognized? In short, both the stack section and the CDP gathers show subtle responses for differentiating the wet sand from the gas sand. So let's examine the reflection clusters on the *NI* versus *PR* crossplot for the CDP gather located at the red trace in the lower section of Fig. 7.C.1.

In Fig. 7.C.3, the crossplot of the extracted *NI* and *PR* reflectivity traces illustrates the following features:

- shale/shale reflections (green) cluster along a −45° line running from the upper left to the lower right,

- shale/wet-sand and wet-sand/shale reflections cluster along the shale line, but just on the outside (yellow), and
- shale/gas-sand and gas-sand/shale reflections lie near the *PR* axis (red). The large red dots are individual points associated with the gas-sand response.

There is a large overlap of lithology and pore-fluid clusters with respect to the *NI* axis. Therefore, it is not surprising that the amplitude of the *NI* section (Fig. 7.C.4) does not discriminate different lithologies or pore-fluid content. (The color background in Fig. 7.C.4 represents the actual model lithology). In fact, as shown in Fig. 7.C.5, amplitude in the AVO product section ($NI \times PR$) does not discriminate lithologies or pore-fluid content either.

Obviously, additional AVO attributes are needed. Let's examine the color crossplot display of (*NI, PR*) where the *NI* traces are overplotted (Fig. 7.C.6). For ease in identifying sands, a sand-percentage curve for the model is superimposed on the display, with the gas sand shaded purple.

Notice the strong correlation of the color background in Fig.7.C.6 to the color backgrounds in Figs. 7.C.4 and 7.C.5. There is one main difference—the color background in Fig. 7.C.6 came from the seismic data themselves! By using the color matrix table (the lower left side of Fig. 7.C.6), the (*NI, PR*) crossplot yields an excellent estimate of the actual lithology and pore fluid. Also, this color matrix table is similar to the well-log crossplot of *NI* and *PR* lithologies shown in Fig. 7.C.3. This demonstrates the calibration of rock properties to seismic data for the generation of a seismic lithologic section.

One salient feature about Fig. 7.C.6 is that the trace values are reflectivities and not impedances; therefore, the (*NI, PR*) crossplot colors essentially correspond to the boundaries of lithologic and pore-fluid changes.

An AVO option that is still desirable is the ability for a trace to represent lithology or pore-fluid content by a range of numeric values rather than a color. With numeric coding, events in 3-D volumes could be automatically searched for lithologic and pore-fluid variations. To accomplish this, the cluster behavior of a Class 2 AVO reflector in a sand/shale sequence is examined.

Typical Class 2 (*NI, PR*) values for different lithologic and pore-fluid boundaries have been plotted in the left of Fig. 7.C.7. The shale/gas-sand and the shale/wet-sand clusters occupy almost the same range of *NI,* and these values are relatively small. The contours of the product $NI \times PR$ are overlain on the clusters. In the left crossplot, notice how the contour nearest the *NI* and *PR* axes cuts through all three lithology clusters. Obviously, the values from $NI \times PR$ cannot distinguish the different clusters as they did for the previous Class 3 anomalies. The inability of some AVO product sections to discriminate Class 1 and Class 2 sands has been previously pointed out by Castagna and Smith (1994).

However, there is a slight separation of the clusters along the *PR* axis, so in principle the lithologies should be separable. An easy way to accomplish our goal is to apply a transform to the *NI* and *PR* reflectivity traces, which essentially rotates them 45°, as shown in the right diagram of Fig. 7.C.7. The relative positions of the clusters have not changed. However, when the rotated $NI \times PR$ contours are examined, each lithology gets a unique value. In fact, with the rotation, gas sands should appear as large-amplitude peaks on an $NI \times PR$ section. Essentially, the rotated NI and PR reflectivities now have Class 3 AVO attributes. For this special case, when the rotation is 45°, the rotated product is equivalent to the nonrotated expression of $(PR^2 - NI^2)/2$.

The original NI and PR traces used in Fig. 7.C.5 were rotated by −45°, and the new product traces yield a bright-spot anomaly (Fig. 7.C.8). The actual lithology of the model is color-coded in the background to show the correspondence of high amplitudes to gas sands, middle amplitudes to wet sands, and low amplitudes to shales.

Gulf of Mexico Field Data

With an understanding of the behavior of Class 2 AVO attributes from model data, let's look at some field data. These data are Miocene rocks from the offshore Gulf of Mexico (GOM). Hydrocarbon production in this area is known to exhibit Class 2 AVO anomalies.

Figure 7.C.9 is a migrated section that traverses a discovery well with 110 ft (30 m) of gas sand. The gas zone has high-velocity and low-density properties with respect to the encasing shale formation. Thus, the NI reflectivity is close to zero. The CDP gather at the well location does not show any appreciable amplitude on the near or far-offset traces (Fig. 7.C.10). Thus, visually comparing the near-angle stack with the far-angle stack can be misleading. Likewise, the migrated section (Fig. 7.C.9) has no significant reflection amplitude that is associated with the gas sand at 3.25 s.

Initially, the NI and PR reflectivities were extracted and a product term was produced, as shown in Fig. 7.C.11. The high and low amplitudes for the product term are represented by red and yellow colors. No red or yellow events cross the borehole in Fig. 7.C.11, thus illustrating once again that $NI \times PR$ products are not always reliable hydrocarbon indicators (particularly for Class 2 AVO reflectors).

Now, if an (NI, PR) color crossplot is generated using a color matrix table for Class 2 AVO anomalies, the gas zone pops out as a bright red event, as shown in Fig. 7.C.12. In the color matrix table, the gray diagonal identifies the shale zones, yellow represents water-wet sands, and of course, red is for the gas zones. The dark green events represent shale-over-shale reflections that have a significant acoustic-impedance contrast. Notice how the lithology on this display is consistent with geologic principles. This area of the gulf is dominated by growth faults, and sand deposits should be expected on the downthrown side of the faults, exactly where several yellow packages are shown in Fig. 7.C.12.

As a final demonstration of converting this Class 2 AVO anomaly into a Class 3 anomaly, the $NI \times PR$ product after a −45° rotation is displayed in Fig. 7.C.13. In this case, the colors were chosen to highlight water-wet sands (yellow), gas-filled sands (red), and high-acoustic-impedance shale/shale boundaries (green). In Fig. 7.C.13, there is a lack of yellow events (identifier of wet sands) in the shallower portion of the well. This interpretation is consistent with the borehole information that showed almost exclusively shale sediments. There is an indication of a gas sand (red event) just beneath the bottom-hole location. However, this color crossplot analysis was performed after the completion of the well.

Comments

For many years, log analysts have crossplotted two borehole attributes for lithologic and pore-fluid discrimination. Only recently have geophysicists utilized this principle by extending the one-reflectivity analysis (*NI*) to a two-reflectivity analysis (*NI* and *PR*, *A* and *B*, etc.). By color-coding the (*NI*, *PR*) matrix, a more effective discriminator of lithologies and pore-fluid content results because the separation of reflection clusters increases. Color was introduced to illustrate this separation, along with axis rotation to discriminate the lithologies with a numeric value.

It is not difficult to see that additional (*NI*, *PR*) transforms or search functions are available for assigning the lithologic clusters a numeric value. These transformations convert the two attributes of a 3-D AVO analysis into a single 3-D volume that can be automatically searched for lithologic or pore-fluid changes using current workstation software.

7D. Class 2—Pore-Fluid Identification Using Anisotropic NMO

The material in this portion supports the concept that a time lag often occurs between theoretical developments and practical applications, similar to the time lag between Koefeld's (1955) theoretical work and Ostrander's (1982, 1984) verification of AVO. In his classic 1986 paper, Thomsen published the weak anisotropic parameters that allowed anisotropic wave propagation to be conveniently related to exploration seismic. This work was expanded upon, and extensive publications continued through a consortium at Colorado School of Mines (CSM). From this CSM effort, the article by Alkhalifah and Tsvankin (1995) contained the anisotropic NMO equation that is employed by most processing centers today. In 1995 Bryan DeVault recognized the significance of the CSM anisotropic work to hydrocarbon signatures that were often observed on very-long offset seismic data. From his observation, the following case history was developed and subsequently published by Hilterman et al. (1998).

Introduction

Throughout the Tertiary basins in the Gulf of Mexico (GOM) are areas where acoustic-impedance values of shales and gas sands are approximately equal, as mentioned in the preceding sections. This means that hydrocarbon zones do not appear as bright spots and are difficult to detect with conventional 3-D seismic data. Furthermore, in some areas, geophysicists have had no success using AVO for predicting where to drill. This normally occurs when the rock properties are not calibrated to the various AVO attributes.

To resolve this dilemma, a 3-D AVO study was conducted utilizing numerous well-log suites, core analyses, and field-production histories. With the inclusion of anisotropic effects, a robust AVO analysis based on a lithologic model was possible. Results from this study are illustrated in Fig. 7.D.1: a conventional 3-D section with the AVO analysis over-plotted in red and yellow. Correlation to the well-log curves and the field production histories indicates that all the red and yellow events are associated with proven hydrocarbon zones.

It is obvious that the reflection amplitudes on the conventional 3-D seismic do not identify lithology or pore-fluid if the red and yellow events are truly hydrocarbon events. However, as the remainder of this case study will show, in some environments, the petrophysical AVO model can be constrained so that reflections from very clean wet sands and gas sands overshadow all other reflections. These dominant lithostratigraphic reflections are related to Poisson's ratio.

Chronostratigraphic and Lithostratigraphic Reflections

Vail and his colleagues at Exxon published the basic principles underlying seismic stratigraphy in AAPG Memoir 26 (Vail et al., 1977). Fig. 7.D.2, one of the most remembered illustrations from their work, displays several sonic logs across a Tertiary basin in South America along with three chronostratigraphic or equal time surfaces numbered 15, 10, and 8. Of importance is that chronostratigraphic surface 8 cuts right through a major sand deposit that overlies an unconformity. The lower portion of Fig. 7.D.2 shows a series of normal-incident synthetic seismograms generated from the sonics. What astounded geophysicists when this synthetic section was first presented was that the reflection events follow the chronostratigraphic surfaces, rather than the upper and lower surfaces of the sand package that would be the lithostratigraphic surfaces. From this example and the many that have been produced since 1977, it was concluded that the normal-incident section and conventional seismic data basically consist of chronostratigraphic reflections. It should be noted that this conclusion results from empirical observations and not a rigid theoretical model.

Shortly afterward, another Exxon geoscientist (Tucker, 1982) warned (in *Pitfalls Revisited*) that "stacking enhances continuity and parallelism of the reflection, ... but over-stacking can destroy the geology. ... Stacking can also distort the stratigraphy ... thus playing havoc with successful stratigraphic mapping." These astute observations were made before the advent of AVO and before the information content of the reflection stack was fully understood. *Is it possible that, because of the long offsets employed in today's seismic, a mixing of two petrophysical properties—acoustic impedance and Poisson's ratio—leads to stratigraphic distortion? Are chronostratigraphic and lithostratigraphic reflections being mixed together?*

Petrophysical Model

As noted before, the relationship of chronostratigraphic and lithostratigraphic events to the reflection amplitude is difficult to envision if the exact Zoeppritz equation is examined. This is why Shuey's linear approximation equation that was later approximated to

$$RC(\theta) \approx NI \cos^2(\theta) + PR \sin^2(\theta) \qquad [29]$$

was introduced.

This equation provides useful insight into the AVO response, and it is often used as the model for approximating *NI* and *PR* from seismic CDP gathers. The main benefit is that the resulting *PR* can be thought of as a signal that reflects from the earth's Poisson's ratio profile. As Vail related *NI* to chronostratigraphy, we ask, "Can it be that *PR* is related to lithostratigraphy, i.e., to sand versus shale?" Verm and Hilterman (1995), in fact, noted how Poisson's ratio curve in a sand-shale sequence closely resembles the SP curve, a primary lithostratigraphic tool of the log analyst. The correlation between SP and Poisson's ratio curves can be explained by examining Castagna's (1993) empirical V_P-to-V_S relationships (Fig. 7.D.3).

An interesting observation from this figure is that sand appears to have a Poisson's ratio that is consistently smaller than shale's Poisson's ratio. This is similar to an SP curve in which the sand value falls beneath the shale baseline. From the diagram, for a Poisson's ratio curve to resemble an SP curve, the *P*-wave velocity of sand and shale should be approximately the same. If shale and sand have the *P*-wave velocities as depicted by points A and B, respectively, in Fig.7.D 3, then the Poisson's ratio for sand is less than for shale. This is similar to an SP relationship. However, as the sand *P*-wave velocity value decreases from point B to C, the Poisson's ratio difference between sand and shale disappears. Thus, for the correlation of the SP and Poisson's ratio to be similar, the sand's *P*-wave velocity must be greater than .84 that of shale's *P*-wave velocity. This condition exists for a majority of the GOM. In short, the Poisson's ratio curve indicates lithology similar to an SP curve, and thus reflection amplitude associated with the Poisson reflectivity, *PR*, will be lithostratigraphic. Also, as the Shuey equation indicates, the conventional seismic stack does indeed mix the lithostratigraphic *PR* with the chronostratigraphic *NI*, especially in a Class 2 environment where *NI* is small.

The *PR* contribution to the reflection amplitude is not significant until larger incident angles are reached. When the source-receiver offset is the same as the depth of investigation, the incident angle is approximately 30° for most Tertiary environments such as the Gulf of Mexico. At this incident angle, the reflection amplitude (according to Shuey's approximation) has a contribution of 75% from chronostratigraphy (*NI*) and 25% from lithostratigraphy (*PR*). However, at 60° incident angles, the situation is opposite, with 25% from *NI* and 75% from *PR*. Thus, if lithologic estimation is the goal, it is desirable to record seismic data at angles approaching 60°.

If reflections at 60° angles are desired, and assuming that the critical angle has not been reached, the petrophysical model described by the modified Shuey's approximation must be reviewed. A higher-order term that can be approximated by $(1/2)(\Delta\alpha/\alpha)(\tan^2\theta - \sin^2\theta)$ was dropped from the modified approximation. This term can't be ignored unless the change in *P*-wave velocity across the interface is small. Thus, the direct evaluation of lithology from the large-offset reflection amplitude is modeled for small velocity variations—which occur for Class 2 AVO anomalies.

Well-Log Data

The study area involved Tertiary rocks that are commonly found in the transition zone of offshore Texas and Louisiana. Fig. 7.D.4 illustrates a typical suite of well-log curves from the area. The SP curve resembles the Poisson's ratio curve shown next to it. Pay zones around the 8000-ft (2400-m) depth are indicated by red rectangles. The acoustic impedance curve that is overplotted on the sand-percentage curve has little character resemblance to the sand percentage, suggesting that acoustic impedance is not a good indicator of lithology in this environment.

In order to calibrate this well to the AVO response, a crossplot of ln(*AI*) versus

Poisson's ratio for the depth around the hydrocarbon zones was generated (Fig. 7.D.5). Also included in the figure are wet-sand points from the fluid substitution of the hydrocarbon zones. While the shale and fluid-replacement wet-sand clusters have a small vertical separation, the shale and gas-sand clusters have no separation. Thus, *NI* will have a small response for shale/wet-sand interfaces, but *NI* will be close to zero for shale/gas-sand interfaces. This is not a very diagnostic HCI condition. However, the horizontal distance (*PR*) for a shale/gas-sand interface is approximately four times larger than the horizontal distance for a shale/wet sand interface. This indicates that *PR*, and not *NI*, will differentiate lithology. The ln[ρV]-versus-σ crossplot provides a quick-look method of quantifying *NI* and *PR* to various lithologic interfaces.

As previously noted by Cambois (1998) and Hendrickson (1995), AVO slope inversions are often contaminated with noise, and angle-stack traces are more robust. In light of this, an elastic impedance (*EI*) curve was generated and crossplotted against the acoustic impedance curve (Fig. 7.D.6). The elastic impedance angle was set to 40°, an angle that is normally not included in the conventional stack. An analysis of this crossplot is very encouraging. For shale/wet-sand interfaces, the amplitude on angle stacks centered on 40° will be zero, while the amplitude for shale/gas-sand interfaces will be large. In short, the large-angle stack will be a good AVO attribute for discriminating pore-fluid content in this area.

Anisotropic Effect

In an effort to stabilize the estimation of *PR* from a CDP gather and to obtain large-angle stacks, offset distances that were greater than depth (incident angles greater than 30°) were desired. In Fig. 7.D.7, a 3-D migrated CDP gather at a well location is shown beside the well's AVO synthetic response. The model was isotropic and NMO-corrected with the well's rms velocity. At 2.25 s (≈ 8000 ft [2400 m]), the model's 14,000-ft (4000-m) offset trace exhibits an NMO overcorrection of 45 ms (caused by the isotropic ray bending). The field data had an overcorrection at the same offset of 125 ms. This additional overcorrection (125 ms − 45 ms) was identified as an anisotropic effect. In essence, the horizontal velocity is faster than the vertical velocity.

In this area, it is believed that the sediments exhibit vertical transverse isotropy. Three-dimensional fields of both velocity and anisotropy are obtained from NMO analyses. With the extraction of the anisotropic parameter η from the 3-D NMO analysis, anisotropic corrections can then be applied not only in NMO but also in DMO and migration. With velocity information from borehole measurements, the other Thomsen anisotropic functions, ε and δ, can be estimated for control in anisotropic modeling.

Figure 7.D.8 presents three CDP gathers with conventional (isotropic) NMO and anisotropic NMO corrections. An interesting effect in the far traces is the reduction of NMO stretch when anisotropy is included in the NMO correction. Often, the NMO overcorrection on the far traces is not observed because the CDP gathers are muted at the line that is equivalent to offset = depth. However, as the modified Shuey equation along with the crossplot indicate, the reflections on the right side of the mute line contain information about lithology and pore-fluid content that needs to be preserved. This lithologic content can be verified by AVO modeling.

Well-log curves along with the anisotropic properties measured from the 3-D seismic were used to generate the AVO anisotropic synthetic shown in the left of Fig. 7.D.9. To the right of the synthetic is the anisotropic-processed CDP gather at the well location. There are two gas zones evident on the SP and resistivity logs. The thickness of the upper gas sand at 2.25 s ($\approx$ 8000-ft depth) is 40 ft (12 m), while the lower sand at 2.39 s is 35 ft (11 m). Offset traces up to 16,000 ft (5000 m) were usable in the CDP gather. Because the anisotropy in this area causes the wavefront to flatten from its isotropic spherical shape, the incident angle at 2.39 s on the maximum offset trace is 50° for anisotropic modeling, while isotropic modeling predicts 60°. This means critical angle reflections occur on traces with farther offsets than conventionally assumed.

Anisotropic AVO synthetics, in place of 1-D synthetics, offer several interpretational benefits. First, the AVO synthetics correlate to the CDP gathers, especially if the thick clean sands and gas sands are matched at the far traces. This is evident by comparing the AVO synthetic with the field CDP gather in Fig. 7.D.9. Also, when the acoustic impedances of the sand and shale are almost equal, small errors due to invasion on the sonic and density logs have significant impact on the 1-D synthetic. Not only can the magnitude of the reflection be several times off, but also the polarity of the reflection can be reversed, thus making it difficult to match the 1-D synthetic to the field data. However, the Poisson's ratio curve is strongly dependent on the more robust estimate of lithology from the gamma and SP logs. Thus on the AVO synthetic, the far-offset traces are more likely to show the correct correlation with the field data than is the 1-D normal-incident synthetic. As an experiment, try tying an SP log displayed in time to the far-offset traces in a CDP gather (far-offset traces $\equiv$ offset > 1.5 depth).

Field Data

The study area was confined to one offshore block (9 mi² [23 km²]). A typical 3-mile line across the block is displayed in the upper portion of Fig. 7.D.10. The conventional 3-D migrated section includes reflections with incident angles from 0° to 35°, while the lower portion is the large-angle stack from 35° to 55°. Two control wells are on this line and two are projected onto the line. The onset of abnormal pore pressure occurs around 2.6 s.

No false indicators or missing indicators of gas zones are present on the lower section. What is interesting is the high that appears between Wells F and D at approximately 2.8 s in the bottom section. Originally, this high was a prospect to be drilled. However, subsequent interpretation of the large-angle stack volume changed this decision. The two events at 2.8 s near Wells F and D are now interpreted to be two separate channels that cut into the flanks of a preexisting topographic high. The crest of this feature does not appear to be sand prone.

The bottom section of Fig. 7.D.10 is a good representation of lithology and pore-fluid content, while the upper portion contains both lithostratigraphic and chrono-stratigraphic reflections. In fact, Fig. 7.D.1 is a combination of the upper portion of Fig. 7.D.10 with the red and yellow events from the bottom portion of Fig. 7.D.10 superimposed.

Figure 7.D.11 contains time slices at 2.54 s across both the conventional 3-D volume and the large-angle stack. The left portrays the results from the conventional 3-D volume, while the right presents the large-angle stack. Both time slices have similar patterns, but only the large-angle stack properly depicts the known limits of the major reservoir in the northeastern portion of the study area.

Discussion

When a wet sand is very clean, its Poisson's ratio lies between that of a gas sand's and a slightly shaly sand's. Also, clean sands tend to be blocky in appearance on the SP log, and thus do not suffer from a reduction in *PR* amplitude caused by a transitional shaliness. These observations suggest that caution should be exercised when evaluating high-amplitude events on large-angle stacks, because they can be clean-sand reflections. Normally, clean wet sands can be differentiated from gas sands by crossplotting the (*NI*, *PR*) volumes, as described by Verm and Hilterman (1995).

It was fortuitous that this area had numerous gas reservoirs and also had several clean blanket sands. At the same time, without the availability of the 3-D long-offset seismic data in a good reflection area, the application of anisotropic processing would not have been attempted. The repeated high-amplitude reflections throughout the block from the very clean sands and gas sands allowed the anisotropic factor η to be estimated with NMO corrections. Other reflections were buried in the noise on the far-offset traces.

One obvious omission in this case history is the contribution of anisotropy to the reflection-coefficient equation. Using the estimate of the η function from the NMO analysis and using the available sonic log, low-frequency estimates of Thomsen's (1986) anisotropic functions δ and ε are obtainable. These two time functions are then adjusted using the shale volume curve to force the anisotropy to reside in the shale zones and to allow the sand zones to be basically isotropic. This procedure provides the additional parameters needed to generate VTI (vertical transverse isotropy) AVO synthetics. However, anisotropic AVO synthetics generated as described are questionable at best. More in-situ measurements of Thomsen's anisotropic parameters are needed if large-angle reflection amplitudes are to be quantified and verified.

Conclusions

When the acoustic impedances of sands and shales are nearly equal, Poisson's ratio curve is similar to the SP curve. In this situation, the amplitude on the large-angle traces is essentially the Poisson reflectivity, which is an indicator of lithology and pore-fluid content. The conventional stack, especially in Class 2 environments, will be composed of chronostratigraphic and lithostratigraphic reflections. Assuming shale to be the bounding medium, *PR* reflections from gas sands have the highest amplitudes, very clean wet sands have the next highest amplitudes, and shaly wet sands are weaker.

7E. Class 1—Pore-Fluid Identification: Anisotropic NMO and Modeling

Class 3 and 4 anomalies are recognized as amplitude bright spots on stack data, and pore-fluid prediction is routinely accomplished by anomaly/background amplitude analyses. For Class 2 anomalies, AVO interpretation of the prestack data is often needed just to recognize potential reservoirs. Finally, AVO interpretation in Class 1 environments is difficult because hydrocarbons don't yield bright spots or amplitude brightening with source-receiver offset. In short, the success for recognizing an anomaly and validating its composition is best for Class 3 environments and poorest for Class 1.

However, the exploration risk associated with Class 1 anomalies could be reduced if they could be treated like Class 2 anomalies, because the latter can be interpreted by examining CDP traces with large-angle offsets, as discussed in the previous case history. Could this apply to Class 1 anomalies if source-receiver offsets are extended to distances that are twice the target depth? This was the question that Hilterman et al. (2000) addressed with the following case history.

Introduction

The possibility of extending the conventional Class 1 AVO interpretation led Fugro-Geoteam and SEI to acquire a 2-D seismic survey in offshore Texas using a 9000-m (29,000-ft) streamer to evaluate Miocene sands. Preliminary AVO modeling revealed that deeper sands in the area have sufficient velocity contrast with surrounding shales so that potential hydrocarbon plays fall between Class 1 and Class 2.

Offshore Texas had major sand deposits during two geologic epochs. A shale-prone area separates these sand deposits (Fig. 7.E.1 and 7.E.2). The shale-prone area is sparsely populated with wells (it is situated around the Wanda Fault System noted in Fig. 7.E.1). As can be observed on the paleo profile line in Fig. 7.E.2, the shale region separates thick Pliocene–Pleistocene deposits of Louisiana origin from the Miocene deposits of Texas.

The seismic lines and the specific lease blocks associated with the two studies are also indicated in Fig. 7.E.1. Only one of the case studies will be discussed in these notes.

Deep Turbidite Play

The example, a deep turbidite play, involves the Elf-Acquitaine well in Galveston Block A142, drilled and abandoned in the late 1980s. Fig. 7.E.3 is a prestack-migrated section (0°–30° angle stack) across the well. The zone of interest is highlighted. Fig. 7.E.4 shows well-log curves from this well. No borehole shear-wave velocity information was available. An immediate concern about this well is the proper identification of the pore fluid in the thick sand sections. Are the sands water-saturated or slightly gas-saturated (fizz water)? Of course, other options are available, but the significant concept for this study is the presence of some gas. Unfortunately, no sands are obviously water-saturated for log-analysis comparison with the zone of interest.

Fortunately, generation of a 1-D synthetic does not require pore-fluid information if invasion effects are ignored. Fig. 7.E.5 illustrates the correlation of the 1-D synthetic to the portion of the seismic that is highlighted in Fig. 7.E.3. The wiggle traces in the middle of Fig. 7.E. 5 are divided into two groups: the three on the left are from the actual seismic, and the other three represent the synthetic. In general, it is felt that this 1-D well tie is more than adequate to continue with AVO modeling. Generally, the 1-D synthetic is tied to a normal-incident section or near-angle stack. This was done, and similar results were obtained.

The AVO modeling will be compared with the prestack migrated CDP gather in Fig.

7.E.6. On the left of this figure, the NMO correction is performed using an rms velocity derived from conventional velocity analysis. The line labeled *offset = depth* represents the routine mute pattern. However, if anisotropic NMO is performed, then additional amplitude information from the CDP gathers is available out to offsets $\approx 2 \times$ depth. Note that the black peak event at the top of the turbidite has a decrease in amplitude with offset out to the normal mute pattern and then reverses phase and increases in magnitude. Basically, applying anisotropic NMO has transformed a Class 1 anomaly into a Class 2 anomaly. Will modeling validate this claim and also show that the amplitude is from a reflection and not a refraction?

Fig. 7.E.7 shows the first attempt at matching the field CDP gather with a ray-trace synthetic. The pore-fluid is assumed to be water. The Batzle-Wang (1992) pore-fluid transforms and the Greenberg-Castagna (1992) shear-wave estimation technique are used. The ray-trace AVO response in the middle of Fig. 7.E.7 is a disappointing match with the field CDP gather. Two significant differences are evident. First, the ray-trace solution doesn't reach the desired long offsets because of critical-angle issues. Around the critical angle, ray-trace solutions fail and more sophisticated codes are necessary. Second, the phase-reversal portion of the turbidite event on the field CDP gather is not evident on the ray-trace synthetic. Both differences deal with nonzero-offset traces (the 1-D synthetic was a good fit to the zero-offset field seismic).

In order to address the critical-angle issue, a total elastic solution (program SOLID) is employed to generate the synthetic shown in the right of Fig. 7.E.7. The same well-log curves were used in the elastic model as in the ray-trace model. Now the far traces have a response, but the large amplitude on the far traces of the elastic synthetic are noticeably different than on the field gather. This large energy is associated with refraction and reflection components around the critical angle. Thus, even though a synthetic was generated for the long offsets, it appears that it was of little value because of the mistie to the field data. Let's first address the missing phase-reversal event on the synthetic.

In Fig. 7.E.8, the ray-trace AVO synthetic of Fig. 7.E.7 has been decomposed into three AVO synthetics as suggested by Shuey's equation. The far-left AVO synthetic is derived mainly from the variations in *P*-wave acoustic impedance, the middle from variations in Poisson's ratio, and the right from variations in the *P*-wave velocity. The associated rock-property curves are shown beneath each AVO synthetic. If the three AVO responses are added, the total ray-trace response is obtained. The field gather is also shown for comparison with the synthetic total response. A significant difference between the total synthetic response and the field gather is seen in the phase-reversal portion (see box on the field CDP gather). The Poisson's ratio AVO synthetic is highlighted at a similar position. Note that the acoustic-impedance AVO response and the total synthetic response are very similar. This means that the Poisson's ratio contribution to the total response is essentially being cancelled by the *P*-wave velocity contribution. This is typical for high-velocity sands beneath low-velocity shales. For the event of interest, the acoustic impedance and *P*-wave AVO responses are in phase with each other but opposite to the Poisson's ratio response. Thus, in order to have the phase-reversal effect appear in the total response, either the *P*-wave contribution has to be reduced or the Poisson's ratio effect increased. Reducing the *P*-wave contribution is difficult to justify because a logged sonic curve produces a good match between the 1-D synthetic and stack section. Thus, the Poisson's ratio curve in the turbidite zone needs to be reduced if an AVO match with the field data is desired. Of course, nonelastic effects such as anisotropy, fractures, or attenuation could be suggested as mechanisms for obtaining a better match of the nonzero offset traces of the AVO synthetic to the field CDP gather.

One way to increase the Poisson's ratio variation would be to assume that the pores contain fizz water. This is not unrealistic (note the well-log curves in Fig. 7.E.4). With this assumption, a new Poisson's ratio curve was computed, and a new total elastic synthetic was generated. The results are in the middle of Fig. 7.E.9. When the elastic response is compared to the field gather, the phase-reversal matches. However, once again, the high energy on the far-offset traces of the synthetic is not evident on the field CDP gather.

One possible explanation is anisotropy. As mentioned previously, the CDP gather at the well location (Fig. 7.E.6) exhibits nonhyperbolic moveout. Using the procedures described by Tsvankin and Thomsen (1994), the anisotropic parameter η, which is derived during the velocity analysis, was combined with check-shot information and the short-spread *rms*-velocity function to generate interval δ and ε functions. Both δ and ε functions had essentially zero values from the surface to a depth of 6000 ft (2000 m). From 6000 ft to 16000 ft (5000 m), ε ranged from 0.10 to 0.14 and δ from 0.06 to 0.09. These two anisotropic functions were then incorporated into an anisotropic ray-trace modeling code. From this code, incident angles for the various offsets were predicted.

These incident angles are different from those predicted for the isotropic model, a result that one would expect. Normally, the horizontal velocity is slightly faster than the vertical velocity. Thus, the propagating wavefront in an anisotropic medium tends to be flatter than in an isotropic medium. For the isotropic model for the Elf-Acquitaine well, the incident angle at 9200 m is 60°, while the incident angle for the anisotropic model at the same offset is only 52°. Another way of saying this is that the incident angle for the field seismic at an offset of 9200 m is the same as that for the isotropic model at 7600 m. An anisotropic incident-angle correction was made to the total elastic synthetic, and the result is on the right of Fig. 7.E.9. In essence, the large amplitudes associated with the critical-angle region were not recorded in the field because of the anisotropic flattening of the wavefront. Now, the total elastic model on the right matches the field gather on the left.

Discussion

Fig. 7.E.10 contains two Zoeppritz curves derived from the well-log curves of the Elf-Acquitaine well. The black curve represents the amplitude for the model with water as the pore fluid in the turbidite sand. The red curve represents fizz water as the pore fluid. The results of this case study can be related to these curves. They are:

- By analyzing offsets greater than depth (30°), a Class 1 AVO anomaly (dim out) was changed into a Class 2 AVO anomaly (phase reversal or amplitude increase with off-set). This is represented by the red curve in Fig. 7.E.10.

- At a depth of 16,000 ft (5000 m), long offsets are needed to recognize and quantify the Poisson's ratio of the turbidite sand. In Fig. 7.E.10, there is little difference between the black and red curves between 0° and 30° incident angles. It is between 30° and 50° angles that the effect of Poisson's ratio (pore-fluid content) is most evident.

- For large velocity contrasts, a total-elastic solution is needed to model offsets greater than depth.

- The large-amplitude reflections near 50° in Fig. 7.E.10 are found on the elastic model in Fig. 7.E.9, if corrections for the anisotropic incident angle are not made.

Figures

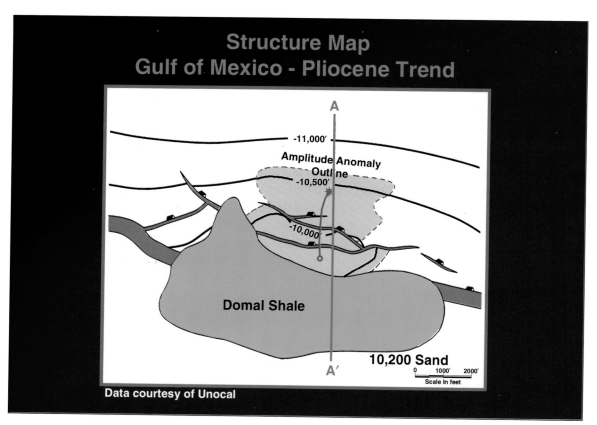

Figure 7.A.1

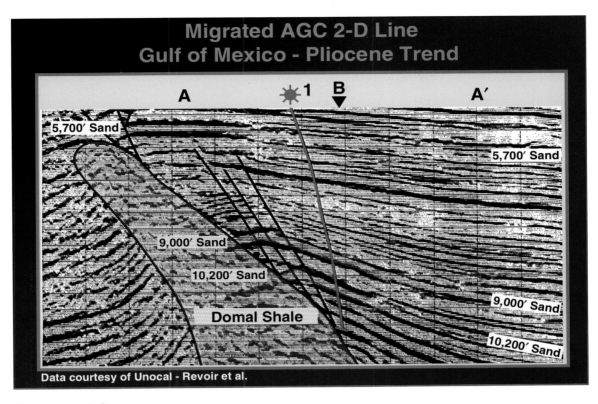

Figure 7.A.2

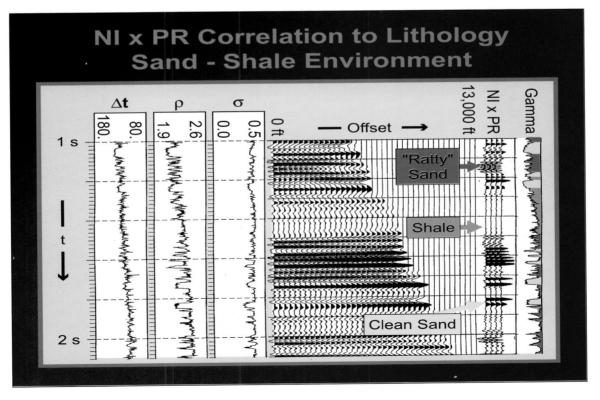

Figure 7.A.3

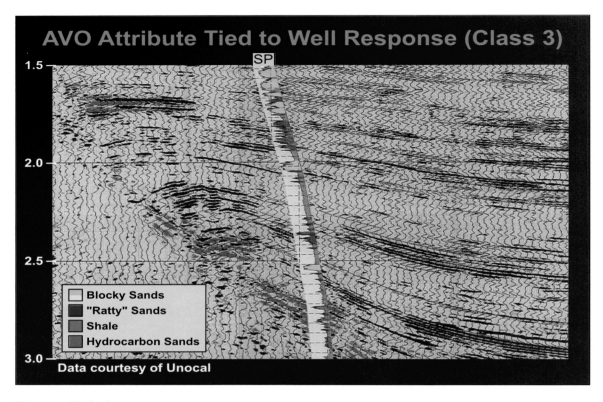

Figure 7.A.4

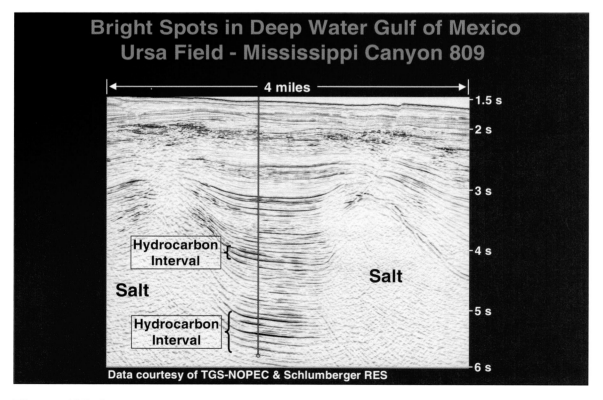

Figure 7.B.1

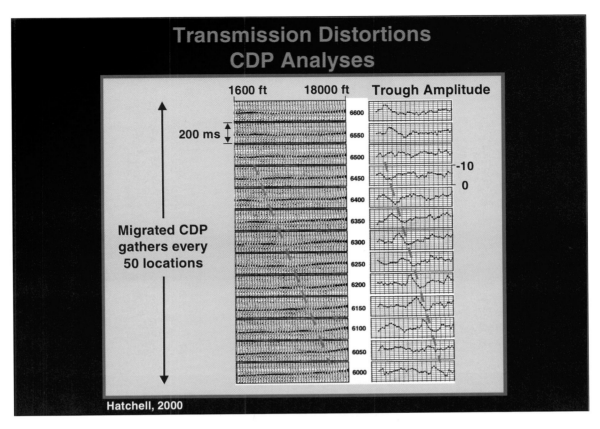

Figure 7.B.2

Figure 7.B.3

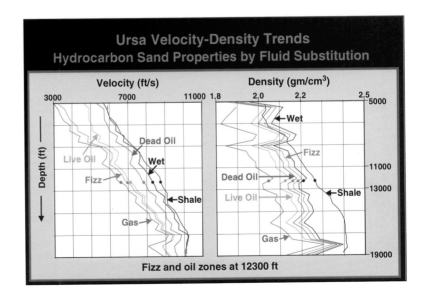

Figure 7.B.4

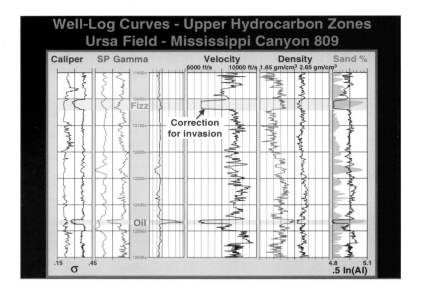

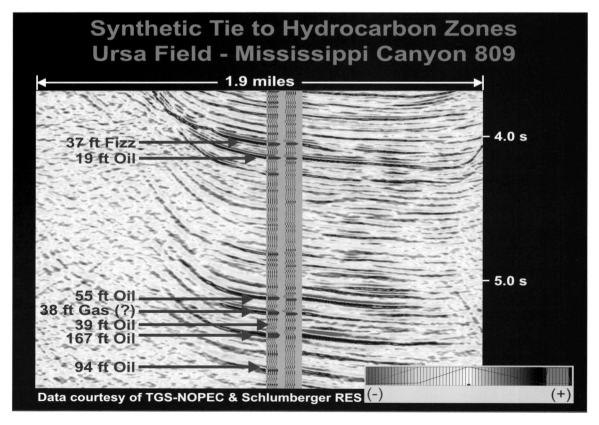

Figure 7.B.5

Figure 7.B.6

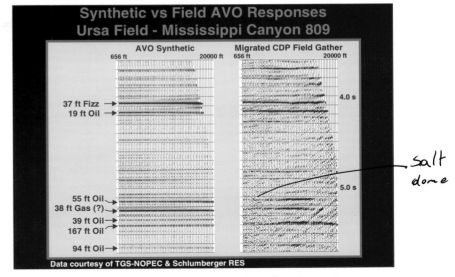

Figure 7.B.7

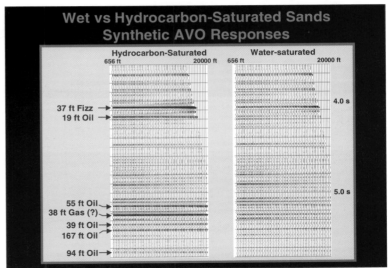

Figure 7.B.8

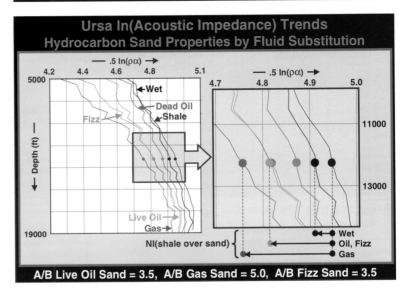

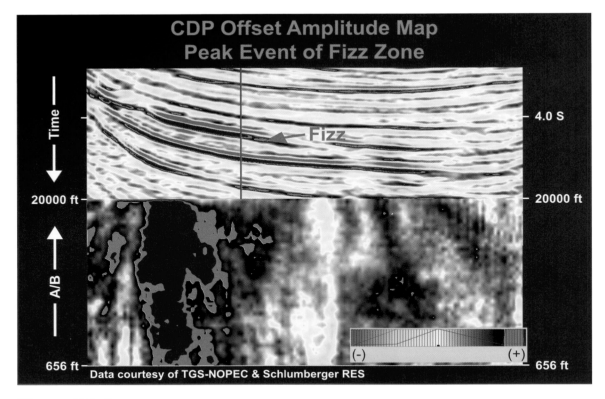

Figure 7.B.9

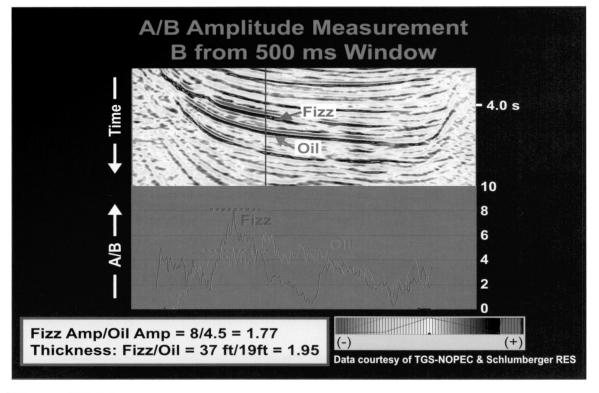

Figure 7.B.10

Figure 7.B.11

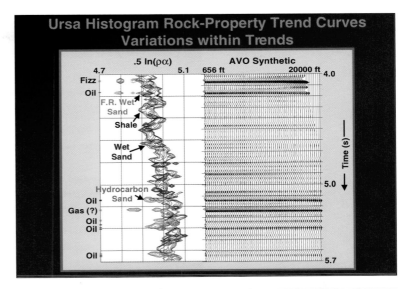

Figure 7.B.12

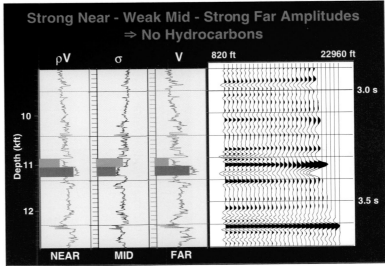

Figure 7.C.1

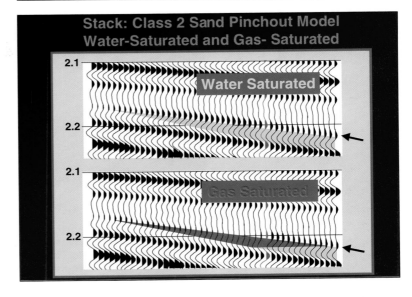

Figure 7.C.2

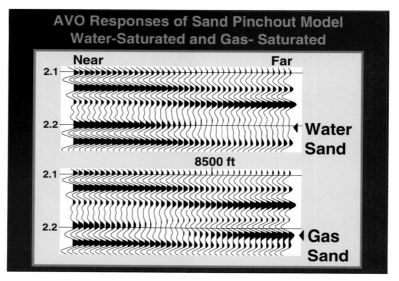

Figure 7.C.3

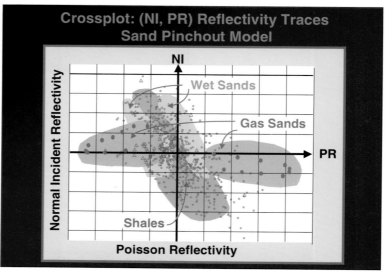

Figure 7.C.4

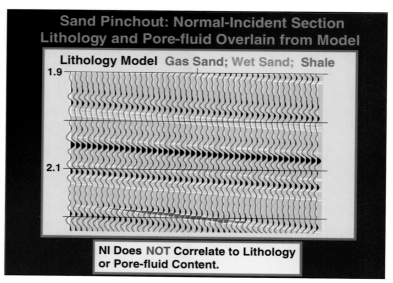

Figure 7.C.5

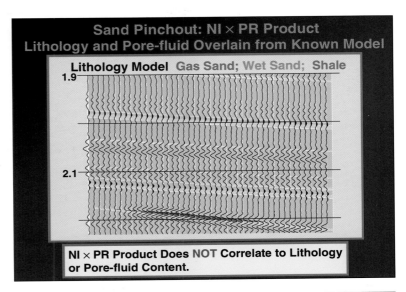

Figure 7.C.6

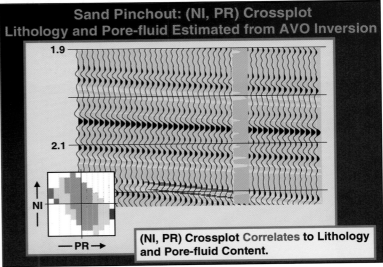

Figure 7.C.7

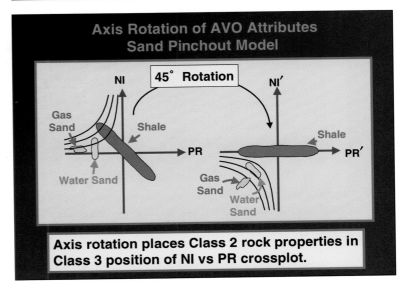

Figure 7.C.8

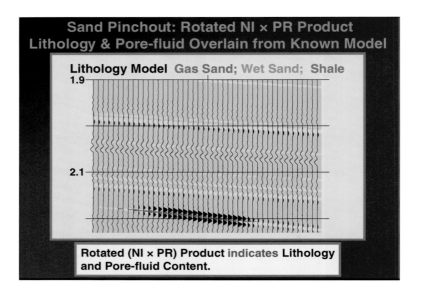

Figure 7.C.9

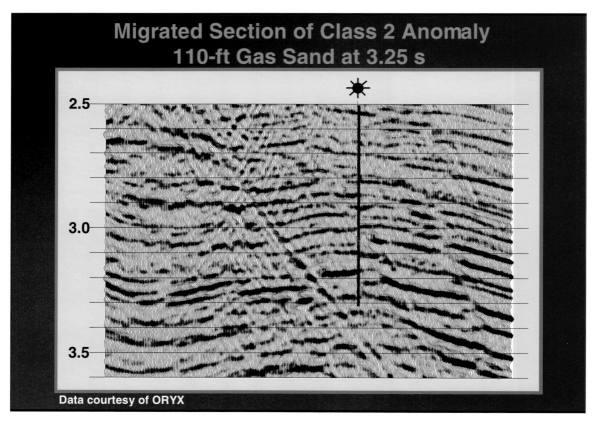

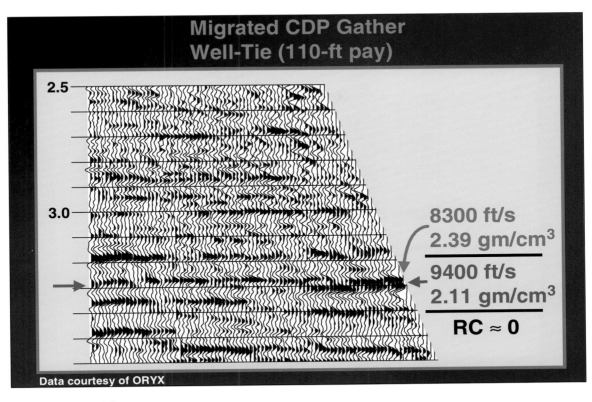

Figure 7.C.10

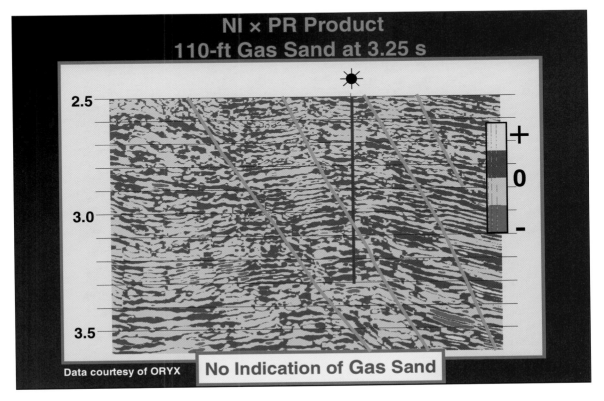

Figure 7.C.11

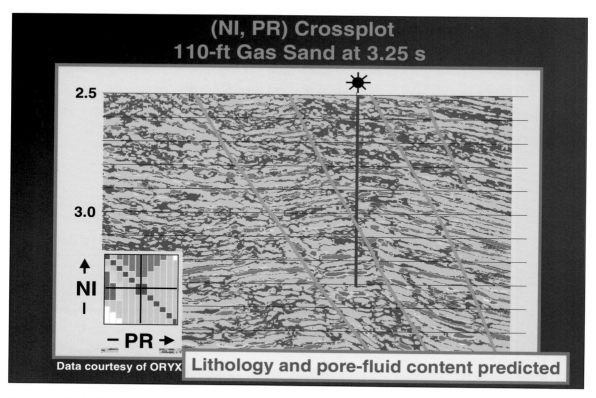

Figure 7.C.12

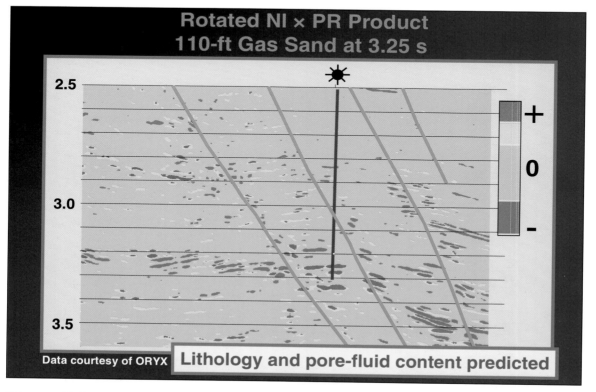

Figure 7.C.13

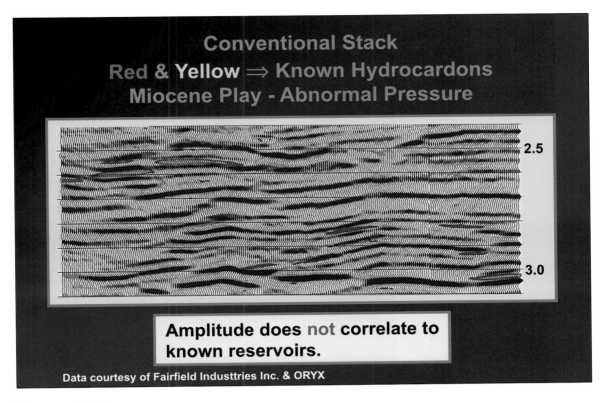

Figure 7.D.1

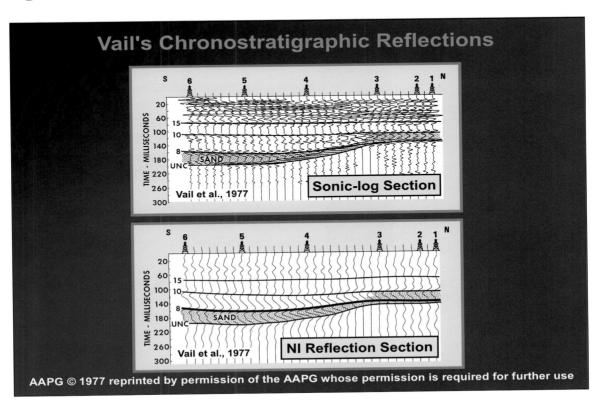

Figure 7.D.2

Figure 7.D.3

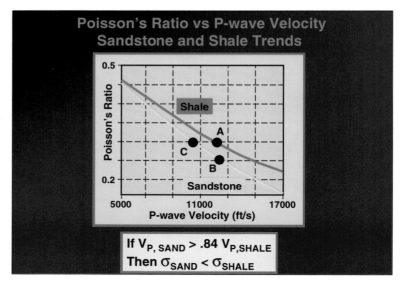

Figure 7.D.4

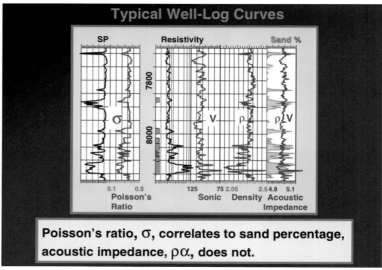

Figure 7.D.5

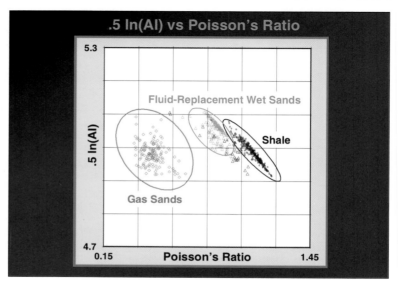

Figure 7.D.6

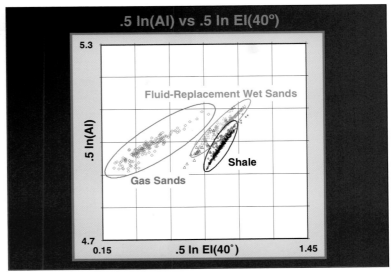

Figure 7.D.7

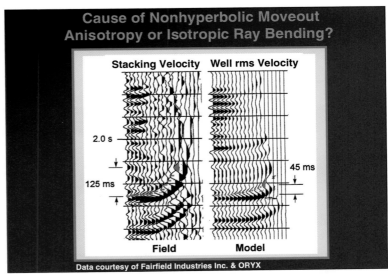

Figure 7.D.8

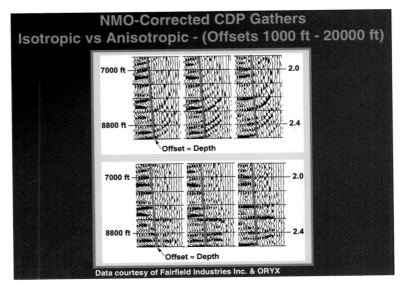

Figure 7.D.9

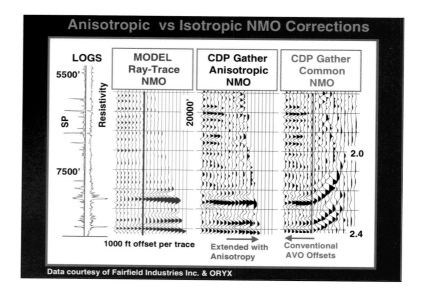

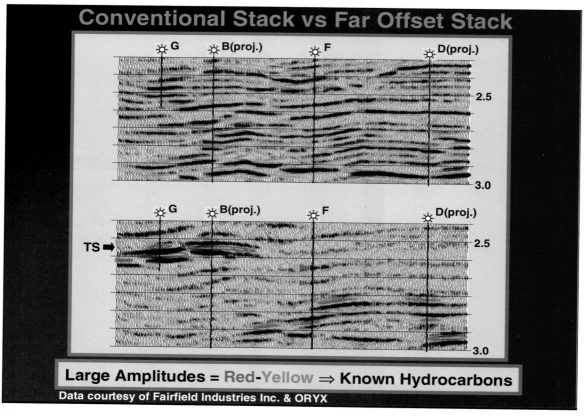

Figure 7.D.10

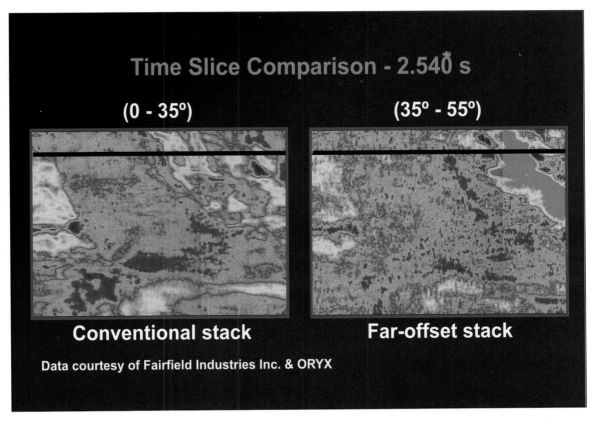

Figure 7.D.11

Figure 7.E.1

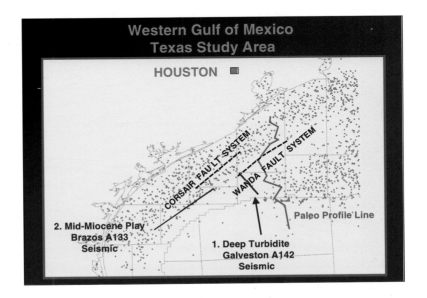

Figure 7.E.2

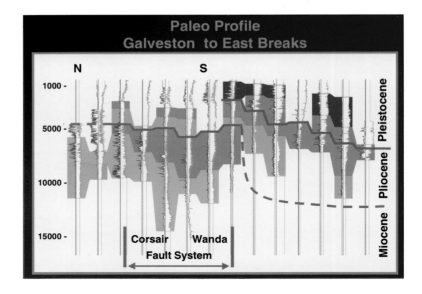

Figure 7.E.3

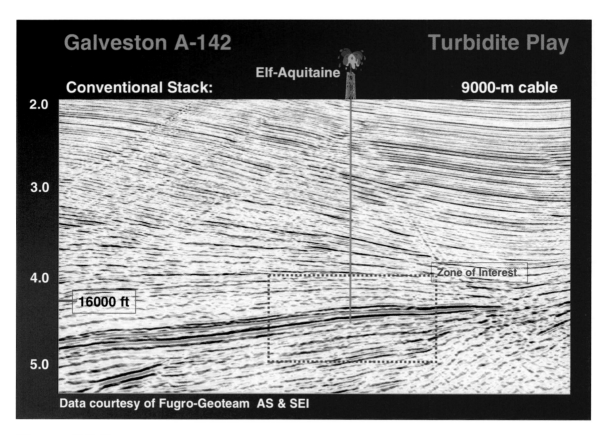

Figure 7.E.4

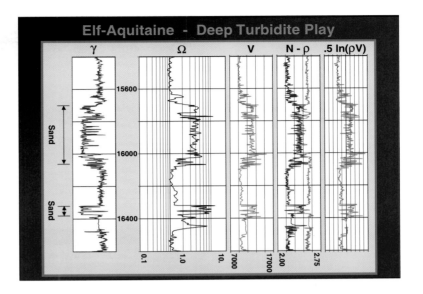

Figure 7.E.5

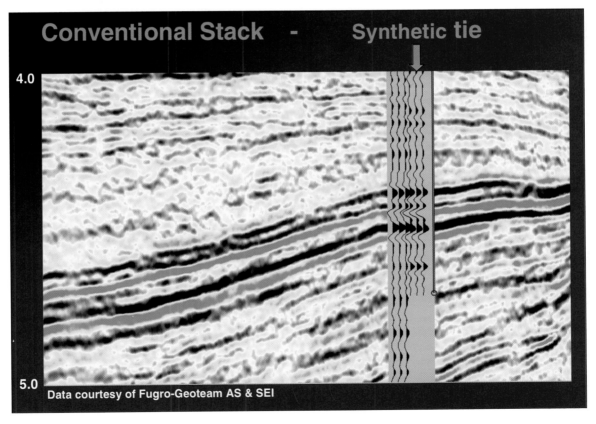

Figure 7.E.6

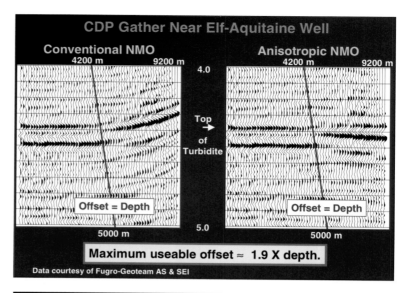

Figure 7.E.7

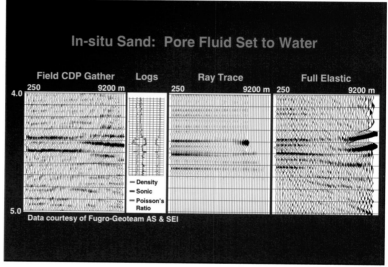

Figure 7.E.8

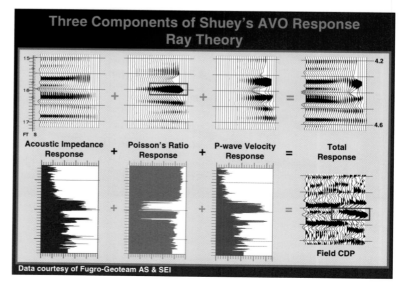

Figure 7.E.9

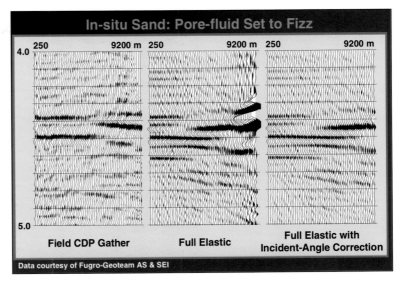

Figure 7.E.10

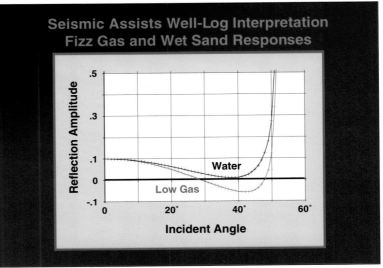

Section 8. Final Comments and Future Expectations

Objective:

1. Review growth of amplitude interpretation

2. Suggest future applications for amplitude interpretation

3. Speculate on future challenges for amplitude interpretation

8A. Second Era of Amplitude Interpretation

As noted earlier in Fig. 1.B.5, the beginning of the second era of amplitude interpretation is keyed to Ostrander's 1982 verification of AVO with prestack field data tied to drilling results. Since that time, the field of amplitude interpretation using AVO has been a fertile area of research, discoveries, and practical applications. The interpretation procedure in Fig. 8.A.1 outlines the AVO philosophy on validation that was followed in these notes. The sections in these notes on petrophysics, modeling, and amplitude attributes were key items that were discussed to reach the goal of validation through "Compute and Compare," as defined in Fig. 1.A.3. However, this amplitude procedure is not new—it is almost identical to Pan's amplitude procedure of the 1970s (Fig. 1.B.4). Little has changed in our validation philosophy. Only the available amplitude attributes have changed. Figure 8.A.2 summarizes some of the amplitude attributes that were developed or expanded in this second era of amplitude interpretation. Starting with the CDP gathers, there are two paths that can be followed in the figure. The path on the right of the figure provides the more robust attribute estimates. As one proceeds downward in either path more information to distinguish pore-fluid and/or lithology is derived from the amplitude attributes. At the same time, though, more interpretative bias is added to the amplitude interpretation in the downward path. This is not necessarily an unwanted result if petrophysical constraints are available. However, the interpreter must always be cognizant of the assumptions and interpretative bias that the amplitude attributes contain.

In a recent issue of THE LEADING EDGE, Castagna (2000) reminisced about the various frontiers in AVO analysis since 1982. Figure 8.A.3 reflects some of his thoughts about AVO progress. A majority of the topics and applications that Castagna mentions are presented in these notes. With the brevity of these notes, however, little emphasis has been given to some other research areas that have greatly advanced our understanding of pore-fluid and lithology discrimination. A few are:

- Geostatistics ⇒ Borehole to seismic calibration
- 4-D seismic ⇒ Fluid movement
- Cross-well seismic ⇒ Fluid continuity
- Multicomponent ⇒ Fracture density quantification

However, there are other applications of AVO suggested in Fig. 8.A.4 that might not be as apparent as the applications in Fig 8.A.3. AVO responses associated with geologic surfaces are often difficult to verify with current petrophysical or seismic models. Should we ignore these anomalous amplitudes if we can't verify them? As an example, in offshore Korea, there are numerous incised submarine canyons. On the 3-D seismic data from this area, the base and sides of the channel produce large amplitudes on the far-offset traces. However, even with dipole sonics available, these large amplitudes are difficult to duplicate with either ray theory or total elastic modeling. Is it possible that reduced-rigidity surfaces (nonwelded boundaries) are introduced parallel to these channel cuts? This is also a question for fault-plane reflections. In numerous areas, fault-plane reflections are more pronounced for those faults that are still active than for those that are dormant. Once again, are there low-rigidity surfaces parallel to fault planes that influence the AVO response? Or on a similar thought pattern, do permeability pathways produce stress-field surfaces that are aligned with the flow pattern?

Little work has been associated with variable earth stress fields associated with geologic surfaces that have a reduced rigidity. While we might not be able to verify these observed amplitude variations with today's theory, interest in quantifying these observations has been activated by the recent seismic stress-field work of Pisetski (1997).

In short, while the verification of amplitude variations associated with various geologic surfaces might be beyond our current mathematical or petrophysical capabilities, the recognition and classification of these amplitude anomalies to geologic features still produces a method to reduce exploration risk. They can be "unusual" anomalies, but sometimes these unusual anomalies turn into usable signal.

8B. Unusual Amplitude Anomalies

As an example of unusual amplitude anomalies, several years ago, an amplitude investigation to detect porosity variations within reefs was conducted. Fig. 8.B.1 contains a cartoon of a reef along with a borehole sonic and a portion of the 2-D seismic line across the reef. The reef was capped with a high-velocity, low-porosity layer, with the high-porosity zone just beneath. The porosity values were largest just beneath the high-velocity layer, and the porosity slowly decreased with depth as the gas-water contact was approached. Seismic offset distances were available that were three times the depth to the top of the reef. There were two questions to answer. First, will there be any useful information from far-offset AVO and/or refraction analyses? Second, with the gradual change in velocity beneath the high-velocity layer, how will the porosity zone and possible gas-water contact be recognized with seismic? In addition, there were "unusual" events on the far-offset traces that appeared to be sideswipe or possibly some form of refraction energy. What were these events? The total-elastic synthetics in Figs. 8.B.2 and 8.B.3 address a portion of these concerns (Al-Otaibi and Hilterman, 2000).

In Fig. 8.B.2, the top of the reef AVO response as a function of the thickness of a high-velocity layer was examined. When the layer was 600 ft (200 m) thick, a refraction arrival was noted that occurred at an offset that was slightly greater than the depth to the top of the reef. The events in these figures and the next two were NMO corrected with a static correction based on the reflection traveltime to the top of the reef.

For the 600-ft layer, the reflection from the top of the reef changes phase going from the near offset to the far. However, as the thickness of the model approached what was observed on the actual top of the reef, the refraction and phase change disappeared. Fig. 8.B.3 addresses the vertical variation in the velocity that was exhibited by the sonic log from the reef. Once again, a thick high-velocity layer was used as the base model. The second model from the top (Fig. 8.B.3) offered no surprises when its AVO response was examined. One would not expect a reflection from the base with a gradual velocity variation. However, when the transitional velocity model had the high velocity at the base, an unusual response occurred. The near-trace response was anticipated, and at first, the far-trace response was also expected. However, the high energy on the far offsets of the third model (Fig. 8.B.3) comes from grazing reflections from the top of the bed rather than the base. In addition, a portion of the energy just past the critical angle was identified as a diving wave. The final model in the bottom of Fig. 8.B.3 indicates that no seismic response is evident until offsets greater than the depth to the top of the reef are reached. The next step was to examine three AVO models for the actual reef. These are shown in Fig. 8.B.4.

The upper two models in the figure have a constant-velocity layer just beneath the upper high-velocity zone. The reflection and refraction from the last interface are evident on these upper two models. However, when the vertical velocity gradient was introduced (bottom of Fig. 8.B.4), the base reflection and refraction disappear. However, there is a strong event between the offsets that are equal to one and two times the depth. This last response is compared with the migrated CDP gather near the well location in Fig. 8.B.5. Both the field data and the model exhibit this strong dipping event. The AVO model has the same character response as do the field data. (Remember, both the model response and field CDP gather were NMO corrected with a static correction to the top of the reef.) As mentioned, the strong event is a diving wave associated with the layer that has an increase in velocity. On the field CDP gather, offsets A and B define the start and end of the strong event. These two offsets, along with the time slope of the diving wave, provide enough information to estimate the pore volume of the reef. Of course on the petrophysical side, the interval velocity of the reef was calibrated to the porosity.

Besides the unusual diving wave, this reef example illustrates that interpreters are often required to view data in nonstandard formats to find the wave propagation feature that best illuminates the exploration task at hand. In the reef example, the top of the reef horizon was digitized from the stack section, and then all the CDP gathers were static corrected based on the digitized time to the top of the reef. If standard NMO corrections were applied, NMO stretch and NMO crossover events would have made it impossible to recognize anomalies on the very-far offset traces. In short, the large-amplitude event (diving wave) was initially interpreted to be a noise component that needed to be eliminated during data processing. However, the validation of this event changed a noise event into a useful signal.

8C. Major Challenges to Resolve

What other areas or frontiers of seismic should our researchers investigate for amplitude interpretation? Should the objective of their future research be the minimization of exploration risk? Or, is it product development rather than research that is needed today? Fortunately, I am unable to answer these questions, so I'll ignore them. Instead, in the last few paragraphs, I will concentrate my thoughts on future challenges and expectations.

Difficult Exploration Areas

There are many areas in the world where high-velocity layers make structure and amplitude interpretations difficult, if not impossible. Until a robust solution is found, areas such as the Gulf of Suez, Timur Sea, and Gulf of Mexico (subsalt) will continue to hide their wealth of hydrocarbons from the drill bit. Figs. 8.C.1 and 8.C.2 illustrate the subsalt imaging problem found in the Gulf of Mexico. The well-log model in Fig. 8.C.1 contains a 2000-ft (600-m) layer of salt, while the well logs in Fig. 8.C.2 are the same but with the salt layer replaced with shale properties. There are three AVO responses shown in both figures: ray trace, total elastic with water in the upper half space, and total elastic with air in the upper half space. Comparing the air with the water responses helps to differentiate the converted waves from the surface multiples. Without the salt layer (Fig. 8.C.2), the three AVO responses are practically identical for amplitude interpretation purposes. However, there are significant differences between the three AVO responses in Fig. 8.C.1. The AVO response labeled *Air* most closely matches real life conditions. Definitely, ray-trace theory is inadequate. But this is the theory on which our processing and interpretation are based.

Future Challenges

If not ray theory, then what? Fig. 8.C.3 contains a suggestion for long-term research. And by no means do I claim this future challenge as an original thought—it is constantly on the minds of our researchers. However, other challenges, such as lack of computer capacity, have hindered research in this area.

Developing a unified vector wavefield processing system is definitely a long-term challenge where intermediate solutions will be needed before the final objective is reached. If useful interpretation by-products are not forthcoming, then the necessary moneys will not be available. Basically, the challenge is depth imaging using the elastic-wave equation, rather than the acoustic. When this is accomplished, amplitude interpretation will be related to the elastic constants of the depth model. However, the significance of amplitude interpretation will change as the "true" model of the earth is imaged. In order to accomplish this goal, multicomponent acquisition and total azimuthal shooting need to be more prevalent in our industry. Unfortunately, with the current trend toward product-driven development rather than research, multicomponent acquisition is still limited to areas where verification of better products has been proven, such as under-shooting gas clouds. Thankfully, recent advances in better lithology identification with multicomponent acquisition, such as those reported by MacLeod et al. (1999), have provided incentive for more multicomponent acquisition.

The challenges listed in Fig. 8.C.3 are definitely long term, but those challenges suggested in Fig. 8.C.4 are more immediate. There are numerous software packages available for both structure and amplitude interpretation. Each year, the degree of sophistication needed to operate a particular software package increases as new product lines are added. Are the requirements for being current with software skills overriding the requirements for keeping current in one's field of expertise? The other three challenges in the figure are obvious but are worth noting.

The next challenge listed in the figure is to avoid the oversell of one amplitude attribute as the panacea for all exploration areas. *VSP's* were subject to overselling in their early days, and it took considerable effort to reverse the stigma caused by this. One might claim that *PR*, Poisson's reflectivity, has been oversold in these notes. I apologize if I left you with that feeling. However, my intentions were to select *PR* more as a vehicle for comparison with other amplitude attributes. The local rock properties, quality of seismic data, nature of the exploration or exploitation problem, and the like, are the driving forces for the proper selection of the amplitude attribute in a given area.

The third challenge is to provide the necessary visualization technology that is independent of interpretative bias. We realize that viewing stack data alone is not sufficient to capitalize on today's technology. At the same time, viewing amplitude maps based on picked horizons is not sufficient to detect the subtle stratigraphic changes that are associated with the horizon pick. The details of the character changes along the horizon need evaluation. The variation in amplitude from different offset or angle-stack volumes needs to be viewed for unbiased analysis. In what domain does one visualize 120-fold data?

If the first three challenges are met, will our interpreters be provided the gestation time needed to analyze the various seismic attributes and the petrophysical data that are necessary to evaluate an area? Will the team effort assist in this challenge? Or is it necessary for the seismic interpreter to be more integrated in the other specialized fields?

With the total-elastic imaging as the long-term objective, what new bright spot or AVO by-products do we see on the immediate horizon for interpretation? I don't know! But I will place my money on the next breakthrough coming from an interpreter. As Fig. 8.C.5 notes, historically, interpreters have provided the initiative for amplitude breakthroughs ... not researchers. But when the initiative from the interpreter arrives, will the basic research be completed to capitalize on the breakthrough?

Final Comments

The final comments shown in Fig. 8.C.6 require no additional explanation. They are:

- An inexpensive amplitude validation of seismic data can often be the most profitable risk reducer ... the "silver bullet."
- Amplitude validation and risk measurements are fundamental geophysical outputs.

Figures

Figure 8.A.1

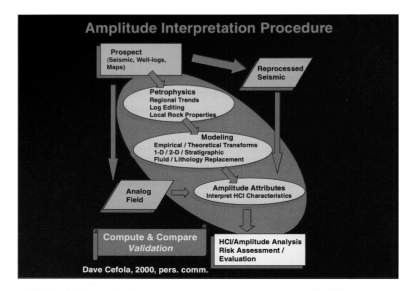

Figure 8.A.2

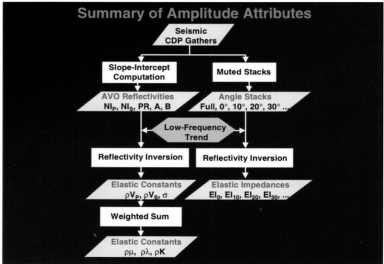

Figure 8.A.3

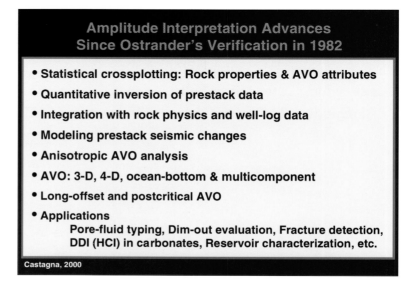

Figure 8.A.4

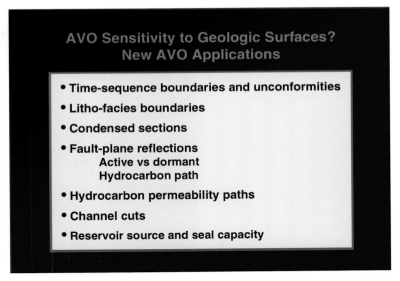

Figure 8.B.1

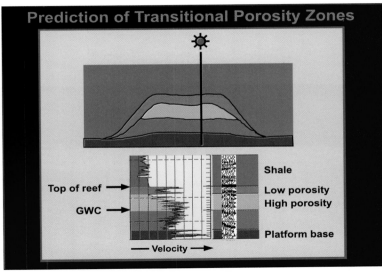

Figure 8.B.2

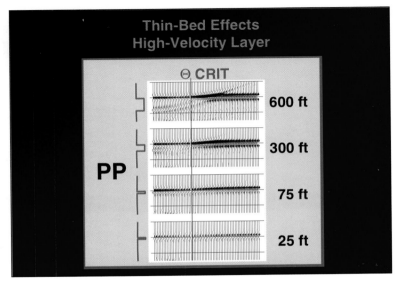

Figure 8.B.3

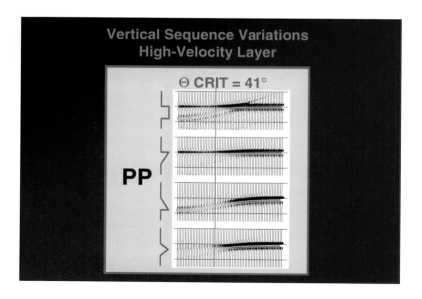

Figure 8.B.4

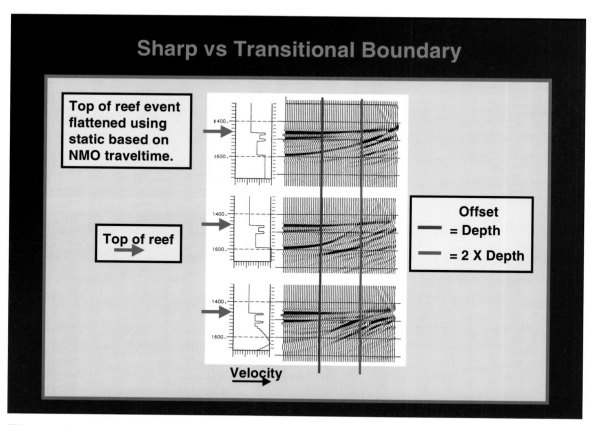

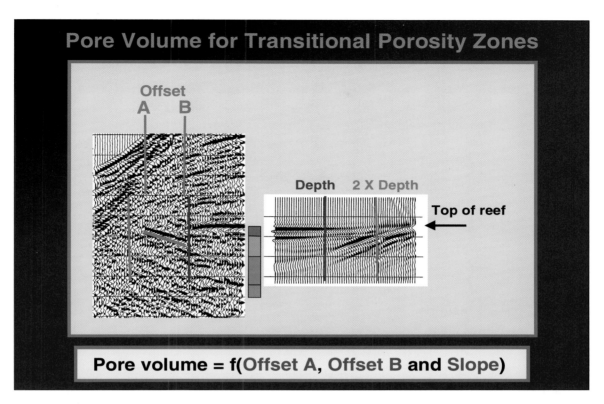

Figure 8.B.5

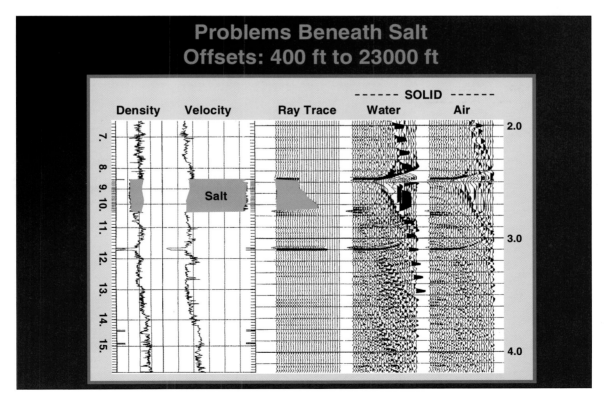

Figure 8.C.1

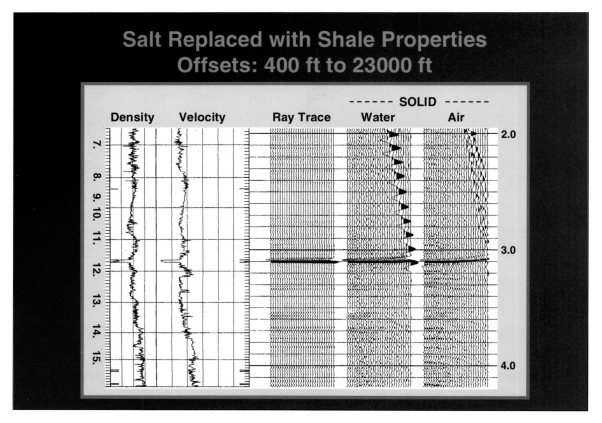

Figure 8.C.2

Figure 8.C.3

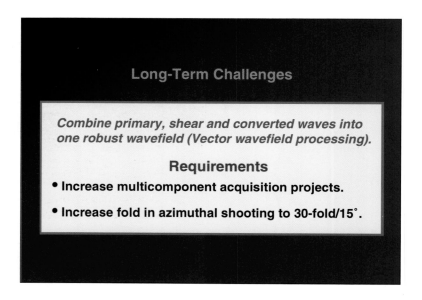

Figure 8.C.4

Immediate Challenges

- Emphasize technical knowledge over workstation skills.

- Avoid the oversell of applying one amplitude attribute to all areas.

- Provide visualization technology that is independent of interpretative bias.

- Provide gestation period for interpreters to allow all data to be viewed and validated.

Figure 8.C.5

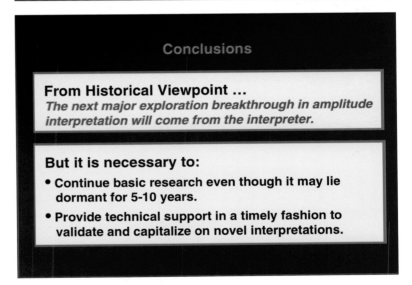

Conclusions

From Historical Viewpoint …
The next major exploration breakthrough in amplitude interpretation will come from the interpreter.

But it is necessary to:
- Continue basic research even though it may lie dormant for 5-10 years.
- Provide technical support in a timely fashion to validate and capitalize on novel interpretations.

Figure 8.C.6

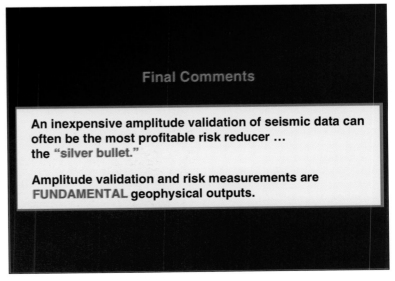

Final Comments

An inexpensive amplitude validation of seismic data can often be the most profitable risk reducer …
the "silver bullet."

Amplitude validation and risk measurements are FUNDAMENTAL geophysical outputs.

Section 9. References

Aki, K., and Richards, P. G., 1980, Quantitative seismology—Theory and Methods, **1**: W.H. Freeman and Co., San Francisco.

Alkhalifah, T. and Tsvankin, I., 1995, Velocity analysis for transversely isotropic media: Geophysics, **60**, 1550–1566.

Allen, J. L., and Peddy, C. P., 1993, Amplitude variations with offset: Gulf Coast case studies: SEG Geophysical Development Series, **4**.

Al-Otaibi, M., and Hilterman, F., 2000, PP and PS amplitude observations pre- and post-critical angle: Presented at the 70th Ann. Internat. Mtg., Soc. Expl. Geophys.

Anstey, N. A., 1991, Velocity in thin section: First Break, **9**, 449–457.

Backus, M. M., and Chen, R. L., 1975, Flat spot exploration: Geophys. Prosp., **23**, 533–577.

Barry, K. M., and Shugart, T. R., 1973, Seismic hydrocarbon indicators and models: Presented at the Geophysical Society of Houston "Lithology and direct detection of hydrocarbons using geophysical methods" symposium.

Batzle, M., and Wang, Z., 1992, Seismic properties of fluids: Geophysics, **57**, 1396–1408.

Biot, M. A., 1956a, Theory of propagation of elastic waves in a fluid-saturated porous solid. I. Low frequency range: J. Acoust. Soc. Am., **28**, 168–178.

Biot, M. A., 1956b, Theory of propagation of elastic waves in a fluid-saturated porous solid. II. Higher frequency range: J. Acoust. Soc. Am., **28**, 179–191.

Bork, J., Yin, C., Castagna, J., Karazincir, H., Wood, L., and Schneider, R., 1997, An investigation into unusual AVO signatures in the Gulf of Mexico and Trinidad: Presented at the 67th Ann. Internat. Mtg., Soc. Expl. Geophys., Expanded Abstracts, 199–201.

Bortfeld, R., 1961, Approximation to the reflection and transmission coefficients of plane longitudinal and transverse waves: Geophys. Prosp., **9**, 485–503.

Bowers, G. L., 1995, Pore pressure estimation from velocity data: Accounting for over-pressure mechanisms besides undercompaction: Soc. Petr. Eng., Drilling & Completion, June, 89-95.

Brown, A. R., 1999, Interpretation of three-dimensional seismic data, 5th ed. AAPG Memoir 42 and SEG Investigations in Geophysics 9: AAPG and SEG, Tulsa, OK.

Cambois, G., 1998, AVO attributes and noise: pitfalls in crossplotting: Presented at the 68th Ann. Internat. Mtg., Soc. Expl. Geophys., Expanded Abstracts, 244–247.

Castagna, J. P., 1993, AVO analysis: Tutorial and review: *in* Castagna, J.P. and Backus, M.M., eds., Offset-dependent reflectivity – Theory and practice of AVO anomalies, Soc. Expl. Geophys. Investigations in Geophysics no. 8, 3–36.

Castagna, J. P., 2000, An introduction to this special section: AVO – The next step: The Leading Edge, **19**, 1187.

Castagna, J. P., Batzle, M. L., and Kan, T. K., 1993, Rock physics – The link between rock properties and AVO response: *in* Castagna, J.P. and Backus, M.M., eds., Offset-dependent reflectivity – Theory and practice of AVO anomalies, Soc. Expl. Geophys. Investigations in Geophysics no. 8, 135–171.

Castagna, J. P., Batzle, M. L., and Eastwood, R. L., 1985, Relationships between compressional-wave and shear-wave velocities in clastic silicate rocks: Geophysics, **50**, 571–581.

Castagna, J. P., and Smith, S. W., 1994, Comparison of AVO indicators: A modeling study: Geophysics, **59**, 1849–1855.

Castagna, J. P., Swan, H. W., and Foster, D. J., 1998, Framework for AVO gradient and intercept interpretation: Geophysics, **63**, 948–956.

Cefola, D. P., 2000, personal communication.

Cerveny, V., and Ravindra, R., 1971, Theory of seismic head waves: Univ. of Toronto Press.

Chesser, K., 1997, Missing data problems in forward AVO modeling: Presented at the 67th Ann. Internat. Mtg., Soc. Expl. Geophys., Expanded Abstracts, 1187–1190.

Chiburis, E. F., 1993, AVO applications in Saudi Arabia: *in* Castagna, J.P. and Backus, M.M., eds., Offset-dependent reflectivity – Theory and practice of AVO anomalies, Soc. Expl. Geophys. Investigations in Geophysics no. 8, 211–229.

Churlin, V. V., and Sergeyev, L. A., 1963, Application of seismic surveying to recognition of productive part of gas-oil strata: Geolog. Nefti i Gaza, 7, p. 363.

Connolly, P., 1999, Elastic impedance: The Leading Edge, **18**, 438–452.

DiSiena, J. P., Parsons, B. E., and Hilterman, F. J., 1995, Two-term inversion from AVO to detect the combined effect of porosity and gas in a Cretaceous sand reservoir: Presented at the 65th Ann. Internat. Mtg., Soc. Expl. Geophys., Expanded Abstracts, 111–114.

Domenico, S. N., 1974, Effect of water saturation on seismic reflectivity of sand reservoirs encased in shale: Geophysics, **39**, 759–769.

Domenico, S. N., 1984, Velocity and lithology: Unpublished notes from AAPG Continuing Education Short Course—Stratigraphic interpretation of seismic data.

Dutta, N. C., and Levin, F. K., 1987, Geopressure: Soc. Expl. Geophys. Geophysics Reprint Series no. 7.

Ebrom, D., and Sheriff, R.E., 1992, Anisotropy and reservoir development:

Sheriff, R.E., ed., Reservoir Geophysics, Soc. Expl. Geophys. Investigations in Geophysics no. 7, 353–361.

Forrest, M., 2000, Bright ideas still needed persistence: AAPG Explorer, **21**, no. 5, 20–21.

Gardner, G.H.F., and Forel, D. 1987, Connections between rock properties and seismic data: Refresher course in geophysics, Univ. of Houston, Allied Geophysical Laboratories.

Gardner, G. H. F., Gardner, L. W., and Gregory, A. R., 1974, Formation velocity and density – The diagnostic basics for stratigraphic traps: Geophysics, **39**, 770–780.

Gassmann, F., 1951, Uber die elastizitat poroser medien: Vierteljahrsschr. Der Naturforsch. Gesellschaft Zurich, **96**, 1–21.

Geerstma, J., 1961, Velocity-log interpretation: The effect of rock bulk compressibility. Soc. Petr. Eng. J., **1**, 235–248.

Gidlow, P. M., Smith, G. C., and Vail, P. J., 1992, Hydrocarbon detection using fluid factor traces: A case history: Presented at the Joint Soc. Expl. Geophys./EAEG Summer Research Workshop on "How useful is amplitude-versus-offset (AVO) analysis?", 78–89.

Goodway, B., Chen, T., and Downton, J., 1997, Improved AVO fluid detection and lithology discrimination using Lame petrophysical parameters; lr, mr & l/m fluid stack, from P and S inversions: Presented at the 67th **Ann. Internat. Mtg., Soc. Expl. Geophys.**, Expanded Abstracts, 183–186.

Graul, J. M., 1999, Amplitude variations with offset: AVO – Seismic lithology: unpublished course notes for Soc. Expl. Geophys. Continuing Education Course.

Greenberg, M. L., and Castagna, J. P., 1992, Shear-wave velocity estimation in porous rocks: Theoretical formulation, preliminary verification and applications: Geophys. Prosp., **40**, 195–210.

Gregory, A. R., 1977, Aspects of rock physics from laboratory and log data that are important to seismic interpretation: *in* Payton, C. E., ed., Seismic Stratigraphy—Applications to Hydrocarbon Exploration, AAPG Memoir **26**, 15–46.

Greve, G. M., 1997, Seismic quality—Let's tell it like it is: The Leading Edge, **16**, 145–148.

Hamilton, E. L., 1979, VP/VS and Poisson's ratio in marine sediments and rocks: *in* Nur, A.M. and Wang, Z., eds., Seismic and acoustic velocities in reservoir rocks, vol. **1**, Experimental Studies, Soc. Expl. Geophys. Reprint Series, **10**, 272–280.

Han, D. -H., 1986, Effects of porosity and clay content on acoustic properties of sandstones and unconsolidated sediments: Ph.D. dissertation, Stanford Univ.

Han, D. -H., Nur, A., and Morgan, D., 1986, Effects of porosity and clay content on wave velocities in sandstones: Geophysics, **51**, 2093–2107.

Hatchell, P. J., 2000, Fault whispers: Transmission distortions on prestack seismic reflection data: Geophysics, **65**, 377–389.

Hendrickson, J. S., 1999, Stacked: Geophys. Prosp., **47**, 663-706.

Hill, R.W., 1952, The elastic behavior of crystalline aggregate: Proc. Physical Soc., London, **A65**, 349–354.

Hilterman, F. J., 1975, Amplitude of Seismic waves—A quick look: Geophysics, **40**, 745–762.

Hilterman, F. J., 1982, Interpretative lessons in three-dimensional modeling: Geophysics, **47**, 784-808.

Hilterman, F. J., 1990, Is AVO the seismic signature of lithology? A case history of Ship Shoal—South Addition: The Leading Edge, **9**, no. 6, 15–22.

Hilterman, F. J., Sherwood, J. W. C., Schellhorn, R., Bankhead, B., and DeVault, B., 1998, Identification of lithology in the Gulf of Mexico: The Leading Edge, **17**, No. 2, 215–222.

Hilterman, F., Van Schuyver, C., and Sbar, M., 2000, AVO examples of long-offset 2-D data in the Gulf of Mexico: The Leading Edge, **19**, no. 11, 1200–1213.

Hilterman, F. J., Verm, R., Wilson, M., and Liang, L., 1999, Calibration of rock properties for deep-water seismic: Presented at the 31th Offshore Technology Conference, OTC 10844, 451–458.

Hottmann, C. E., and Johnson, R. K., 1965, Estimation of formation pressures from log-derived shale properties: J. Petr. Tech., **17**, 717–722.

Jakosky, J. J., 1960, Exploration geophysics, 2nd ed.: Trija Publishing Company.

Knott, C. G., 1899, Reflection and refraction of elastic waves with seismological applications: Phil. Mag., **48**, 64–97.

Koefoed, O., 1955, On the effect of Poisson's ratios of rock strata on the reflection coefficients of plane waves: Geophys. Prosp., **3**, 381–387.

Kozman, J. B., and Hilterman, F. J., 2000, AVO analysis of long offset 2D data in the western Gulf of Mexico: Presented at the 2000 AAPG Annual Convention, Abstracts, p. A80.

Krief, M., Garat, J., Stellingwerff, J., and Ventre, J., 1990, A petrophysical interpretation using the velocities of P and S waves (full-waveform sonic): The Log Analyst, **31**, Nov., 355-369.

Kuster, G.T., and Toksöz, M.N., 1974, Velocity and attenuation of seismic waves in two-phase media: Geophysics, **39**, 587-618.

Lin, T. L., and Phair, R., 1993, AVO tuning: Presented at the 70th Ann. Internat. Mtg., Soc. Expl. Geophys., Expanded Abstracts, 727-730.

MacLeod, M. K., Hanson, R.A., Bell, C.R., and McHugo, S., 1999, The Alba Field ocean bottom cable seismic survey: Impact on development: The Leading Edge, 18, 1306–1312.

Mavko, G., Mukerji, T., and Dvorkin, J., 1998, The rock physics handbook—Tools for seismic analysis in porous media: Cambridge Univ. Press.

Merlini, E., 1959, Un nouveau dispositif auxiliarie dans la recherche sismique: Geophys. Prosp. 7, p.129.

Neidell, N. S., and Poggiagliolmi, E., 1977, Stratigraphic modeling and interpretation—geophysical principles and techniques: *in* Payton, C. E., ed., Seismic Stratigraphy—Applications to hydrocarbon exploration, AAPG Memoir 26, 389–416.

Neff, D., 1992, Estimated pay mapping using three-dimensional seismic data and incremental pay thickness modeling: *in* Sheriff, R. E., ed., Reservoir geophysics, Soc. Expl. Geophys., Investigations in Geophysics 7, 207–214.

Nickerson, R. L., and Tuttle, S., 2000, Lower exploration risk—Using a maximum likelihood clustering and AVO analysis: Presented at the 70th Ann. Internat. Mtg., Soc. Expl. Geophys., Expanded Abstracts, 110–113.

Nur, A. M., and Wang, Z., eds., 1989, Seismic and acoustic velocities in reservoir rocks—Experimental studies: v. 1, Soc. Expl. Geophys. Geophysics Reprint Series no. 10.

Nur, A., Marion, D., and Yin, H., 1991, Wave velocities in sediments, *in* Hovem, J.M., Richardson, M.D., and Stoll, R.D., eds., Shear Waves in Marine Sediments, Kluwer Academic Publishers, Dordrecht, The Netherlands, 131–140.

Ostrander, W. J., 1982, Plane wave reflection coefficients for gas sands at nonnormal angles of incidence: Presented at the 52nd Ann. Internat. Mtg., Soc. Expl. Geophys., Expanded Abstracts, 216–218.

Ostrander, W. J., 1984, Plane wave reflection coefficients for gas sands at nonnormal angles of incidence: Geophysics, 49, 1637–1648.

Paige, D. S., 1973, The dark side of the bright spot: Presented at the GSH Lithology and direct detection of hydrocarbons using geophysical methods symposium.

Pan, P. P., 1969, Direct location of oil and gas by the seismic reflection method: Ph.D. Thesis, Rice Univ.

Pan, P. P., and de Bremaecker, J. C., 1970, Direct location of oil and gas by the seismic reflection method: Geophys. Prosp., 18, 712–727.

Pennebaker, E. S., 1968, Seismic data indicate depth, magnitude of abnormal pressure: World Oil, 171, 78–82.

Pickett, G., 1963, Acoustic character logs and their applications in formation evaluation: J. Petr. Tech. , 15, 650–667.

Pisetski, V. B., 1997, Methods for determining the presence of fluids in a subterranean formation; U.S.A. Patent Application 57274744.

Prescott, W. T., 1973, VIBROSEIS bright spot—An example: Presented at the GSH Lithology and direct detection of hydrocarbons using geophysical methods symposium.

Press, W. H., Teukolsky, S. A., Vetterling, W. T., and Flannery, B. P., 1996, Numerical recipes in Fortran 77– 2nd Ed. –The art of scientific computing: Cambridge Univ. Press.

Raymer, L. L., Hunt, E. R. and Gardner, J. S., 1980, An improved sonic transit time-to-porosity transform: Presented at the Soc. Prof. Well Log Analysts 21st Annual Logging Symposium, Transactions.

Resnick, J. R., 1993. Seismic data processing for AVO and AVA analysis: *in* Castagna, J. P. and Backus, M. M., eds., Offset-dependent reflectivity – Theory and practice of AVO anomalies, Soc. Expl. Geophys. Investigations in Geophysics 8, 175–189.

Reuss, A., 1929, Berechnung der Fliessgrenzen von Mischkristallen auf Grund der Plastizitätsbedingung für Einkristalle: Zeitschrift für Angewandte Mathematik und Mechanik, **9**, 49–58.

Revoir, M. E., Hawkins, J. G., and Duffy, R. E., 1992, Integrating AVO modeling and processing products—An offshore Gulf of Mexico case study for the applied explorationist: Presented at the Joint Soc. Expl. Geophys./EAEG Summer Research Workshop on "How useful is amplitude-versus-offset (AVO) analysis?" 140–153.

Richards, P. G., and Frasier, C. W., 1976, Scattering of elastic waves from depth-dependent inhomogeneities; Geophysics, **41**, 441–458.

Rosa, A. L. R., 1976, Extraction of elastic parameters using seismic reflection amplitudes with offset variations: M.S. Thesis, Univ. of Houston.

Ross, C. P., 2000, Effective AVO crossplot modeling: A tutorial: Geophysics, **65**, 700–711.

Ross, C. P., and Beale, P. C., 1994, Seismic offset balancing: Geophysics, **59**, 93–101.

Ross, C. P., and Kinman, D. L., 1995, Nonbright-spot AVO: Two examples: Geophysics, **60**, 1398–1408.

Ruger, A., 1996, Reflection coefficients and azimuthal AVO analysis in anisotropic media: PhD thesis, Center for Wave Phenomena, Colorado School of Mines, Golden, CO.

Russell, B., Hawkins, J. G., Lashgari, B., and Revoir, M. E., 1992, AVO modeling and inversion- An offshore Gulf of Mexico case study: Presented at the Joint Soc. Expl. Geophys./EAEG Summer Research Workshop on "How useful is amplitude-versus-offset (AVO) analysis?", 154–163.

Rutherford, S. R., and Williams, R.H., 1989, Amplitude-versus-offset in gas sands: Geophysics, **54**, 680–688.

Savit, C. H., 1960, Preliminary report, A stratigraphic seismogram: Geophysics, **25**, 312–325.

Schlumberger, 1972, Log interpretation—Volume 1—Principles: Schlumberger Ltd.

Sengbush, R. L., 1983, Seismic exploration methods: Internat. Human Res. Dev. Corp.

Sengbush, R. L., Lawrence, P. L., and McDonal, F. J., 1961, Interpretation of synthetic seismograms: Geophysics, **26**, 138–157.

Sheriff, R. E., 1989, Geophysical Methods: Prentice Hall.

Sherwood, J. W. C., Hilterman, F. J., Neale, R., and Chen, K. C., 1983, Synthetic seismogram with offset for a layered elastic medium: Presented at the 15th Offshore Technology Conference, OTC 4508, 539–546.

Shuey, R. T., 1985, A simplification of the Zoeppritz equations: Geophysics, **50**, 609–614.

Simmons, J. L. Jr., and Backus, M. M., 1994, AVO modeling and the locally converted shear wave: Geophysics, **59**, 1237–1248.

Smith, G. C., and Gidlow, P. M., 1987, Weighted stacking for rock property estimation and detection of gas: Geophys. Prosp., **35**, 993–1014.

Smith, G. C., and Sutherland, R. A., 1996, The fluid factor as an AVO indicator: Geophysics, **61**, 1425–1428.

Spratt, S., 1987, Effect of normal moveout errors on amplitude versus offset-derived shear reflectivity: 57th SEG Expanded Abstracts, 634–637.

Swan, H. W., 1993, Properties of direct AVO hydrocarbon indicators: *in* Castagna, J.P. and Backus, M.M., eds., Offset-dependent reflectivity —Theory and practice of AVO anomalies, Soc. Expl. Geophys. Investigations in Geophysics no. **8**, 78–92.

Thomsen, L., 1986, Weak elastic anisotropy: Geophysics, **51**, 1954–1966.

Tsvankin, I., and Thomsen, L., 1994, Nonhyperbolic reflection moveout in anisotropic media: Geophysics, **59**, 1290–1304.

Tsvankin, I., and Thomsen, L., 1995, Inversion of reflection traveltimes for transverse isotropy: Geophysics, **60**, 1095–1107.

Tucker, P. M., 1982, Pitfalls revisited: Soc. Expl. Geophys.,Tulsa, OK.

Vail, P. R., Todd, R.G., and Sangree, J. B., 1977, Seismic stratigraphy and global changes in sea level, Part 5: Chronostratigraphic significance of seismic reflections, *in* Payton, C. E., Ed., Seismic stratigraphy—Applications to hydrocarbon exploration: Memoir 26, AAPG, 99–116.

Verm, R., and Hilterman, F., 1995, Lithology color-coded seismic sections, The calibration of AVO crossplotting to rock properties: The Leading Edge, **14**, 847–853.

Verm, R., Liang, L., and Hilterman, F. J., 1998, Significance of geopressure in predicting lithology: The Leading Edge, **17**, 227–234.

Voigt, W., 1928, Lehrbuch der Kristallphysik: Teubner, Leipzig, Germany.

Wang, Y., 1999, Approximations to the Zoeppritz equations and their use in AVO analysis: Geophysics, **64**, 1920–1937.

Wang, Z., and Nur, A. M., 1992, Seismic and acoustic velocities in reservoir rocks— Theoretical and model studies: v. **2**, Soc. Expl. Geophys. Geophysics Reprint Series no. **10**.

Widess, M. B., 1973, How thin is a thin bed?: Geophysics, 38, 1176–1180.

Wiggins, R. K., Kenny, G. S., and McClure, C. D., 1983, A method for determining and displaying the shear-velocity reflectivities of a geologic formation: European Patent Application 0113944.

Wood, A. W., 1955, A textbook of sound: The MacMillan Co.

Wright, J., 1986, Reflection coefficients at pore-fluid contacts as a function of offset: Geophysics, 51, 1858–1860.

Wyllie, M. R. J., 1963, The fundamentals of electric log interpretation, 2nd ed.: Academic Press.

Wyllie, M. R. J., Gregory, A. R. and Gardner, G. H. F., 1958, An experimental investigation of factors affecting elastic wave velocities in porous media: Geophysics, **23**, 459–493.

Wyllie, M. R. J., Gregory, A. R. and Gardner, L. W., 1956, Elastic wave velocities in heterogeneous and porous media: Geophysics, **21**, 41–70.

Xu, S., and White, R.E., 1995, A new velocity for clay-sand mixtures: Geophys. Prosp., **43**, no. 1, 91–118.

Zoeppritz, K., 1919, Erdbebenwellen VIIIB, On the reflection and propagation of seismic waves: Gottinger Nachrichten, I, 66–84.

Section 10. Acknowledgments

Numerous concepts, discussions, and figures presented in these notes were developed over the past 20 years with the assistance of many professionals who were and/or are associated with Geophysical Development Corporation (GDC). They are: Mohammed Al-Otaibi, Brad Bankhead, Scott Burns, David Cefola, Kevin Chesser, Prakash Desai, Bryan DeVault, Jim DiSiena, Peg Guthrie, Dan Kinman, Luh Liang, Liz Nettles, Marc Sbar, Karl Schleicher, Connie Van Schuyver, Ashish Shah, John Sherwood, Pam Todd, Richard Verm, Don Verrett, Ron Ward, Mark Wilson, and Martin Wood. I apologize to any whom I may have missed.

I am also indebted to seismic contractors, Fairfield Industries, Inc., TGS-NOPEC, Schlumberger RES, Fugro-Geoteam AS, and Seismic Exchange, Inc. for agreeing to show examples from their data sets. My appreciation goes to Unocal and ORYX for supplying data also.

I am thankful for the time and effort that Mike Schoenberger, Bryan DeVault, and John Castagna have provided me with their review of the notes. This was an enormous task that Mike, Bryan, and John undertook, and they did it in a very timely and professional fashion. Any errors that remain are solely my responsibility.

To commit oneself to writing these course notes is one thing, but to commit an "innocent" bystander is another. My partner in this commitment was Nicolas Gonzales, Jr. As I wrote the text, Nicolas kept pace creating, pasting, scanning, editing, and transcribing all the figures. SEG, EAGE, and I owe a big thanks to Nicolas for his dedication to 2001 DISC.

It is a great honor and privilege to present the 2001 DISC. I am thankful to the members of the SEG Continuing Education Committee and the Executive Committees of SEG and EAGE who have selected me. In addition, this work would not have been possible without the support and effort provided by the professional staffs at the SEG and EAGE Business Offices. My thanks to all.

Of course, I am indebted to the management of GDC for the time and support that they have provided me. To all my fellow colleagues at GDC, thanks for taking up the extra load during this time period.

Without the financial contributions to the DISC program from the various companies, the ability of SEG and EAGE to meet their future goals and objectives would have been limited. Thanks for the help.

Though stated at the end, by no means does that reflect any lack of appreciation I have for the support that my wife Kathi gave me during the preparation of the notes.

—Fred J. Hilterman